EDMUND G. BROWN JR.
Governor

HUEY D. JOHNSON
Secretary for Resources
The California Resources Agency

LEWIS A. MORAN
Director
Department of Forestry

CALIFORNIA FORESTRY HANDBOOK

by

T. F. Arvola

State of California
The Resources Agency
DEPARTMENT OF FORESTRY
Sacramento 1978

This book may be purchased from

OFFICE OF PROCUREMENT
Publications Section
P.O. Box 20191
Sacramento, California 95820

All Sales Subject to Payment in Advance

Price postpaid $2.50 including tax. Prices subject to change

Money Orders and checks should be made to:
STATE OF CALIFORNIA

FOREWORD

In the late 1940s the California Division of Forestry published two handbooks that proved to be very popular and useful. These were respectively the Redwood Forest Handbook by Jack Reveal and Arnold Wallen and the California Pine Region Forest Handbook by George A. Craig and William P. Maguire. Although these handbooks have been out of stock for a number of years, there still has been a demand for them, despite the fact that they contain some outdated information and lack recent knowledge of value in forestry practices today.

To fill this need we decided to publish a new combined version of these handbooks; this was made possible by financial assistance from the U.S. Forest Service. The main purpose of this book is to provide a practical forestry guide for the management of the 3.6 million acres of commercial forest lands held in farm and small ownerships in California. These lands represent 47 percent of the 7.6 million acres of privately owned commercial forest land in the state. This reference is therefore written for use principally by such forest owners, timber operators, and forest technicians. Of course, forestry students and professional foresters may have some use of this text, but in no way will it supplant much more elaborate publications like the Forestry Handbook produced by the Society of American Foresters and many other technical references a forester must utilize. The California Forestry Handbook will not make a forester out of a person, nor preclude the need for use of consulting foresters in the management of many small ownerships. However, this handbook may make it possible for a tree farmer, timber operator, or technician to understand and apply practical forestry knowledge to enhance his or her situation and thereby improve forest management practices in California.

The author of this handbook is Tobe Arvola, a Fellow in the Society of American Foresters. In addition to obtaining a forestry degree from the University of California in 1938, the author took pre-forestry courses at Humboldt State University and did graduate study in meteorology at UCLA and the University of Chicago. He served as Deputy State Forester in charge of resource management programs for the California Division (now Department) of Foresty for 27 years. Early in his career he also had a number of years of experience in timber management with the U. S. Forest Service, the redwood industry, and as the first manager of Jackson State Forest. Since retiring in 1975, the author produced an earlier CDF production—Regulation of Logging in California: 1945–1975.

L. A. Moran
Director of Forestry

iii

ACKNOWLEDGEMENTS

The author has had fine cooperation and assistance from many people and organizations in this endeavor. First to be recognized are the authors and their collaborators of the two original CDF forest handbooks, whose pioneering made it so much easier to produce this work. In fact, some of the organization, figures, and tables which are still appropriate were retained in this combined version.

In addition to generous financial support, U. S. Forest Service staff in San Francisco, through Robert W. Gustafson, was very helpful in supplying technical data, editorial advice, and other assistance. Peter C. Passof of the University of California Cooperative Extension Service deserves special mention for his comprehensive review of the manuscript. Much of the workload fell on the California Department of Forestry, principally Chief of Resource Management James C. Denny, Robert J. Malain, Brian R. Barrette, and other CDF specialists. Credit is also due to Gerald Brown and the CDF graphic services unit, Mae McFadin and assistants of the Department of Conserviation for preparation of some tables, Marjorie Blair for typing and proofing, my wife Margaret for proofing help and moral support, Allison Haapala for the cover design, Nancy Rogers for many favors during processing of the manuscript, and the Office of State Printing. There were many other persons within and without the CDF that furnished valuable advice and help, but are too numerous to mention individually, but certainly deserve recognition and a word of appreciation.

T.F.A.

TABLE OF CONTENTS

Chapter   Page

I   The Tree 1
      Definition and Composition 1
      How a Tree Grows 3
      Kinds of Trees 3
      Wood Characteristics 5
II   The Forest and Its Management 8
      Silvics and Silviculture 8
          Site 8
          Age and Forest Types 9
          Growth 13
          Growth Prediction 13
      Management Planning 19
          Regulation 19
          Allowable Cut 20
          Management Plans 22
      Silvicultural Systems 24
          Clear Cutting 24
          Seed-Tree Cutting 24
          Shelterwood 25
          Selection 25
          Other Systems 25
      Environmental Factors 25
          Soil and Water 26
          Fish and Wildlife 26
          Aesthetics and Recreation 26
      Timber Stand Improvement 26
          Thinning 26
          Pruning 28
          Herbicides and Fertilizers 28
      Reforestation 30
          Natural Seeding 30
          Artificial Seeding 32
          Planting 34
      Economics 38
III   Wood Products of the Forest 39
      Conifer Sawlogs 39
      Conifer Veneer Logs 39
      Hardwoods 40
      Pulpwood and Chipwood 40
      Poles, Piling, and Posts 41
      Split Products 42
      Fuelwood 43
      Christmas Trees 44
      Miscellaneous Forest Products 45
          Greenery 45
          Cones for Seed 45
          Burls and Rounds 46
          Other Possibilities 46

Chapter		Page
IV	Harvesting Tree Crops	47
	Timing and Location of Harvests	47
	Marking the Harvest	47
	Advance Information Needed	48
	Timber Cruise	48
	Timber Harvesting Plan	49
	Stumpage Appraisal	50
	Logging Operations	50
	Felling and Bucking	50
	Yarding, Loading, and Hauling	51
	How to Sell	53
	Sale Offers	53
	Measurement	53
	Sale Contract	54
	Bidding and Negotiation	54
	Supervision	54
	Legal Requirements	55
	Forest Practice Act	55
	Environmental Protection	55
	Licensing of Foresters	56
	Taxation	56
	Property and Yield Taxes	57
	Income Taxes	57
	Other Taxes	58
	Forestry Organizations	58
V	Forest Inventory	60
	Land Subdivision	60
	Maps and Aerial Photographs	63
	Measuring and Running Lines	65
	Horizontal Chaining	65
	Slope Chaining	65
	Pacing	67
	Measurement of Direction	67
	Measurement of Trees	68
	Diameter Measurement	68
	Tree Heights	69
	Volume Measurement	71
	Timber Cruising	72
	Cruise Accuracy	72
	Recording Data	73
	Preparations for Cruise	74
	Strip Cruising	75
	Plot Cruising	75
	Other methods	77
	Calculating Volumes	77
	Use of Prisms	78
VI	Log Scaling	81
	Required Knowledge	81
	Board-Foot Measure	81
	Log Rules	82
	Scaling Equipment	83
	Measurement Procedures	83
	Defect Deductions	86

Chapter		Page
	Weight Scaling	88
	Other Forms of Scaling	90
VII	Forest Roads	91
	Road Planning	91
	Rights-of-Way	91
	Routing	92
	Road Location	92
	Grade Considerations	94
	Alinement and Curvature	94
	Width, Cuts, and Fills	98
	Subgrade and Surface	99
	Drainage and Erosion Control	100
	Surface Drainage	100
	Side Ditches	102
	Cross-Road Drainage	102
	Revegetation of Slopes	105
	Roadside Treatment	105
	Road Maintenance	105
VIII	Forest Protection	107
	Forest Fires	107
	Prevention	107
	Hazard Reduction	108
	Fire Readiness	110
	Fire Control	111
	Prescribed Burning	114
	Forest Insects	114
	Insect Identification	115
	Detection, Reporting, and Investigation	120
	Prevention	120
	Control	122
	Forest Diseases	123
	Kinds of Diseases	123
	Detection, Reporting, and Investigation	126
	Prevention and Control	126
	Animal Damage	127
	Animal Pests	127
	Checking Damage	127
	Prevention and Control	128
	Other Tree Losses	128
IX	Forest-Range Management	130
	Multiple Use	130
	Forest-Range Use	130
	Range Plants and Types	131
	Kinds of Plants	131
	Range Types	132
	Range Evaluation	134
	Basic Site	134
	Range Condition	134
	Carrying Capacity	137
	Management Practices	138
	Watering Facilities	138
	Salt Needs	138

Chapter		Page
	Control of Stock Movement	139
	Seeding and Fertilization	139
	Poisonous Plants	139
	Control of Rodents	140
	Erosion and Watershed Repair	140
	Controlled Burning	140
	Grazing Systems	141
	Continuous Grazing	141
	Deferred Grazing	141
	Rotation Grazing	141
	Deferred-Rotation Grazing	142
	Rest-Rotation Grazing	142
	Choosing the System	142
	Protection of Timber	143
X	Water, Wildlife, Recreation	144
	Watershed Management	144
	The Hydrologic Cycle	144
	Effects of Soil and Vegetation	146
	Water Utilization	147
	Impact of Forest Land Management	148
	Prevention and Control of Damage	150
	Fish and Wildlife	151
	Forests and Fish	151
	Terrestrial Wildlife	153
	Wildlife Management	154
	Species Protection	155
	Forest Recreation	156
	Protection of Recreational Resources	156
	Recreation Programs	157
	Precautionary Measures	158
	Appendix	161
	Terminology in Forestry	162
	Various Conversion Tables	174
	Basal Area Table	179
	Various Volume Tables	180
	Various Site Curves and Yield Tables	214
	Log Rules (board feet and cubic feet)	224
	List of Tables in Handbook	229
	Some Practical References	232

Timber and wood products are very much a part of our economic base and that base has to be built, protected and enhanced.

Edmund G. Brown Jr.
Governor
1978 Budget Message

Chapter I

THE TREE

The tree is a wonderous thing in countless ways. It provides us with food, shelter, beauty, inspiration, and over 5,000 different wood products. The tree forms the basic unit of the forest community, so we need to know and understand it in order to use our commercial forests wisely.

Definition and Composition

A tree is a woody perennial plant, typically larger than other plants, and usually with a single, well defined stem supporting a crown of branches. As a conglomerate of roots, stem or trunk, branches, leaves, and fruit, all of which have specialized functions (see Figure I-1)*, the tree is a complex organism. Trees, even of the same species, vary widely in size and shape. This diversity offers us many opportunities for making good use of the great variety of trees that we have.

The roots hold the tree upright, absorb water and nutrients from the soil, conduct them upward, and store food made by the foliage. Oxygen from within the soil is necessary for roots to function. The larger and older roots, which like branches have heartwood, sapwood, and bark, provide the physical support for the tree. The smaller roots, which are hairlike at the extremities, absorb water and minerals needed for growth.

The trunk also serves a number of purposes. It conducts water and nutrients from the roots to the crown, moves food from the crown to other parts of the tree, and it lifts the branches and leaves to collect the sun's energy. The heartwood of the trunk is relatively lifeless compared to the outside layer, from which it was formed. It is darker because its cells contain a deposition of complex compounds, which in many species improve the durability of the wood. The outer sapwood is lighter in color, and composed of living cells that move water and nutrients upward. A microscopic growth layer, called the cambium, located between the sapwood and the inner bark, produces new sapwood and bark cells each year; this causes the tree to grow in diameter.

Like the woody part of the trunk, the bark has its live and dead parts. The spongy, wet inner bark carries food from the leaves to the adjacent cambium layer and the growing tips of branches and roots. The outer bark layer is dry and lifeless; it protects the tree from damage by weather, fire, pests, and physical contact.

The crown of the tree is composed of branches, twigs, foliage, and reproductive organs like flowers and fruit. Using sunlight, water and nutrients from the roots, and carbon dioxide from the air, the leaves manufacture (photosynthesize) the tree's own food in the form of various sugars. Oxygen is a valuable by-product of photosynthesis.

Flowers and fruits of trees vary greatly among species. They provide the most reliable means for identifying different species of plants. Some spe-

---

* The first digit (roman) of the figure and table numbers represent the chapter, and the second digit (arabic) is the sequential number within the chapter. Tables and figures in the appendix are preceded by A followed by a sequential number.

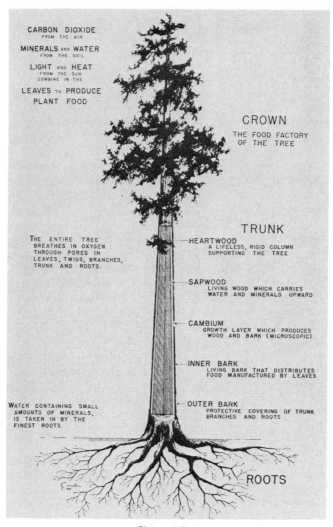

CARBON DIOXIDE
FROM THE AIR

MINERALS AND WATER
FROM THE SOIL

LIGHT AND HEAT
FROM THE SUN
COMBINE IN THE

LEAVES TO PRODUCE
PLANT FOOD

CROWN
THE FOOD FACTORY
OF THE TREE

TRUNK

THE ENTIRE TREE
BREATHES IN OXYGEN
THROUGH PORES IN
LEAVES, TWIGS, BRANCHES,
TRUNK AND ROOTS.

HEARTWOOD
A LIFELESS, RIGID COLUMN
SUPPORTING THE TREE

SAPWOOD
LIVING WOOD WHICH CARRIES
WATER AND MINERALS UPWARD

CAMBIUM
GROWTH LAYER WHICH PRODUCES
WOOD AND BARK (MICROSCOPIC)

INNER BARK
LIVING BARK THAT DISTRIBUTES
FOOD MANUFACTURED BY LEAVES

WATER CONTAINING SMALL
AMOUNTS OF MINERALS,
IS TAKEN IN BY THE
FINEST ROOTS.

OUTER BARK
PROTECTIVE COVERING OF TRUNK
BRANCHES AND ROOTS

ROOTS

Figure I-1
Structure and growth of the tree.

cies are monoecious, meaning they contain both male and female flowers on the same tree. Other species are dioecious, having male and female flowers separately on different trees. All the California conifers, except juniper and yew, are monoecious. Similarly, most of our broadleaved trees have flowers of both sexes on the same tree, excepting only Oregon ash, aspen, cottonwood, and the willows. The pines, Sierra redwood, cypress, Port Orford cedar, juniper, and nutmeg require two years to produce mature fruits and seeds; all other conifers require only one year. Most of our broadleaved trees grow their fruits in one·year, excepting only some oaks.

How a Tree Grows

All the main parts of a tree contribute to its growth (Figure I-1). As a tree grows, each year its roots, trunk, and branches add a new layer of wood just inside the bark. These annual rings can be readily seen on tree stumps, cross sections of limbs, and the ends of lumber. These concentric rings stand out because each ring has a light-colored band of springwood and a usually narrower and darker band of summerwood. The springwood part is generally wider because it is formed in the growing season when water and other conditions are most favorable. We shall see later that the age and growth information reflected in annual rings is very useful in the management of forests.

The bark layer is also continually growing. Each year a narrow ring is grown on the inside of the bark. This gradually forces the older bark out and causes it to form plates, ridges, and troughs, which slowly deteriorate and erode, especially on the lower trunk.

Elongation of tree stem and branches is a much different process. It is brought about by the formation of terminal and side buds during the fall, which burst and grow lengthwise in the spring. This growth is always an additive process, so the middle of the branches and trunk do not elongate at all, nor is the tree pushed out of the soil like corn or bamboo.

Roots also extend themselves to seek water and nutrients. They elongate in the area behind their tips, whose caps continually produce new cells. Lateral root hairs absorb water and nutrients.

Tree growth depends on the species, age, soil, climate, and growing conditions. Fast-growing, thrifty trees have thick annual rings and large crowns. In conifers, usually one whorl of branches on the stem is produced each year, the spacing of which is a good indicator of growth. Spacing of 12 inches or more between whorls in young trees represents good growth. As a tree matures its top begins to flatten and the whorl spacing diminishes or even ceases.

Trees reproduce from seed or by sprouts (sometimes known as suckers or coppice growth). All of our tree species produce seed. Many hardwoods develop sprouts also, particularly after cutting, but among our conifers only the coast redwood is a sprouter. It also produces burls made up of many buds that are capable of sprouting.

Kinds of Trees

There are many kinds of trees having some value as wood. They are divided into two broad classes—conifers or softwoods, and broadleaved or hardwoods. The softwood-hardwood terminology is somewhat confusing because some softwoods like Douglas-fir are harder than some hardwoods like aspen.

All plants have two kinds of names—common and scientific. Common names often vary by locality, although within professional circles only one common name is usually used. For instance, ponderosa pine is sometimes termed western yellow pine, blackjack pine, or bull pine, but ponderosa is the accepted common name by botanists and foresters. To avoid this kind of confusion, and to classify plants, botanists developed scientific names. Thus ponderosa pine is named *Pinus ponderosa, Pinus* being the genus the tree belongs to and *ponderosa* being the species name. Sometimes a third category is added, the variety; e.g., our boxelder is called *Acer negundo californicum* to distinguish it from the eastern boxelder. See Table I-1 for a listing of our more common native trees, and the Appendix for a reference on tree identification.

Table I-1. The more common native trees of California.

CONIFERS

Common Name	Scientific Name
Bigcone-spruce	Pseudotsuga macrocarpa
Cypress, MacNab	Cupressus macnabiana
Cypress, Monterey	Cupressus macrocarpa
Cypress, pygmy	Cupressus pygmaea
Cypress, Sargent	Cupressus sargentii
Douglas-fir	Pseudotsuga menziesii
Fir, California red	Abies magnifica
Fir, grand	Abies grandis
Fir, white	Abies concolor
Hemlock, mountain	Tsuga mertensiana
Hemlock, western	Tsuga heterophylla
Incense-cedar	Libocedrus (Calocedrus) decurrens
Juniper, California	Juniperus californica
Juniper, Utah	Juniperus utahensis
Juniper, western	Juniperus occidentalis
Nutmeg, California	Torreya, californica
Pine, Bishop	Pinus muricata
Pine, Coulter	Pinus coulteri
Pine, Digger	Pinus sabiniana
Pine, Jeffrey	Pinus jeffreyi
Pine, knobcone	Pinus attenuata
Pine, limber	Pinus flexilis
Pine, lodgepole	Pinus contorta
Pine, Monterey	Pinus radiata
Pine, ponderosa	Pinus ponderosa
Pine, sugar	Pinus lambertiana
Pine, western white	Pinus monticola
Pine, whitebark	Pinus albicaulis
Port Orford-cedar	Chamaecyparis lawsoniana
Redwood, coast	Sequoia sempervirens
Redwood, Sierra	Sequoia gigantea (Sequoiadendron giganteum)
Spruce, Sitka	Picea sitchensis
Western red-cedar	Thuja plicata
Yew, Pacific	Taxus brevifolia

HARDWOODS

Common Name	Scientific Name
Alder, red	Alnus rubra
Alder, white	Alnus rhombifolia
Ash, Oregon	Fraxinus latifolia
Aspen	Populus tremuloides
Boxelder	Acer negundo var. californicum
Buckeye, California	Aesculus californica
California myrtle	Myrica californica
Cascara	Rhamnus purshiana
Chinkapin, golden	Castanea chrysolphylla
Cottonwood, black	Populus trichocarpa
Dogwood, Pacific	Cornus nutallii
Laurel, California	Umbellularia californica
Madrone	Arbutus menziesii
Maple, bigleaf	Acer marcrophyllum
Oak, blue	Quercus douglasii
Oak, California black	Quercus kelloggi
Oak, California live	Quercus agrifolia
Oak, canyon live	Quercus chrysolepis
Oak, interior live	Quercus wislizenii
Oak, Oregon white	Quercus garryana
Oak, valley	Quercus lobata
Sycamore	Platanus racemosa
Tanoak	Lithocarpus densiflora
Walnut, California black	Juglans hindsii
Willow	Salix, sp.

The conifers are the more important to us here in California. All of them are evergreen, most bear cones, and have needles or scale-like leaves. The principal ones are the pines, the true firs, and Douglas-fir. We also have a few cedars, hemlocks, and spruces that have commercial value.

The hardwoods, although very valuable in eastern United States, at present do not have as much commercial importance in the west as the conifers. However, a few of our broadleaved species have a good potential for specialty lumber and veneer, and most of them will have increasing use as fuel. They are characterized by flat, usually broad leaves, irregular branching, wide crowns, and varying kinds of fruits. Most of our hardwoods are deciduous, but several are evergreen, e.g., madrone, California laurel, tanoak, and a few oaks.

Wood Characteristics

Taking a close look at wood, we find a remarkable structure (Figure I-2). It is largely composed of millions of small, narrow, hollow cells, or fibers which are oriented parallel to the tree's stem. Some cells form rays that are perpendicular to the axis. There are a number of other cells that have specialized functions, like resin ducts in some conifers, and vessels or pores in broadleaved trees.

SOFTWOOD UNDER THE MICROSCOPE
(BLOCK, ORIGINALLY 3/16″ ON SIDE)

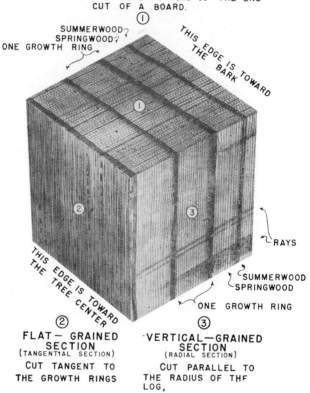

CROSS SECTION
(TRANSVERSE SECTION)

CUT AT RIGHT ANGLE TO
THE LENGTH. THIS IS THE END
CUT OF A BOARD.
①

SUMMERWOOD
SPRINGWOOD
ONE GROWTH RING

THIS EDGE IS TOWARD THE BARK

①

②

③

RAYS

SUMMERWOOD
SPRINGWOOD

ONE GROWTH RING

THIS EDGE IS TOWARD THE TREE CENTER

②
FLAT — GRAINED
SECTION
(TANGENTIAL SECTION)
CUT TANGENT TO
THE GROWTH RINGS

③
VERTICAL—GRAINED
SECTION
(RADIAL SECTION)
CUT PARALLEL TO
THE RADIUS OF THE
LOG,

From Emanuel Fritz,
School of Forestry, Berkeley, California

Figure I-2
A detailed view of the structure of wood
Emanuel Fritz

The composition and arrangement of these various elements, along with the springwood, summerwood, heartwood, and sapwood, determine the characteristics and properties of wood. This can vary widely among the different species, and also between trees of the same species, or even within the same tree. Grain, texture, and figure of wood are affected by these elements and the way a log is sawn. Flat grained lumber is cut tangentally with the annual rings and vertical grained or quarter sawn boards are cut parallel to the radius of the log (Figure I-2). The cellular make-up of the wood affects weight (which is also influenced greatly by the moisture content), stability (shrink and swell), strength, hardness, workability, and durability.

Scientists have developed a lot of quantitative data of this kind about woods from all over the world, which are readily available for use by wood processors and users. Table I-2 presents data on weight, fuel value, and durability of our more common species in California.

Table I-2. Some properties of selected woods.

| Species | Weight | | Fuel Value Thousand BTU[c] Cu. Ft. | Decay Resistance |
	Air-Dry Sawn[a] Lbs./Cu. Ft.	Average Logs[b] Lbs./Bd. Ft.		
Alder, red	27	8.5	173	Low
Ash, Oregon	34	–	250	Low
Aspen	25	–	156	Low
Chinkapin, California	32	–	–	Medium
Cottonwood	24	10.0	160	Low
Dogwood	45	–	307	Low
Douglas-fir	32	8.0	213	Medium
Eucalyptus, blue gum	52	–	389	Low
Fir, true	27	8.5	187	Low
Hemlock, mountain	33	–	227	Low
Hemlock, western..	27	10.0	224	Low
Incense-cedar	26	–	187	High
Laurel, California ..	39	–	289	Low
Madrone	45	–	307	Low
Maple, bigleaf	34	–	240	Low
Oak, California black	40	–	280	Low
Oak, canyon live....	54	–	373	Low
Oak, Oregon white	50	–	347	High
Pine, Jeffrey	28	–	213	Low
Pine, lodgepole	29	–	213	Medium
Pine, ponderosa	28	9.0	213	Low
Pine, sugar	25	10.0	173	Medium
Pine, western white	27	–	213	Medium
Port Orford-cedar..	29	10.0	–	High
Redwood, coast	28	7.5	200	High
Spruce, Sitka	28	6.5	227	Low
Tanoak	40	–	280	Low
Walnut, black	38	–	267	High
Western red-cedar	23	8.0	223	High
Willow	31	–	213	Low
Yew	44	–	307	High

[a] At 12% moisture content
[b] For green logs 18″ in diameter at small end (weight varies widely)
[c] British Thermal Unit
Source: various

Chapter II

THE FOREST AND ITS MANAGEMENT

An extensive grouping of trees makes a forest. More specifically, it is a plant community composed predominantly of trees and other vegetation, growing more or less close together. A forest is a complicated and delicate ecosystem consisting of soil, trees, and many associated flora and fauna. Great care and skill are necessary in the use of the forest in order to maintain this balance of nature to a reasonable degree, to prevent irreparable environmental damage, and to keep the forest continually providing its many benefits to us. It is a renewable resource and a big energy producer.

This husbandry requires the application of forestry or forest management—the science, art, and practice of managing and using for human benefit the various natural resources that occur on and in association with forest lands. The forest values include protection of watersheds (a very important function in California), habitat for wildlife, outdoor recreation, other environmental benefits, grazing for livestock, and a whole host of forest products, which is of prime interest to us in this handbook.

Silvics and Silviculture

In order to manage our forests properly for wood crops, we should have some basic knowledge about silviculture in addition to the information about the tree covered in the previous chapter. This gives us an understanding of the life history and characteristics of trees and forest stands (silvics) and how they can be established, grown, and tended (silviculture). How well a tree grows depends on its native characteristics, its relationships with other trees and plants, its setting, and how we treat it.

Site

The growth rate is determined largely by what is called the forest or timber site—a measure of productivity based on how trees respond to the soil and climate of the immediate area. Generally, deep, well-drained, clay-loam soils with plenty of moisture are the best. Soils are classified by series names. Some of the more common better forest soils are shown below (see Watershed Management section in Chapter X for a listing of erosive soils):

Redwood–Douglas-Fir Region	Pine Region
Empire	Aiken
Hely	Cohasset
Hugo	Holland
Josephine	Josephine
Larabee	McCarthy
Masterson	Musick
Melbourne	Shaver
Mendocino	Sites
Orick	
Sites	

(C.D.F., Stone, 1978)

Many of the forest soils in California have been surveyed by the State Cooperative Soil-Vegetation Survey, and maps delineating the various series of soils and the principal vegetation are available at low cost. These maps and legends are of immense value to tree farmers and forest managers. In addition to kinds of soil, they provide data on depth, slope, predominant plant species, erosion potential, and timber site. You can obtain literature, instructions on ordering the maps, and assistance in using them from forest advisers located in various offices of the California Department of Forestry. Soils information is also available from county farm advisers and the U.S. Soil Conservation Service.

Climate in California is the most diverse in the U.S. Usually forest growth is better where annual precipitation is greater. For example, the coast redwood type occurs where rainfall is the highest in the state, and it also has the best growth. In most cases, except in areas of summer rain showers, like the eastside of the Cascade Range and the Sierra Nevada, about 18 inches or more of precipitation is required yearly to sustain natural coniferous forests.

The site quality naturally varies a great deal among forests and even within a single forest. A measurement called site index is used by foresters for various purposes. It represents the height of dominant and codominant trees in a stand at a standard age, usually 100 years. Height in feet of such trees is found by methods described in Chapter V. The age is determined by using an increment borer (see section below on growth). This auger is used to extract a pencil-like core out of a tree trunk at breast height on which the number of annual rings to the center of the tree can be counted. When trees are too thick to bore, the age can be found by counting rings on stumps of felled trees nearby. Using a prepared table like Tables II-1, 2, 3, or site curves in the Appendix, a person can look up the site index. For instance, using Table II-1, a 70-year-old, 134-feet tall dominant tree in the pine region would indicate a site index of 160—a good site. To simplify matters site indices are usually grouped into classes. The classes employed are shown in Table II-4.

There is an easy method to roughly estimate the site quality of a forest, which was briefly mentioned in Chapter I; that is by looking at the distance between the upper branch whorls of thrifty trees. Two-foot or more spacing indicates high site, between one-half and two feet represents a medium site, and less than that a poor site.

Age and Forest Types

Most natural timber stands in California are all-aged (also called uneven-aged); that is, they contain a mixture of immature, mature, and overmature trees. Typical of all-aged forests is the extensive mixed conifer type in the pine region. Douglas-fir and redwood are also all-aged, but may also grow in even-aged stands, meaning that most trees are approximately of the same age. Red fir and lodgepole pine stands are mostly even-aged. The structure of these two categories is much different; all-aged stands have trees of varying diameters and heights while even-aged stands have trees that are more uniform. Age class is another common term in forestry. It denotes the interval, usually 10 years, into which the age range of tree

Table II-1. Height of average dominant and codominant ponderosa pine at 100 years.

Age	Height, by site index—											
	50	60	70	80	90	100	110	120	130	140	150	160
	Feet	Feet	Feet	Feet	Feet	Feet	Feet	Feet	Feet	Feet	Feet	Feet
20	9	12	16	20	25	30	35	40	45	50	55	60
30	15	20	26	32	38	44	51	57	64	70	77	84
40	22	28	35	42	49	55	63	70	77	85	93	100
50	28	35	43	51	58	65	73	80	89	97	105	113
60	34	42	50	58	66	73	81	90	99	107	115	124
70	39	47	56	64	73	80	89	98	108	116	125	134
80	43	52	61	70	79	88	97	106	116	124	133	143
90	47	57	66	75	85	94	104	113	123	132	142	152
100	50	60	70	80	90	100	110	120	130	140	150	160
110	53	63	74	84	95	106	116	127	137	147	158	168
120	55	66	77	88	100	111	122	133	144	154	165	175
130	57	69	80	92	104	116	128	139	151	161	172	182
140	59	71	83	96	108	121	133	145	157	167	179	189
150	60	73	86	99	112	125	138	151	163	173	185	195
160	61	75	89	102	116	129	143	156	169	179	191	201
170	62	77	91	105	119	133	147	161	174	184	196	206
180	63	78	93	108	122	136	151	165	179	189	201	211
190	63	79	95	110	125	139	154	169	183	194	205	216
200	64	80	97	112	128	143	157	172	187	198	209	220

U.S.F.S., Meyer, 1938

Table II-2. Height (in feet) of average dominant and codominant Douglas-fir at 100 years.

Age (years)	Site Class V		Site Class IV			Site Class III			Site Class II			Site Class I		
	Site index 80	Site index 90	Site index 100	Site index 110	Site index 120	Site index 130	Site index 140	Site index 150	Site index 160	Site index 170	Site index 180	Site index 190	Site index 200	Site index 210
	Feet	Feet	Feet	Feet	Feet	Feet	Feet	Feet	Feet	Feet	Feet	Feet	Feet	Feet
20	21	24	26	29	31	34	37	39	42	44	47	49	52	54
30	37	41	46	50	55	60	64	69	74	78	83	88	92	96
40	48	54	60	66	72	78	84	90	96	102	108	114	120	126
50	56	63	70	77	84	91	98	105	112	119	125	132	139	146
60	63	70	78	86	93	101	109	117	124	132	140	148	156	163
70	68	77	85	94	102	110	119	127	135	144	152	161	170	178
80	73	82	91	100	109	118	127	136	145	154	163	172	181	190
90	77	86	96	105	115	125	134	144	153	163	172	182	192	201
100	80	90	100	110	120	130	140	150	160	170	180	190	200	210
110	83	93	100	114	124	135	145	155	166	176	187	197	207	218
120	85	96	106	117	128	138	149	160	170	181	192	202	213	224
130	87	98	109	119	131	141	152	163	174	185	196	207	218	228
140	88	99	110	121	133	144	154	166	177	188	199	210	221	232
150	89	101	112	123	134	145	156	168	179	190	201	213	224	235
160	90	102	113	124	136	147	158	170	181	192	203	215	226	237

U.S.F.S., McArdle, Meyer, Bruce, 1949

Table II-3. Average total heights of dominant coast redwood by breast-high age and site index.

Age at b. h. (years)	Total height (feet), by site index							
	100	120	140	160	180	200	220	240
20........	21	31	42	53	63	74	84	95
30........	34	48	62	76	89	103	117	131
40........	47	62	76	92	107	122	137	152
50........	57	73	89	106	122	138	155	171
60........	67	84	102	119	136	154	171	188
70........	76	94	112	130	148	166	184	202
80........	85	104	123	142	161	180	198	217
90........	93	113	132	152	171	190	210	229
100........	100	120	140	160	180	200	220	240

U.C., Lindquist and Palley, 1963

Table II-4. Timber site classification systems in California.

Young Growth Coast Redwood		Douglas-Fir		Ponderosa Pine	
Site Class	Site Index*	Site Class	Site Index*	Site Class	Site Index*
I .... 180 or more		I .... 194 or more		I .... 114 or more	
II 155–179		II 164–193		II 93–113	
III 130–154		III....................134–163		III.......................75–92	
IV 105–129		IV....................103–133		IV.........................60–74	
V .... Less than 105		V.......... Less than 103		V............. Less than 60	

* Height in feet at 100 years age.
California Board of Forestry, CAC 14-1060, 1974

crops is divided, e.g., the 10-year age class, 20-year age class. An all-aged forest would contain all age classes, while an even-aged stand would be mostly composed of trees in one class.

Forests are also classed by the type of species found in them. The principal forest types we have are as follows:

Name	*Common Species Contained*
Pine	Pure stands of various pines
Redwood	Coast redwood, Douglas-fir, grand fir, hemlock
Douglas-fir	Douglas-fir
Fir (true)	Red and white fir
Pine—Douglas-fir—fir (Mixed Conifer)	Ponderosa, Jeffrey, and sugar pine, Douglas-fir, white and red fir, incense-cedar

Where these forest types are found in California is shown in Figure II-1. These commercial forests make up about 16.3 million acres.

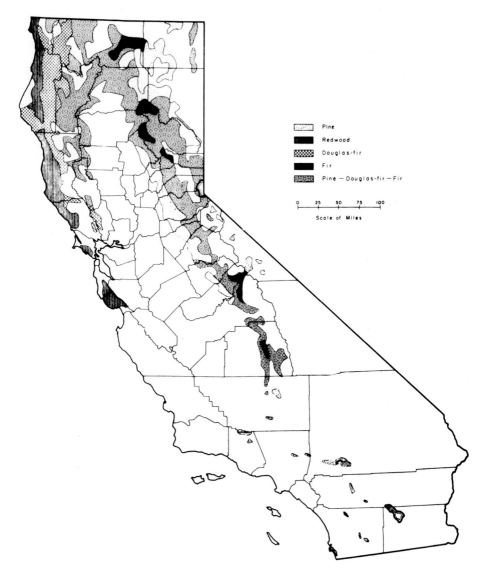

Figure II-1
Timber croplands of California.
U.S.F.S., Pacific Southwest Forest and Range Experiment Station, 1945

Growth

As noted above, growth depends on site, but it also is related to the age of the trees, the number per acre (called stocking or density), and how well they are distributed. Trees grow well when they are young, and as they reach maturity the growth begins to slow down. For the most favorable growth, ideal stocking and distribution are achieved when trees still have room to grow but none to waste.

Forest growth is affected by competition between trees within a stand and other forms of vegetation. Trees that are too crowded may stagnate, or even die, but still enough trees should be present to utilize the site fully and to make use of available moisture and nutrients. Also, some shading is necessary to cause the dying and self-pruning of lower branches. This makes better grades of sawlogs.

Some trees grow better then others under shade. These are classed tolerant trees, and include species like grand and white fir, the cedars, the hemlocks, and coast redwood. Douglas-fir, Sierra redwood, and red fir are intermediate in tolerance. Intolerant trees include the pines, with sugar pine being somewhat more tolerant than the other pines.

Competition, spacing, and tolerance are all involved in the formation of a forest. Thrifty young trees are tall and have sharp-pointed crowns. As they become older, the trees grow slower in height and the tops become broader. Some trees lose out in the struggle, become suppressed, and succumb. In an all-aged forest having trees of different sizes and ages, the larger and usually older trees have the dominant position. Others nearly like them are codominant, and the laggards are intermediate or suppressed. Foresters use the Dunning's Tree Classification System (Figure II-2) showing this relationship to help decide what trees should be selected for harvest. Although this system was designed primarily for pine, its principles can be used with the application of some judgement to all-age stands of other species.

A measure called basal area is a convenient method used by foresters to keep tab on growing stock of a stand. It is the sum of the cross-section area at breast height of all trees on an acre expressed in square feet. Basal areas on uncut areas may exceed 300 sq. ft. Often basal area needs to be reduced to place the stand in a better growing state. See Figure II-5 and Basal Area Table in the Appendix. How to measure basal area by using a prism is explained in Chapter V.

Growth Prediction

The growth of a forest is the foundation for its management and the basis of continuous production. A tree farmer needs some growth information in order to tell how well the forest is responding to its care, and more importantly, to help decide what amount can be harvested safely. Unfortunately, growth measurements are not easy to obtain, nor are they easy to use in making predictions of the growth of a stand in the future. There are many methods to forecast forest growth, most of which are rather complicated and laborious, and all of them require a lot of professional judgement and skill to give reliable results. Therefore, only a general

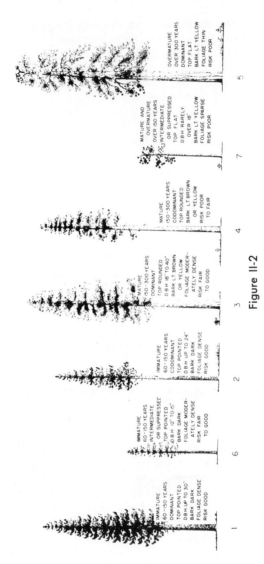

Figure II-2

Dunning's Tree Classification shows ponderosa pine by classes based on age, size, and appearance of bark and crown. Classes 1, 3 and sometimes 5 have crowns 65% or more of total height.

treatment of this subject can be included in this handbook, and a person wanting to measure and predict growth would be well advised to seek professional assistance. Also, Chapter V on forest inventory should be studied if a better understanding of the mechanics is desired.

A handy tool to use to obtain growth information is the increment borer (Fig. II-3) mentioned in the previous section on Site. The growth in diameter (twice the radial growth) in relation to a specified number of years can be measured on the core. For example, if the radial growth of wood (excluding bark) in the past 10 years of a tree 20.1 in. diameter outside the bark was measured to be 2.3 inches, the diameter growth would be 4.6. The expected diameter 10 years hence would be 20.1 plus 4.6 or 24.7 inches. This assumes that the bark thickness remains constant and that the growth would continue at the same rate, which may not be necessarily true in all cases. It should be realized that measuring growth with increment borers, unless carefully done and interpreted, can produce misleading results.

Figure II-3
Using an increment borer.

The growth during the past year is termed current annual growth, while the average growth per year over a period is called periodic annual growth. This periodic measure is the one used the most. The yearly average growth determined by dividing the total volume of a tree or a stand by its age is named mean annual growth.

Basically, growth of a forest can be estimated by three approaches: (1) indirectly by comparison or general observation, (2) indirectly from yield tables, and (3) by direct measurement of the stand. The last category includes many specific methods that can be utilized to meet the wide variety of conditions found in American forestry.

General observations on growth are the easiest and cheapest, and may in some cases be all that would be necessary, especially for smaller forests, or those that are first coming under a management program. However, the results certainly are not precise and should be cautiously used until better information becomes readily available. Under the method, the average net growth per acre per year, e.g., 500 bd. ft., of a similar stand in terms of forest type, age, site, and stocking is accepted and applied to the forest in question. Such growth information may be available from nearby national, state, and industrial forests.

Using *yield tables* under special circumstances is also a convenient and inexpensive way to estimate growth. Yield tables have been prepared for some of the more important species. Some yield tables along with site curves * are shown in the Appendix. In essence, these tables show the volume of timber produced by fully stocked, even-aged stands by decades on different sites. Because most forests are not fully stocked, these production figures have to be proportionately reduced. Thus, where a forest is only 50 percent stocked the yield may be only one-half of that indicated by a normal yield table. One major disadvantage of these tables is that they are mostly based on even-aged stands, so it is difficult to apply them properly to all-aged stands. Also, yield tables are lacking for some important California species and most of our forests are composed of a number of species. Nonetheless, professional foresters with good judgement and experience can make use of such tables to predict growth even for some all-aged stands.

Direct measurement of growth of the stand being managed can be the most accurate approach to take, but all the methods that have been developed require a great deal of detailed technical work, both in the field and the office, and consequently they are quite expensive. This effort and cost may not be justified in all instances. In addition, there are many chances for errors and misinterpretation. However, to give the reader some general idea of this direct approach three of the more common methods are briefly described. A person using them should refer to pertinent references or seek professional help.

The *stand-table projection* or diameter step-up method, of which there are several variants, has been used a lot by foresters. From timber cruise data, a stand table is prepared to show the number of trees by diameter at breast height (dbh) classes—usually two-inch, i.e., 10, 12, 14, etc., by

---

*The curves are needed to find what the site index is for the stand for which yield data are wanted from the accompanying yield tables.

species or species groups for an average acre of the stand. Thus the current volume of the average acre can be found in an appropriate volume table (Chapt. V); this will be the base for the growth prediction. How much these trees in each diameter class have grown on the average in diameter for a stated period, say 10 years, is determined by making increment borings of a sufficient number of trees that are representative of the forest as a whole. Using that data, the stand table for the average acre can be revised to show what the diameters in each class would be 10 years hence. This assumes that the next decade's growth will be the same as in the past 10 years. The new diameters can be rounded off by two-inch classes so that forecasted volume can be read from a volume table, but this is rather rough. By using the actual anticipated diameters to the nearest tenth-inch and making interpolations between diameter classes in the volume table the accuracy can be improved considerably.

The average gross annual growth of the average acre is the difference between the present volume and the forecasted volume divided by the number of years in the period. However, before this figure can be used for management purposes it should be reduced somewhat to a net growth basis to account for anticipated loss of trees by natural causes—competition, fire, pests, weather, etc. This adjustment cannot be easily made by exact methodology, but it can be arrived at by judgement. In California the forests as a whole lose approximately an average of 129 bd. ft. per acre yearly to mortality, but the range of values is wide.

The second and easier direct method is by using *growth percentages.* Because growth percentages vary by diameter for the same number of annual rings per inch—low for large trees and high for small ones—it is hard to apply a single growth percentage to a stand of trees to forecast growth (Table II-5). Here again, it is necessary to take increment borings of a representative sample of the forest to get the average growth percent

Table II-5. Interest rates being grown by trees.

D.b.h. (i.b.) inches	Number of annual rings per last radial inch of growth											
	1	2	3	4	5	6	7	8	9	10	11	12
						Percent						
2		340.0	144.4	83.3	57.1	37.5	32.0	29.4	24.2	22.2		
3	880.0	122.7	68.9	44.4	32.4	28.9	25.6	19.5	16.7	14.0		
4	295.4	77.5	45.0	30.0	22.5	19.2	16.0	13.0	11.5	10.1		
5	177.5	56.3	33.3	23.6	18.2	15.2	12.4	10.5	8.8	7.9	7.1	6.2
6	125.2	44.1	26.4	18.8	14.6	12.0	10.1	8.8	7.7	7.1	6.5	6.0
7	96.3	36.4	22.5	16.1	12.1	9.8	8.5	7.2	6.3	5.9	5.1	4.2
8	77.5	30.7	19.1	13.6	10.8	9.0	7.7	6.7	5.8	5.1	4.5	4.0
9	65.5	26.6	16.6	12.2	9.7	7.8	6.7	6.0	5.3	4.7	4.2	4.0
10	56.1	23.3	14.7	10.7	8.3	6.9	6.0	5.3	4.5	4.0	3.6	3.4
11	49.3	21.1	13.4	9.8	7.6	6.3	5.6	4.7	4.1	3.8	3.4	3.1
12	44.0	18.9	12.1	8.9	6.9	5.5	4.9	4.3	3.7	3.4	3.0	2.9
13	39.7	17.5	11.2	8.2	6.5	5.2	4.6	3.9	3.5	3.1	2.8	2.7
14	36.2	15.9	10.3	7.6	5.9	4.9	4.2	3.5	3.2	2.9	2.6	2.4
15	33.1	14.8	9.5	6.9	5.5	4.5	3.9	3.3	2.9	2.7	2.4	2.2
16	30.6	13.8	8.8	6.5	5.2	4.2	3.7	3.2	2.8	2.5	2.3	2.1
17	28.4	12.9	8.4	6.1	4.8	4.0	3.5	3.1	2.7	2.4	2.1	2.0
18	26.6	12.0	7.9	5.8	4.6	3.8	3.3	2.9	2.5	2.3	2.0	1.9
19	24.9	11.4	7.4	5.5	4.3	3.5	3.1	2.7	2.3	2.1	1.9	1.8
20	23.5	10.8	7.1	5.2	4.1	3.4	3.0	2.6	2.2	2.0	1.8	1.7
21	22.1	10.2	6.8	4.9	3.9	3.2	2.9	2.4	2.1	1.9	1.7	1.6
22	21.0	9.8	6.4	4.7	3.7	3.1	2.7	2.3	2.0	1.8	1.6	1.5
23	20.0	9.3	6.1	4.5	3.5	2.9	2.6	2.2	1.9	1.7	1.5	1.4
24	19.0	8.9	5.8	4.3	3.4	2.8	2.5	2.1	1.8	1.7	1.5	1.4

U.S.F.S., Region 1, Foresters Field Handbook, 1971.

for each diameter class. The growth percent can be calculated by various formulas, such as the Gevorkiantz formula:

$$p = 456/(ND)$$

where p = growth percent per year

        N = number of rings in the last inch

        D = present dbh

A stock table is prepared from the stand table of the average acre of the forest by multiplying the number of trees in each diameter class by the corresponding value from the right volume table. This then gives the volume in each diameter class, which when totalled is the present volume on the average acre. The corresponding volumes for the next year of the diameter classes are computed by multiplying the present volume in each class by the average growth percent of that class. These figures are added to obtain the forecasted volume of the average acre. The differences between that volume and the present volume is the expected growth in one year. Before this value can be used it has to be adjusted the same way for anticipated mortality as is done in the above stand table projection method.

The third common method to measure the growth of a forest is by using permanent sample plots. This system, often called the *continuous forest inventory* (CFI), usually is the most accurate, but it involves a considerable expenditure of time and money. It requires the establishment of enough sample plots to produce information that is statistically sound. The number of plots, commonly one-fifth or one-fourth acre, depends on area of the stand, the stocking, the variability of the stand, and the accuracy desired. More plots are needed for large tracts than small, poor stocking than good, patchy stands than uniform ones, and when a high degree of accuracy is wanted. Assuming a desired accuracy of 90 percent and average stocking and variability, the number of one-fifth acre plots needed would range from 67 for 40 acres to 100 for 5,000 acres and above. The plot number can be calculated exactly by statistical procedures after some preliminary measurements of the forest regarding stocking and variability, or standard tables like V-5 could be used in most cases.

While the CFI plots are located and permanently marked to determine saw-timber growth, all trees over 10 in. dbh have to be carefully measured for diameter and height. Using these measurements the present volume of all the plots is determined from appropriate volume tables. The plots are remeasured at intervals of 5 to 10 years to obtain the timber volume on the plots at that time. The difference in volume between one measurement time and the succeeding one is the growth for the area contained in all the plots for the stated period. This can be translated to average annual growth per acre by dividing it first by the acreage in the plots and next by the number of years between measurement. If some growth information is wanted at the time when the plots are first measured, increment borings can be made of a representative number of trees in each diameter class, and this can be used to make the first growth forecast by the stand-table projection or growth percentage method. Except in this case of the first measurement, no adjustment is necessary to obtain net volume, because loss from mortality would be reflected in the successive measurements. However, any volume removed by harvesting any plot areas since last measurement, should be recorded and this included in the growth for that period.

Before closing this subject of growth, some appropriate observations should be made. Growth rates of forests in California have a wide range— from less than 100 bd. ft. per acre per year to as high as 2000 bd. ft. The net average for all California stands is about 300 bd. ft. per acre per year. In general, when the potential net annual growth is much less than 200 bd. ft. per acre for a property not much intensive forestry can be justified. This means that timber management should be ordinarily concentrated on medium and better sites. Getting specific figures for one's property may be difficult and often costly and time-consuming, and the results may not be entirely dependable, because certain assumptions have to be made, e.g., the future growth will be the same as in the past. In some cases, the forecasted growth will be too high, and in others it may be too low. Any figures that are developed, regardless of the method, should be tentative and adjusted downward or upward by trial and error and practical experience.

Management Planning

Beside the care and improvement of the trees, the concept of forest management includes the regulation of the forest so as to promote maximum continuous production of crops. This is called sustained yield. The objective is to eventually achieve a balance between the growth of a forest and the amount harvested. Maintaining a somewhat even flow of crops over time from the forest may be another objective.

Before going into this subject there are a few more terms that should be defined. The term rotation means the general age to which trees will be grown before they are harvested. Different rotation ages are used, depending on such factors as species, growth, site, forest products to be grown, and desires of the tree farmer. Rotations are usually set at or below the age where the mean annual growth of a stand begins to decline from the peak of biological maturity. Short rotations like 40 years may be appropriate for pulpwood, but longer ones of 50 to 100, or even more, are necessary for saw and veneer logs. The term cutting cycle denotes the number of years from one logging to another on the same area, where repeated cuts are made, none of which remove the entire stand. The cycle should equal the number of years it takes for a partially cut stand to produce trees that are ready for another harvest. Many other terms used in forestry are defined in the Appendix.

Regulation

To regulate the forest the tree farmer tries to convert the stand into a healthy condition, where all of the area is adequately stocked in accordance with the site capabilities and where there is a proper distribution of age classes. In an all-aged stand an owner would want to have a mixture of all age-classes from one year old to the rotation age in the right proportions. Theoretically then, the periodic harvest would be restricted to trees of the rotation age and older classes only, unless some recently defective younger trees also needed removal.

The classic example of a completely regulated even-aged forest would be one containing equal areas of each age class with the area of trees of the rotation age class, e.g., 80 years, being harvested over each decade. Because management of California's forests is relatively recent and has been based largely on virgin timber, we have few examples of a completely regulated forest, yet the principle is still valid for long-range planning purposes.

What can be cut from a forest is dependent upon how well the forest is regulated. One with a great amount of large trees in relation to other sizes would demand a heavier annual cut than usual over enough years to bring about a better distribution of age classes. It also would be necessary in order to convert such slow-growing stands to young, fast-growing trees. Conversely, a forest with little mature timber, poorly stocked areas, or large gaps in age classes should be harvested at a rate less than usual for awhile in order to achieve desired age-class distribution. In other words, the level of cutting should be adjusted so that the forest can be placed into a regulated condition as early as possible (preferably in the first rotation), where all age classes are proportionately represented and an optimum stocking of healthy trees is present.

Allowable Cut

If one has a fully regulated forest, it would be fairly easy to determine the allowable annual cut. It simply would equal the net growth of the stand as indicated by appropriate yield tables or from growth measurements. However, very few, if any, of our forests are yet regulated, and this situation causes a lot of difficulty in arriving at an allowable cut figure.

There are a great many methods for determining allowable cut. They include a few graphic presentations, a wide variety of formulas, and some rather sophisticated computer programs. A lot of data about the forest is required by some of the formulas and by all computer methods. The ease of application depends largely on the complexity of the forest and how it departs from a regulated condition. Nonetheless, a tree farmer should establish by whatever way is most practicable at least a preliminary level of annual allowable cut and be prepared to modify it to meet changing facts and conditions.

It is beyond the scope of this handbook to go very deeply into this subject. The methodology is definitely something that needs professional treatment. However, to illustrate some of the principles involved, a few of the more simple approaches will be explained.

One of these is the *Van Mantel formula* which works best with even-aged stands, and the more regular they are the better the results. It has been principally used for preliminary planning purposes. The formula reads as follows:

$$AC = (2 \times V)/R$$

Where AC = annual allowable cut of the stand

V = timber volume thereon

R = rotation period in years

Note that no growth information is required. This formula gives much too low results, especially when board feet are used, because only merchantable trees are included in the volume. As a result, it grossly underestimates actual growth. When used with caution, this formula is an easily applied and valuable check on what the allowable cut might be for a natural forest, but its limitations must be clearly recognized.

Probably with more reservations than in the case of even-aged forests, the Van Mantel formula has been adapted to selection cutting of all-aged forests. Here annual cut would be twice the timber volume times the cutting cycle expressed in years, all divided by the rotation.

The *current growth formula*, often used by foresters, is an emperical or informal method to calculate the allowable cut of forests being deficient in growing stock that are to be placed under management. Its principle is that, if the current growth is known, all that is required is to harvest less than the growth in order to build up the stocking of the forest. The cut is therefore assessed as a fraction of growth: AC = actual growth of the total stand times a reduction factor. The value of the reduction factor is set by judgement, depending on the shortness of the stocking of the forest and silvicultural and economic conditions. Usually the reduction factor runs from 0.6 to something less than 1.0.

A *stand growth percentage method* is one that can be used to set the allowable cut of an all-aged forest, especially one that has satisfactory stocking. The average annual percentage growth rate of the stand as a whole needs to be estimated or known. It can be derived by finding the total annual growth of a stand by methods discussed earlier and dividing that by the total stand volume. The formula for the stand growth percentage method gives the percentage of the stand volume that may be cut and restored by growth for various rates of stand growth and cutting cycles:

$$I = (i \times CC) / [1 + (i \times CC)]$$

Where I = percentage of stand to be cut

i = average annual growth percent for the stand

CC = cutting cycle in years

Table II-6 gives for different rates of growth and cutting cycles what percentage of the stand can be harvested and replaced by growth during that time period. By that table, a stand with an average annual growth of 5 percent being cut on a 10-year cutting cycle would have 33 percent of its volume cut every ten years. Of course, this harvest could be spread evenly over each year in the cycle and be concentrated on those areas where the cutting would be most beneficial silviculturally and economically.

Table II-6.   Percentage of allowable stand cut for various rates of growth and cutting cycles.

Cutting Cycle (years)	Average Annual Stand Growth Percent (simple interest)						
	2	3	4	5	6	7	8
5	9	13	17	20	23	26	29
10	17	23	29	33	37	41	44
15	23	31	37	43	47	51	55
20	29	37	44	50	55	58	64

It should be remembered that what the forest manager does in the way of improvement of a stand affects the allowable cut possibilities. If the owner has an active, successful reforestation program, uses fast-growing trees, or takes timber stand improvement measures, the allowable cut can be almost immediately set higher than would otherwise be prudent. The reason for this is that in time these practices will increase the yield. Some industrial tree farms also apply fertilizers to increase growth. How much higher the cut can be elevated depends on the amount and intensity of such efforts, and this has to be carefully assessed so that the allowable cut is not raised too much. These kinds of practices have the capacity to increase allowable cut of a forest as much as 30 percent or more.

Management Plans

The reader has seen that the regulation and determination of the allowable cut of a forest are complex, involving many factors. Without going to a great deal of expense, the methodology is not necessarily exact, especially when forests are not in a regulated condition, and much professional judgement based on practical experience has to be exercised. Run-down stands first coming under management certainly do not require precise formulas or methods to determine cut, or sophisticated management planning. In those cases, priority has to be given to rehabilitation and forest improvement until adequate stocking can be established. The basic aim is to have an overall plan to be sure that eventual harvests are within the productive potential of the forest and in line with a reasonable distribution of age and size classes. Whatever is done, it must relate to the owners objectives, the economic situation, the forest itself, and be flexible to take advantage of knowledge gained about the forest and to meet changing conditions.

Forest management is a long-term continuing process and it has to be based on a good knowledge of the property. Decisions have to be made for current operations and also for a long time into the future. Therefore, it is advisable to have a management or working plan for one's forest. It is a written document, including maps and records, that is prepared to maintain the owner's policies and actions by prescribing and controlling the basic operation of a forest over a period of years. The plan should not be rigid and it should be revised periodically. The contents of a forest management plan are outlined below:

- A. Introduction
    - Location and boundaries
    - Acquisition history
- B. General physiographic features
    - Climate
    - Topography
    - Geology
    - Soil
- C. Forest description
    - Forest type
    - Site
    - Previous cutting
    - Growth potential
    - Access and roads
- D. Economic situation
    - Local markets
    - Transportation
- E. Management objectives
    - Wood products
    - Range
    - Water
    - Wildlife
    - Recreation
- F. Silvicultural treatment
    - Silvicultural systems
    - Logging conditions
    - Pest protection measures
    - Stand improvement
    - Reforestation
- G. Regulation
    - Rotation and cutting cycle
    - Allowable cut
    - Cutting budget and order
- H. Sales policy
- I. Other management factors
    - Acquisition plans
    - Other forest uses
    - Road development
    - Fire protection
    - Zoning and land-use regulation
    - Miscellaneous
- J. Appendix
    - Stock and stand tables
    - Cruise reports
    - Growth data
    - Various maps

Silvicultural Systems

Various cutting systems are used to grow, tend, and harvest forest crops in accordance with a planned program. What system is used depends primarily on the nature of the stand, because, unless the harvested area is to be seeded or planted by man, the chosen method should be favorable towards quick natural reproduction. Other factors to consider are the need for improvement of the stand, type of forest regulation chosen, the economic aspects of the cutting, market considerations, and logging conditions. There are four basic systems in use: (1) clear cutting, (2) seed-tree, (3) selection, and (4) shelterwood. In addition, there are combinations and variations of these cutting systems.

Clear Cutting

Clear cutting is what the name implies—removal of all or most of the trees. The system is appropriate to use on merchantable even-aged stands, especially where the species being harvested needs sunlight to reproduce and grow, or where windthrow is a serious threat to partially cut stands. If natural seeding is being depended on, mature trees should surround the cutting, and the area should not be too large—preferably less than 40 acres. Because natural seeding is not too dependable, aerial or hand seeding and planting of seedlings are commonly done after harvests are made. Clear cutting is a drastic treatment in some ways. It reduces the forest cover so much that soil damage can result, unless appropriate erosion control procedures are undertaken. In clear cutting, cable logging is often employed to reduce damage from skidding and road construction associated with tractor logging. The appearance of clear-cuts is often poor; this can be alleviated by keeping them away from roads and streams, and by using irregular shapes. Clear cutting is used on both private and public land, particularly in old-growth redwood and Douglas-fir in northwestern California and also elsewhere in pure pine and red fir stands.

Seed-Tree Cutting

Seed-tree cutting is the removal of all merchantable trees except those required to naturally seed the area. This is accomplished by leaving at least two (preferably more) designated large trees per acre for good seed production, or by leaving blocks of uncut trees to serve the same purpose. This cutting method may be applied to both all-aged and even-aged forests, although the succeeding crop is quite even-aged, except for the residual trees from the original stand. This system has been widely combined in this state with a minimum cutting diameter limit. Under this version, except for desired seed trees and obviously defective trees, all trees are felled above a prescribed minimum diameter, e.g., 18″ dbh. Neither seed-tree cutting nor the combination has been entirely efficient here in regenerating a new crop of trees. Often where the residual stand does not provide enough cover, the site is captured by competing brush which takes many years to be shaded out by trees. Windfall of seed trees and smaller residual timber can also be a problem.

Shelterwood

The shelterwood system is the gradual removal of the timber crop in two or more steps designed for specific purposes. The object is to obtain natural reproduction of the stand under the protection of a forest cover. This system has been rarely used in California, although it has been tried on an experimental virgin redwood forest and an experimental young-growth, mixed conifer forest, both with favorable results.

Selection

The selection cutting method is the most common one in California. It is the periodic removal of certain trees, individually (single tree selection) or in small groups (group selection) from an all-aged forest. The trees or groups of trees selected for harvest are the overmature, suppressed, defective, and some mature trees. The unit-area control system is a form of group selection, where an attempt is made to cut areas of trees of like condition, in effect creating very small clear-cuts. The Dunning's tree classes are a useful guide for marking trees to be cut, especially in older pine forests. Usual practice is to take the poorer risk trees, like numbers 4, 5, and 7 (Figure II-2). Other trees may also be cut for economic reasons, to eliminate unwanted species, or to thin out trees to obtain better spacing. Basal area can also be used as a cutting control. It should not ordinarily be reduced to levels below 70 to 100 square feet, depending on species, forest type, site, stand condition, growth, and other factors.

The cycle beween cuttings should be long enough to obtain some reproduction, but short enough to capture trees of poor risk before they die and yet provide enough volume to justify the logging. Cutting cycles in California range from 10 to 20 years.

Where properly applied, the selection system is an excellent one. It produces a diverse all-aged forest that protects the site, it favors continuous reproduction, and rates high from the aesthetic standpoint.

Other Systems

In addition to these four basic silvicultural systems, there are other cuttings that can be made. These include thinnings, sanitation-salvage harvests, and other special cuttings (see Timber Stand Improvement later).

Environmental Factors

In choosing and applying silvicultural systems, one must give serious thought to not only the protection of the forest from the crop standpoint, but also to preventing environmental damage. Non-wood values of the forest are important to the owner and general public alike. They are of sufficient importance to the general welfare that these other values are protected by the State Forest Practice Act and a number of other laws and regulations, which are discussed in Chapter IV. Therefore, the multiple-use concept should be practiced, whereby the soil, water, range, wildlife, recreation, and aesthetic benefits are retained as much as possible. More will be said about this subject in the last two Chapters.

Soil and Water

The soil is the basic resource to a tree farmer. It is a main element of the growing site and should not be wasted away by erosion. Soil erosion can also cause costly road damage, foul other lands, deteriorate the quality of water in springs, lakes, and streams, and deposit sediments in reservoirs and where fish live and spawn.

Fish and Wildlife

In addition to fish, there are many other kinds of wildlife that are affected by forest operations. Logging an area temporarily changes the habitat; some changes may be good temporarily, such as for deer, quail, and song birds that feed on grasses, herbs, and shrubs that come in after a cutting, but other changes may be detrimental to birds like eagles, ospreys, and others, which nest in trees and snags. Woodpeckers are particularly beneficial to a forest because they help control tree-killing insects by feeding on the insects and larvae in defective and dead trees. How a forest is managed will largely determine what the overall wildlife composition will be. Of course, some species like gophers, mice, rabbits, porcupines, and even deer and bear may cause serious injury at times, so these factors have to be considered also and special measures taken to control the damage (see Chapter VIII).

Aesthetics and Recreation

The appearance and cultural resources of a forest are of special concern to the public, who can be critical of the results of forest harvests. This can lead to more legal restraints and can hamper or, in some cases, even prohibit logging. Besides economic gain, a tree farmer receives personal satisfaction and pride from how well beauty, rare and endangered species, and archaeological and historical sites are protected. In some cases commercial forests can be integrated into a beneficial and profitable recreation program, and these attributes are important to such use.

Timber Stand Improvement

Other measures are often applied in the forest besides the basic systems explained earlier. Their purpose is to improve the composition, condition, health, growth, and quality of the trees.

Thinning

A forest manager can make careful intermediate cuttings or thinnings to a good advantage in young stands. If there is a market or personal need for small logs, posts, poles, piling, pulpwood, firewood, Christmas trees, and similar products; such cuttings may pay; otherwise thinning trees is expensive, slow, hard work. Unless it is a paying proposition in terms of useful products, it is not ordinarily done except in those cases where it is especially desirable for silvicultural reasons.

Trees in well-stocked or crowded stands tend to slow down in growth and many die in time. Thinning actually saves the growth of trees that will die before final harvest. A useful tool to see what is happening is the increment borer, which reveals the annual ring growth. Other indicators of the need for thinning are closeness of trunks, crowding or overlapping of tree crowns, and thin stems. A thinning ordinarily releases the trees from excessive competition and stimulates greater growth on the remaining crop trees. These should be selected early and favored in the thinning process (Figure II-4). This could be done regularly, perhaps every 5 to 10 years, for at least a few decades until the forest reaches a peak condition. However, intermediate cuttings must be carefully done, because as trees grow older they lose their ability to release, and some species release better than others.

Figure II-4

Increase or release in diameter growth of a tree after removal by cutting of some competing trees in the stand is clearly shown in this cross section.

The thinnings should first remove defective, poor-growing, otherwise undesirable trees, and also trees necessary to achieve a better spacing. Here, rules-of-thumb can be handy. One guide that is helpful in the pine region to better space trees is the D + 4 rule, which means that optimum spacing between trees would be equal to the tree diameter plus 4 stated in feet. Thus, the desired spacing for 18" dbh trees would be 22 feet. The rule can be modified to better fit local conditions or extended to other forest types by replacing the figure 4 with another number that experience has shown to be appropriate.

Basal area values also can be useful in determining how much to thin, as they are in selection cutting. Figure II-5 shows the relationships between basal area, average dbh, and tree spacing.

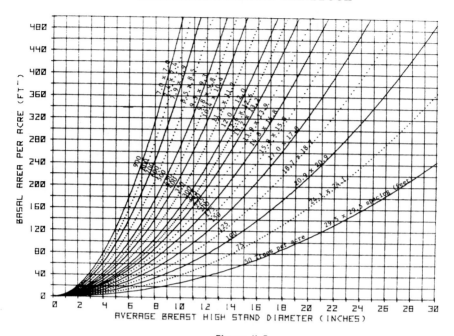

Figure II-5

Stand basal area, average dbh, and tree spacing relationships.
U.S.F.S., Pacific Northwest Forest and Range Experiment Station, 1977.

Pruning

Pruning the lower branches of young trees raises the future quality and value of them for use as saw or veneer logs. Only so-called crop trees that are vigorous, sound, and well-formed should be pruned. Generally, stands are ready for pruning when these trees are from 4 to 12 inches dbh, because they have the potential of putting on another 12 inches of clear wood, which would pay for the pruning. This would take 30 years or more—a long-time investment. Real heavy-limbed trees do not justify pruning because of cost, neither do the lower valued species. Because of the work and expense of pruning, the delimbing is done only to the height that would produce one log 18 feet above ground for a sawlog and 10 feet for a veneer log. Not more than one-fourth the live crown shown should be removed at one time; otherwise the tree's growth could be set back. Curved pruning saws are better to use than axes or clubs, because saws make a neat cut close to the trunk that will heal over sooner (Figure II-6). Light chain saws can be used effectively on the lower and larger limbs, but this has to be carefully done to avoid injury to the operator.

Herbicides and Fertilizers

There are additional stand improvement measures that may be applicable under certain circumstances. Chemicals called herbicides or silvicides are used to decrease competition from unwanted trees and growth. Individual trees or large shrubs, especially sprouting species that grow back after cutting, can be ringed with an axe and the chemical placed in the cut. Hand-spraying of smaller individual plants can be done also. Aerial application is necessary where broadcast treatment of chemicals is required to control competition to crop trees from brush and hardwoods of no value. It takes specialized knowledge to properly and safely (both from the human and environmental standpoints) to use chemicals, and most if not all are strictly regulated by law. Therefore, a tree farmer contemplating their use would be well advised to consult experts like CDF forest advisers, county agricultural commissioners, licensed pest control operators, manufacturer representatives, and aerial applicator companies.

Fertilization of the forest is a growth and stand improvement measure of some promise. Nitrogen is the main additive although some soils may require other elements. Before forests are fertilized the soils and tree foliage should be checked and consideration given to what fertilizers to use, method of application, costs, and probable returns. The help of specialists should be definitely sought before any fertilization program is initiated to avoid wasteful expenditures and to attain satisfactory response.

Figure II-6

Pruning the lower limbs of younger trees can improve the quality of the butt log.

Reforestation

Reforestation, like many other subjects in this handbook, is a big field, and no attempt is made here to cover it thoroughly, but to only bring out the most essential facts. Fortunately, there are readily available some good written material (see Appendix) and advice on the topic. Several options for reforestation are possible as discussed below.

Natural Seeding

The reproduction of a forest by natural means is obviously preferred whenever possible by tree farmers over that done artificially by hand. To accomplish this, the managment practices—cutting systems, logging, site preparation, protection—are designed to favor nature's method and to protect the young unmerchantable trees that are already established and ready to grow to be crop trees. In many cases the results are quite satisfactory and certainly are less costly than artificial reforestation.

To obtain natural reproduction there must be sufficient viable seed, favorable conditions of soil, weather, light, vegetative cover, and minimum chances for depredation by insects, birds, rodents, and other animals. The amount and quality of available seed depends on nearness of seed trees, their species, age, health, and the seed year, which varies greatly from poor to good. In most years seed crops are not satisfactory; depending on species, medium and above crops only occur on the average of every 4 to 5 years. Because the best seed producers are young to mature, thrifty, dominant trees with large crowns, those are the types to be selected for seed trees.

In the case of conifers, one good tree can produce hundreds of cones, each containing scores of seed, but all may not be viable. Thus, literally millions of seed are cast on forest areas when conditions are right. One pound of cleaned seed has thousands of seed, and the viability differs considerably (Table II-7).

Table II-7.   Number of clean seed per pound and average germination capacity after stratification for selected California conifers.

Species	Number	Percent
Douglas-fir	42,000	85
Fir, grand	23,200	28
Fir, red	6,600	25
Fir, white	15,100	34
Hemlock, western	297,000	56
Incense-cedar	15,000	50
Pine, Jeffrey	4,000	68
Pine, lodgepole	102,000	80
Pine, ponderosa	12,000	59
Pine, sugar	2,100	56
Redwood, coast	122,000	10
Redwood, Sierra	91,000	25
Western red-cedar	414,000	51

When cones ripen in the fall, they open and release their seed which descend to the ground or are scattered by wind. Conifers have winged seed that enables the seed to fly away from the tree for some distance depending on species, height of the tree, topography, and wind direction and speed. The distance can vary from the immediate ground area below the crown to a number of times the height of the tree of origin. Of course, most seed fall close to the tree and gradually diminish outward. Characteristics and patterns of seedfall in the forest should be observed and an area harvested accordingly, especially clear cuts, in order to obtain the best chances for the success from natural seeding. As noted, the quality or germination percent of seed is quite variable among species and between seed years, so this fact needs to be taken into account also.

A mineral seedbed devoid of most vegetation and organic material is preferred by most conifers. This is shown dramatically by how well trees become established on road cuts and fills and other bare areas. Logging the area in mid-summer of good seed years can be helpful in this respect in that it scarifies the soil and reduces competing ground vegetation, thereby making the site more receptive to seed. And other site preparation measures, like using a tractor to rake or lightly bulldoze the area, in good seed years to accomplish the same effect may be warranted.

A moist soil with favorable growing temperatures during the spring and early summer months is required for seed germination and enough root penetration to follow the moisture level as it recedes in late summer and fall. Consequently, drought years or an exceptionally dry exposed site can be disastrous. Depending on the tolerance of the species, there has to be enough light to support photosynthesis, and seedlings of intolerant species like most pines will die in too much shade.

Crops of forest cones, seed, and young seedlings, may be diminished considerably by insects, fungi, and animals. Damaging insects include cone beetles, cone worms, seed chalcids, maggots, grasshoppers, and many others which are not readily controllable. Fungi-like molds and damping-off disease brought about by warm moist weather are in the same category. Many animals are involved in cone, seed, or seedling depredation—birds, squirrels, chipmunks, mice, rats, gophers, and rabbits. Some methods are available for control of such animal damage, but this is usually done for artificial seeding rather than for natural seeding, and an expert should be consulted especially regarding use of chemicals, some of which if not carefully used can be dangerous to humans, domestic animals, wildlife, and the environment. To justify the added costs of control it should only be done in areas and at times when good seedfall is expected.

Weather factors other than drought that can cause damage are those brought about by extreme conditions. Severe late spring or early fall freezes can kill immature cones, and prolonged stormy weather during the pollination period can cause abortion of cones and low seed quality. Unseasonal low temperatures can also destroy young cones. Spells of cold temperatures during the early growing season can bring about frost-heaving of tender seedlings; excessive temperatures can be lethal also.

Artificial Seeding

To avoid the vagaries of nature and to speed up a rather slow process, a number of methods of artificial reforestation have been developed and are being increasingly used by tree farmers, both large and small, private and public. These practices to upgrade the stocking of a forest can be very rewarding since this can permit earlier increase of the allowable cut of a forest. Because of its ease and relatively low cost, artificial seeding has been quite popular, although it is giving way more and more to planting. Providing seed can be collected or obtained, one of the advantages of direct seeding is that it can be done promptly after catastrophies like fire or to substitute for natural seeding of recent cut-over areas in need of

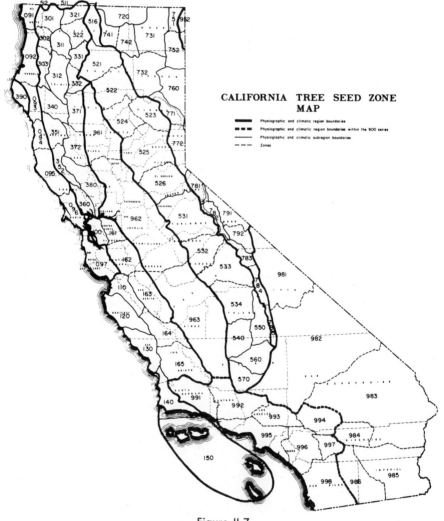

CALIFORNIA TREE SEED ZONE
MAP

━━━ Physiographic and climatic region boundaries
■ ■ ■ Physiographic and climatic region boundaries within the 900 series
────── Physiographic and climatic subregion boundaries
─ ─ ─ Zones

Figure II-7
California tree seed zones.

restocking. The right kind of planting stock is sometimes difficult to procure, and seeding costs generally average one-fourth to one-half planting costs. But seeding results may not be satisfactory in many cases because of seed and seedling depredation, drought during time of germination and early growth, disease attacks, frost damage, and competition from other plants.

The seed that is to be used should be preferably of species native to the area and meet acceptable purity and germination percent standards. The seed should also be from the local area or a tree seed zone that is compatible in terms of latitude and elevation. Figure II-7 shows the zones recognized in California. A larger copy is available from the Department of Forestry. Seed can be purchased from a number of private suppliers, a list of which can also be requested from the Department.

Seeding in the fall is usually preferred over spring sowing because of less risks. The seed should be pre-conditioned by a moist-cold stratification process, which will break the dormancy of the seed and stimulate germination. A simple way to do this is to (1) soak the seed in tap water for 1–2 days, (2) drain off excess moisture, (3) place seed in plastic bags and close them with a rubber band, and (4) store under temperatures of 32° to 36° F. for about two months prior to use.

Three methods are used to sow the seed: (1) broadcast, (2) spot, and (3) drill. The first of these has been most popular, mostly in the northwestern part of the state, where climatic conditions are more favorable. Usually it is done by using aerial contractors, although for smaller areas a cyclone hand seeder can be employed. Depending on species, from one-half to over one pound of seed is used per acre.

Because seed-eating rodents have been the main cause of failures in direct seeding, it is wise to take some measures to prevent this damage. First, some idea of the rodent population in the area should be obtained; this should be done by wildlife biologists who make sample trappings and prescribe the necessary treatment. This can consist of treating the area with certain chemical baits that temporarily lower the rodent population, or by treating the tree seed with chemicals that repel the rodents, or doing a combination of both treatments. The chemicals in the baits and repellents, if not properly used, can cause damage to other wildlife like birds and fish and affect the water quality of streams and lakes. And they can injure man and domestic animals, so the use of rodenticides and repellents is strictly controlled by law, and use permits must be obtained from the county agricultural commissioner.

Spot seeding has been tried to a considerable extent, particularly on experimental plots and by tree farmers on a limited basis, but the results have not always been too satisfactory. The same problems encountered with broadcast seeding are ever present. A few seed are implanted into well-spaced (6–8 feet), prepared spots of bare soil by hand tools, corn planters, or special walking-stick seeders. Here chemicals can also be used to control rodent damage. Another rodent control measure is to cover the seeded spot with a small dome-shaped or cylindrical barrier (Figure II-8) made from hardware screen that is pressed into the soil. These devices are costly when many spots need to be covered and they take more work to pack in, and the screens have to be removed after the start of the second growing season. Before this method is tried it should be tested in the local area to see how well it does the job.

Figure II-8

A metal screen 4″ x 6″ is sometimes used to protect a seed spot from rodents.

The last method of seeding is by tractor-drawn drilling machines like the rangeland drill, modified corn planters, and machines especially made for tree seeding purposes. Although the results of a few experiments in California have been encouraging, not much drill-seeding has taken place in this state because our forest lands are mostly too rough and the site needs to be well prepared.

Planting

Planting has become the more favored artificial reforestation method. Although it takes longer to accomplish and is costly, if the proper procedures are followed, the results can be more consistently positive than by seeding. Planting has also supplemented and even replaced natural methods in more and more cases, because prompt re-establishment of trees is a prerequisite for early sustained yield management.

A key decision is where to plant. In general, priority should be given to the lands needing it most, e.g., unstocked areas, and where the potential success and returns will best pay for the investment being made. Thus, unstocked forest lands should come before those that are only partly stocked, and the high site before medium. From an economic standpoint, low site lands cannot ordinarily justify the expense of planting. Here is where site surveys, soil-vegetation maps, and other references having site and soils information are of inestimable value.

The slope aspect has a bearing also on what trees to plant. Northerly and easterly exposures which are shadier, cooler, and moister, should be planted to the more tolerant species, while the south and west facing slopes should have the more intolerant species.

What species to plant depends on the locality and the wants of the owner. A good rule is that the species to plant should correspond with those that are native to the area, although some proven species of other countries or regions may be in order for special reasons. Most of the planting stock sold in California for timber production consists of ponderosa and Jeffrey pine, coast redwood, Douglas-fir, and sugar pine. Also, mainly for Christmas trees, other species like Monterey pine, red and white fir, Sierra redwood, and Scotch pine are grown by nurseries. Some pine hybrids show much promise in special cases because of fast growth and insect resistance. The trend now is to develop and use super trees which come from seed grown in orchards where the trees have originated from selected wild trees and have demonstrated high growth, good form, and other desirable traits.

Much of the conifer planting stock used in this state is bare-root grown in outside nurseries. It is lifted from nursery beds without soil, packed in a medium of wood waste in bundles of 100 to 1,000, and sold fresh or placed in cold storage until needed. The more common stock is 2-0, meaning it spent 2 years in the seedbed and none in a transplant bed. Some stock may be 1-0, 1-1, 2-2, etc. with the figures representing the years spent in each bed. Trees in the nursery are root-pruned at least once, or sometimes transplanted; both processes promote healthy root development. Increasing amounts of seedlings are grown in greenhouse nurseries, especially by large industrial tree farms in the redwood region. One-year seedlings are grown in special containers having a prepared fertilized growing medium. The trees are carefully removed from the containers with a minimum of root disturbance before placing into the ground upon planting.

Where needs are small, some resourceful tree farmers have successfully planted wild seedlings (wildlings) dug up from the forest or those grown in their own small nursery beds. But this is a painstaking business requiring a "green thumb", and would not ordinarily be the practical thing to do, particularly when plantings to be made are large or sporadic.

When to plant is another important consideration. In California, the best time has been generally in early spring, but late fall and winter planting works in some areas of milder climate. The factors involved here are the physiological condition of the planting stock, soil moisture availability, and anticipated weather during and after planting. The tops of the planting stock must not be growing yet at time of planting and the roots must be ready to start a season of new growth soon after planting. The soil at the planting location should be moist from the top down, and prospects for some further precipitation after planting should exist.

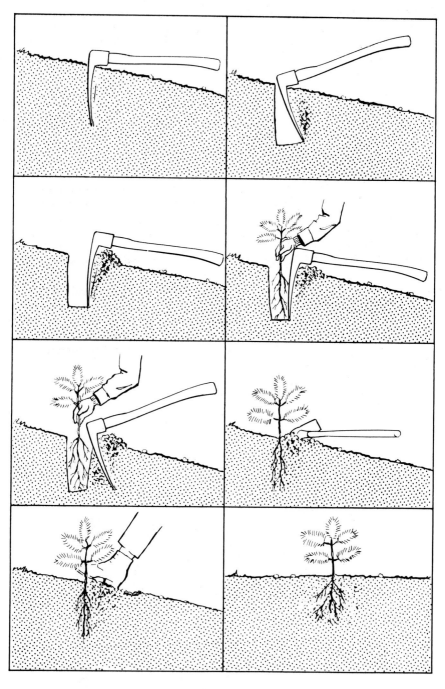

Figure II-9
A western planting tool is a common hand-planting method in California.

To enhance success of expensive planting endeavors, some sites have to be cleared to mineral soil with tractors, removing slash and competing vegetation. The debris is placed in piles or windrows that can be left or burned during safe periods. Herbicides have been used singly or in combination with mechanical clearing. Sometimes gophers, rabbits, and porcupines have to be controlled by baiting or trapping. The use of chemicals for plant and rodent control may require permission of the county agricultural commissioner.

Trees are planted in a number of ways—by hand tools, powered augers, and tractor-drawn planting machines. The former method is still the most adaptable in this state because of our difficult ground conditions. The western planting tool—a special hoe or mattock (Figure II-9)—, a planting bar, or a dibble for tubed seedlings are the hand tools in common use. The planting stock should be stored and handled carefully to prevent drying and planted with great care. Grass and herbs around the planting spot should be scalped to reduce competition.

The usual spacing now for growing timber is 10' x 10' , giving a stocking of 436 trees per acre, but closer or wider spacing may be desired depending on survival expectations, products to be grown, and precommercial thinning plans. The seedlings are ordinarily planted in parallel straight rows. An experienced planter under favorable conditions can plant from 350 to 700 bare-root trees per day. Planting with containerized seedlings is usually much faster. The number of trees per acre resulting from different spacings are given in Table II-8; it is derived from the formula:

$$N = 43,560 / (L \times W)$$

Where N = number of trees per acre

$43,560$ = the square feet in an acre

L = distance between plants in row

W = distance between rows

Table II-8.   Number of trees per acre for various square and rectangular spacings.

Spacing, feet	Number trees, per acre	Spacing, feet	Number trees, per acre
2 x 2	10,890	8 x 10	544
3 x 3	4,840	8 x 12	454
4 x 4	2,722	8 x 25	218
4 x 5	2,178	9 x 9	538
4 x 6	1,815	9 x 12	403
4 x 8	1,362	10 x 10	436
4 x 10	1,089	10 x 12	363
5 x 5	1,742	11 x 11	360
5 x 6	1,452	12 x 12	302
5 x 8	1,089	12 x 18	202
5 x 10	871	13 x 13	258
6 x 6	1,210	14 x 14	222
6 x 8	908	15 x 15	194
6 x 10	726	16 x 16	170
6 x 12	605	18 x 18	134
7 x 7	889	18 x 20	121
7 x 10	622	20 x 20	109
8 x 8	681	25 x 25	70

The chances for good survival of plantations can be increased in a number of ways. Using native mulch (leaves, humus, etc.) from immediately around the seedlings is one practical way to reduce moisture loss. Of course, watering is out of the question except for valuable seed orchards and other special plantings. Spraying the tops with transpiration inhibitors and fertilization at time of planting have not demonstrated consistent satisfactory benefits. Herbicides may be used for control of grass and weeds near the plantings. Shading of the seedlings with shingles or other devices has improved survival under some conditions. Protection from fire by reducing fire hazards and risks, maintaining firebreaks and fuelbreaks, and keeping access roads open should be planned and provided. Similarly, the forest manager should periodically examine the plantings to detect damage from insects, disease, and animals, and take appropriate corrective measures to control those pests if possible and practicable. There are a number of serious pests of plantations. See Chapter VIII for more explanation about forest protection.

Economics

Obviously, in managing a forest for timber production, the owner must be guided by the economics of the efforts put into the undertaking. In the long run, benefits to be derived from silvicultural measures, increasing the stocking base, careful cutting, regulation of the forest, and stand improvement should exceed the investment costs and interest charges. Sometimes financial consideration may suggest heavier harvests, especially of slow-growing, old-growth trees, and shorter rotations. A central objective of tree farming is to get the greatest possible growth from the forest and at the same time leave the smallest amount of timber on the ground as a capital investment.

From the short-term standpoint, regulating the forest to balance cut with growth and improvement of the stand may not seem financially attractive to a tree farmer. Of course, each situation has to be determined from the condition and potential of the forest and the owner's situation. While investments made in the forest may not pay off in the near future, it should be remembered that they do immediately increase the sale or estate value of the property. This can be compared to putting more money in the bank, although it is true that this capital is not nearly as liquid as money. However, prudent forest management brings about a much nicer looking forest with a higher value.

The economic potential of a forest can be increased by means other than regular timber harvests. These include the harvest of special forest products described in the next chapter and taking advantage of the range, water, wildlife, and recreation resources (see Chapters IX and X).

To encourage tree farmers to make long-term investments in their forest land, the costs of some practices are eligible for cost-sharing by the federal government. A major part of the expense of reforestation, thinning, and pruning may qualify for this financial assistance. In addition, the State provides assistance for reforestation projects. Low-interest loans may be available from the Federal Land Bank for forestry purposes. For information about these kinds of financial assistance see a CDF forest adviser.

Chapter III

WOOD PRODUCTS OF THE FOREST

There is a great variety of tangible and marketable products that can be obtained from the forest. They range in size from large sawlogs down to small tree seed, and the values and uses involved are also quite different. A tree farmer is wise to consider harvesting as many products as possible.

Conifer Sawlogs

By far, the commodity that is generated the most from our forests is in the form of conifer sawlogs; they constitute over 90 percent by volume of all our annual wood production. And sawlogs have the highest value in terms of the total yield of California forests. Good markets exist for logs that can be sawn into lumber.

The specifications for sawlogs mainly depend on needs of the market. Generally, merchantable sawlogs have minimum diameters (inside the bark) of five inches and up, and must be at least 10 feet long plus a trim allowance of 4 inches for every 16 feet. In the pine region the standard log is 16 feet (plus trim) in length, but logs may vary from lengths of 10 feet by even feet to 32 or 40 feet. In the redwood–Douglas-fir region the standard log is 20 feet long, but here again variable in length.

The length to which logs are cut for logging depends on size, weight, logging conditions, machinery used, and type of lumber to be cut. In case of small timber, it may be logged and hauled in tree lengths and not cut or bucked into logs until arrival at the mill.

Logs should be reasonably sound; a quarter or more of the volume should be defect free, depending on value and the logging costs. Low-value logs or those that could be expensive to harvest and deliver to a mill must be sounder than others to pay their way. Where logs can be used for pulpwood or chips it is possible to utilize some defective or cull logs.

Logs can be graded according to quality. There are no statewide or even regional standards for logs in California, and if used, they are the result of requirements of the local market or timber seller-buyer contracts. Sometimes a simple grading system is achieved by segregating old-growth logs from young-growth, large from small, and sawlogs from those useable for veneer and plywood purposes. Usually a small tree farmer would not want to be bothered by grades unless he or she chose to personally harvest and sell the logs and the grading was worth the expense.

The measurement of logs for volume and defect is called scaling and is described in Chapter VI.

Conifer Veneer Logs

Conifer logs of high quality and large size can be more profitably utilized by marketing them as veneer logs, or peelers as they are usually called. Douglas-fir is the leading species, although coast redwood, ponderosa pine, sugar pine, and some true fir are also used for veneer, most of which goes into plywood.

At one time peelers were clear, lower-trunk logs of 30 inches or more in diameter, but now sound logs of lower quality and lesser diameter are being increasingly used to manufacture plywood. Before peeling on the lathe, the logs are sawn into lengths of 8 feet plus some trim allowance. Therefore, logs prepared for this market are bucked into multiples of that length.

Some veneer (named shook) is also produced at a few places in California for manufacture into boxes and other containers mainly for the agricultural industry. The veneer can come from large lathes similar to those in plywood plants, or be sliced or peeled from special bolts or blocks smaller than the usual veneer or peeler logs. Shook blocks 19 inches in length by 18 inches in diameter and larger of knot-free wood are peeled on small lathes. Sometimes these blocks can be made from quite limby trees by just cutting them from between the whorls, and using the remaining knotty and poor quality pieces as fuelwood. The species employed for shook are ponderosa, sugar, and digger pine, Douglas-fir, and Sitka spruce.

Hardwoods

Although California hardwoods don't have the size, form, quality, and diversity of those in eastern U. S., they still have good prospects. They are slowly increasing in use for sawing into lumber and for pulpwood and chipwood where the better stands occur. Species used for lumber include alder, black oak, chinkapin, cottonwood, madrone, sycamore, tanoak, white oak, and a few others.

As for pulpwood and chipwood, eucalyptus has been the principal hardwood species used (see section below). Other hardwoods, like tanoak, have been made into chipwood when the market was especially good.

The stump portion, swelled trunk pieces (large burls), sections with forks of the stem, and other pieces having special figure characteristics of some trees are utilized in the furniture, novelty, and special wood products trade. Black walnut, cottonwood, California laurel, and madrone are the main species in demand. The logs or chunks are sold by the ton.

The utilization of our hardwoods for fuel is discussed in a later section on fuelwood.

Pulpwood and Chipwood

With the installation of pulp mills in California and the development of a foreign export market, pulpwood and chipwood are rapidly expanding forest products. This development has resulted in a much better utilization of our commercial forests and enhanced opportunities for tree farmers to practice more intensive forest management.

Most of the raw material for pulp that is marketed in this state is in the form of chips that are made from sawmill and plywood plant waste. The chips are used or sold for domestic pulp production or exported. Chips are also used to make hardboards (like masonite) and less dense, thicker particleboards. Some chips have come from the chipping of woods wastes by mobile chippers. This probably will increase in the future and include chipping of thinnings and hardwoods.

Chips are measured by the "unit" which is equal to a gross content of 200 cubic feet in uncompacted form. Depending on species and moisture content, a unit weighs from 1800 to 2100 pounds. Loosely packed, the average solid-wood content of a unit is only about 72 cubic feet. The "bone-dry unit" or "B.D.U." in use by some chip purchasers is equivalent to 2,400 pounds of oven-dry chips. The B.D.U. of a load of delivered chips is determined by drying and weighing sample lots.

As mentioned earlier, low quality and cull sawlogs may be chipped for pulp where the logging and handling costs are favorable. Also, pulpwood in form of logs or cordwood can be obtained from thinnings, salvage of fire-killed timber, and special harvests as it is done so much in the east and south, but this latter method is not practiced much yet in California. Woods waste like broken logs, chunks, and tops is collected to some extent and brought to chippers at mills and at pulp plants. Pulpwood in sawlog form is measured by board feet while that in smaller sizes may be measured by the cord—128 gross cu. ft. of wood (see Chapter VI); it roughly equals 500 board feet.

Poles, Piling, and Posts

Roundwood products from the forest in form of poles, piling, and posts can be marketed in a number of areas of the state. These are something that a tree farmer can fairly easily harvest personally and not require too much equipment or a high degree of skill. They can be used to some extent by the forest owner for building purposes, fences, etc. Another advantage is that these roundwood products provide an opportunity to utilize some of the material arising from stand improvement measures, thinnings, and salvage before or after regular logging.

Poles are made in many sizes and for a number of purposes, e.g., utility lines, pole-constructed buildings, and other special purposes. Douglas-fir, western hemlock, ponderosa and lodgepole pine, true firs, and a few other species are used. Poles for usual purposes are made from the smaller diameter trees—from 9 to 22 inches dbh—that are live, straight, sound, tall, and free of heavy limbs. Minimum top diameters run from 5 to 9 inches.

Pole operators classify poles by species, length, minimum top diameter, circumference 6 feet from the butt, and into six bending-strength categories established by the industry. Poles are usually sold by the piece. Most poles in the trade are peeled and treated at commercial plants using preservatives like creosote or other special chemicals to improve their resistance to rot and insects.

Pilings are similar to poles; most here are cut from Douglas-fir and coast redwood. They are made from good quality trees 7 to 20 inches dbh—with minimum top diameters of 5 to 12 inches. Standard specifications are somewhat more complex than for poles and are different for friction piles and end-bearing piles. In addition to certain quality factors, piles in the market are specified by length, minimum circumference at the top and 3 feet from the butt, and must meet certain design standards. They are sold by the lineal foot.

Pilings for wharves in salt water have to be peeled and treated to prevent damage from sea creatures like the teredo worm and some crustaceans. Piles for driving deep into the subsoil where insects and rot do not flourish usually are not treated, nor necessarily peeled of bark.

Because of the complexities of the specifications of poles and piling, a tree farmer considering the harvesting of them should consult buyers or plants to determine exactly what they require. Also, care should be taken to not hi-grade the forest by cutting future crop trees that would be more valuable for lumber or veneer, or to interupt the overall silvicultural objectives.

When required, the bark from poles and piles can be more easily removed soon after harvesting to reduce damage from insects and rot and to increase penetration of preservatives. Most peeling is done by machines at the processing plants, which sometimes also shaves or shapes the pieces, rather than by hand peeling with an axe, drawknife, or spud bar.

Round posts are cut from small trees of many species. Those that are naturally durable (see Table I-2) like redwood, cedar, and juniper are preferred, because if sound, close-grained wood is used, no preservative treatment is necessary. However, less durable species and coarse-grained trees can be utilized also, provided the posts are treated. Some forest owners do this themseles by soaking the butts of dried posts in a solution of pentachlorophenol and diesel oil, or other preservatives. Instructions are available from a CDF forest adviser or county farm adviser. Like many chemicals, preservatives have to be handled carefully. The posts should be peeled in any case by hand or rotating drum debarkers. Posts are usually 6 to 8 feet long and 3 to 6 inches in top diameter.

Split Products

Different kinds of split products are marketable from California trees. The species used depends on the product. Posts 6 to 8 feet in length and 4 to 5 inches thick are split from the heartwood of old-growth redwood and cedars. Splitting tools include wedges, sledge, splitting maul, and the broadaxe.

Stakes for supporting young landscape trees, grape vines, and fencing make up a large portion of the split products business. Grapestakes are split mostly from old-growth coast redwood, although Sierra redwood and western red cedar make good stakes also. The most common length is 6 feet and the thickness is 2 x 2 inches. When stakes are to be used for fencing they are usually resplit or sawn to a 1 x 2 inch size. Special split products like paling and rails are occasionally marketed for construction of rustic fences.

At one time California operators produced a large quantity of split and sawn shakes from select, virgin coast redwood trees, but most of these products consumed here now are made from western red cedar in the Pacific Northwest. The old-time shake is uniform in size—⅜ by 6 by 18 or 24 inches, and split across the annual rings to get vertical grain. Besides straight-grained, clear redwood, it can be split from bolts of heartwood of the cedars, sugar pine, and even white fir. A tool with a handle at right angles to the cutting blade, called a froe, is pounded by a wooden mallet to split thin slices.

More popular than the uniform shake is the one that is partly sawn; sometimes it is called the Hollywood shake. Again, it is mainly made from western red cedar and coast redwood. The shakes are first split with a froe from bolts into thick pieces of varying width and then these are each sawn edgewise at an angle to produce tapered shakes. They are either 18 or 24 inches long, and the thickness at the big end is ½ to ¾ inches for medium shakes and ¾ to 1¼ inches for heavy shakes. The operators pack the shakes into bundles where five of them will cover about a "square" or 100 square feet of surface.

There is a limited market for shake and shingle bolts in the northern redwood region. They are sold by the cord. However, bolts for shingle manufacture have virtually disappeared from the California scene. What few shingles that are manufactured here at present mostly come from choice blocks of redwood which are a by-product of sawmill operations.

Fuelwood

Wood is coming into its own again as fuel because of the energy crunch. Until the early 1930s fuelwood was used a lot for both domestic and industrial purposes, but it was gradually replaced by oil and gas. Wood still has a good potential as a source of energy and its use for fuel will increase. Wood is a versatile fuel that can be used in solid form, gasified, or converted into a liquid state. Depending on the heat value of the species (see Table I-2), a cord of some of our denser hardwoods when air dry has about the heat equivalent of a ton of coal. Fuelwood may be in the form of cordwood, hogged and chipped wood, woods and mill wastes, briquets, or charcoal.

Most California hardwoods make excellent fuel. These trees are cut on the lower elevation woodland grazing areas and to some extent from commercial forests having a mixture of hardwoods and conifers. Large limbs, tops, and cull material resulting from harvesting of conifers, can also be made into fuelwood; so can thinnings and salvage from trees killed by fire or pests.

The wood is ordinarily cut and split in 12 to 24 inch lengths mainly for heating purposes—fireplaces, wood-burning heaters, and a little for cookstoves. It should be air dried before marketing. The cord is the standard measure; it is a closely stacked pile 4 x 4 x 8 feet, or 128 cu. ft. gross. However, the net solid wood content of a cord only averages 80 cu. feet. The tier or rick is also used to sell firewood but it is a confusing unit because it depends on the length of the wood pieces. For 12-inch wood 4 tiers make a cord, and a tier then is a pile of such wood 4 feet high and 8 feet long. In case of 16-inch wood, three tiers equals a cord, and for 24-inch wood, 2 tiers make a cord. Thus, a tier of one length wood is not equivalent to a tier of another length.

Where not utilizable for pulp and other by-products, mill wastes in the form of bark, edgings, trimmings, sawdust, and shavings are used for fuel in some plants to generate power to drive mill machinery. A few large mills produce electricity in excess of their needs and this is sold for domestic consumption. Some mill trimmings and larger pieces of waste wood may be sold for firewood.

Some special wastes are manufactured into briquets and charcoal by processing facilities at the mill. Making charcoal in kilns near the woods has not proved to be very successful because of the great amount of labor required and air pollution problems.

Christmas Trees

The growing and harvesting of Christmas trees has developed into a big business in California, although we still depend on imports from other states (principally Douglas-fir from the Pacific Northwest) for much of our needs. It is a venture that is readily adaptable to many tree farmers, either as a sideline to regular timber operations, or exclusively as a Christmas tree farm. The principal species grown here for this are Douglas-fir, Monterey pine, white and red fir (silver-tip), Sierra redwood, and Scotch pine.

The trees are produced in three ways. Natural commercial timber stands occasionally offer chances for thinnings, especially too densely reforested areas. The second source can be some natural forests, especially high elevation fir areas, where stands which are thick, slow-growing, and

Figure III-1

New Christmas trees can be produced on the stem of a cut tree by the turn-up process.

even-aged are set aside for Christmas tree management. The trees are thinned to get better spacing and side growth of the crowns. Others are just topped during harvest to leave at least one whorl of healthy branches, one or a few of which will turn upwards to form a new stem (Figure III-1). These are called "turn-up" trees. The last production method is the plantation where trees are grown, cultured, and harvested solely for Christmas trees. Many are located on open or agricultural land near urban areas and are operated on a choose-and-cut basis, so that families can have an outing to cut their own trees. There is a lot of literature, advice, and assistance that can be had on the subject of Christmas tree management from CDF forest advisers, county farm advisers, and the California Christmas Tree Growers (CCTG).

Christmas trees are sold by the lineal foot or at a fixed price per tree. They are segregated by species and often graded. Standards for grades have been established by the U. S. Department of Agriculture, copies of which can be obtained from CDF forest advisers and county farm advisers. The CCTG above has also adopted some grading rules.

Miscellaneous Forest Products

There are other products that can be profitably utilized from the forest, most of which depend on special or local markets. The producer needs to search them out and learn what the requirements are. A good first source of information would be the CDF forest adviser or county farm adviser.

Greenery

Christmas greenery, toyon berries, mistletoe, and cones for wreaths and other decorations are in demand during the holiday season. Florists also use considerable amounts of foliage of ferns, huckleberry, salal, and conifers in making floral pieces and displays. The cones preferred are those from sugar, Jeffrey, and other pines. Specifications for these decorative products are set by dealers who buy them by the bunch, bundles, bag, or pound.

Cones for Seed

With the increased interest in reforestation, there has been a corresponding increase in the demand for cones for seed purposes. The buyers include public forestry agencies, some industrial tree farms, private nurseries, and seed companies. The more common species collected are Douglas-fir, ponderosa pine, Monterey pine, red and white fir, and redwood, but other species may be wanted also. The easiest way to collect cones is after tree felling on logging operations that coincide with the maturity of the cones. Sometimes, cones severed by wind or squirrels are handy also. Using long pruning hooks or climbing equipment is another method, but safety precautions should be taken to avoid injury. The cones should be tested for ripeness and soundness before harvesting. This is done by carefully slicing the cone lengthwise with a sharp knife and the good seeds counted on the cut surface. For cones to be acceptable, at least 75 percent of the exposed pine seeds and 50 percent of the other species should be full and sound. Cones are sold by the burlap sack (about two bushels), each tagged with species and date, elevation, and location of collection. Before one collects cones, advice should be sought from CDF forest advisers, forest-tree nursery operators, or others having experience in the subject.

Burls and Rounds

Burls and rounds of a few species are salable. In case of coast redwood, live burls that will sprout are sold by curio shops, and large pieces of redwood burls are cut for rustic furniture or manufactured into novelties and highly prized items. Burls of California laurel are also turned and made into beautiful novelties. Rounds or cross sections of small, close-grained cedar and redwood logs that are durable are made into patio or garden stepping blocks. Treating with wood preservatives would be necessary in case of non-durable species.

Other Possibilities

A resourceful and enterprising tree farmer could develop markets for other miscellaneous products. Duff from the forest floor is a good soil conditioner for some gardens. Manzanita branches or tops have decorative value. There is limited market for peeled cascara bark in the northwest part of the state. Tanoak bark once was peeled a great deal for tanning of leather, but it has largely been displaced by chemicals.

Chapter IV

HARVESTING TREE CROPS

Harvesting the crop is a critically important function in the management of the forest. If done right, logging can be used to silviculturally improve a forest, but on the other hand it also can be a destructive force to the forest and the environment if it is not done properly. Harvesting is the operation that enables the owner to effect the management plan for the forest—to bring about better distribution of age classes, improve the stand, and promote growth. And more importantly, periodic harvests are the pay-offs for the planning, investments, and work put into the forest.

Like any other major activity, harvesting must be planned. Consideration needs to be given to the care and betterment of the forest, protection of its associated values, and to many other factors about the crop, cutting methods, selling, and legal requirements.

Timing and Location of Harvests

First of all, the timing and location of the harvests should correspond to the needs of the forest as set forth in the management plan. A good practice is to have a cutting budget prepared for at least five years ahead to indicate what amounts can be harvested, how often, and from what parts of the stand. Generally, annual or periodic harvests at longer intervals of about the same volume in accordance with allowable cut estimates are tentatively prescribed in the cutting budget and revised periodically. The cutting is located where the forest needs it most. High priority is given to trees or areas that are defective, of poor vigor, overmature, and to merchantable trees of any particular age class that are overabundant. Of course, quick salvage of trees damaged or killed by fire and pests is important.

Market conditions need to be taken into account also. Obviously, there is no point making a harvest when the market is poor or non-existant; that would be a waste of material and money. Like other commodities, wood products vary in price according to supply and demand and other economic factors, and these cannot be accurately predicted. Whether to harvest or not should depend on whether there is a fair chance to realize a reasonable profit from the crop. Fortunately, standing timber can be held over from one year to the next without too much spoilage, so harvesting can be deferred when market conditions are not right.

Logging should be timed by season also. In California, it is usually done in the spring, summer, and fall months when climatic conditions are more favorable. In wet weather harvesting is more costly, causes more damage to the forest and roads, and has a more deteriorating impact on the soil, streams, and watershed. The markets for wood crops are ordinarily better in the dry months.

Marking the Harvest

As indicated above, what trees to specifically harvest depends on the objectives of the management plan, the condition of the forest, and the market. Legal requirements also come into play here, because they control such things as stocking to be left and other aspects of logging. These legal factors are discussed in a later section in this chapter.

Depending on the silvicultural method to be employed, the trees or areas to be cut should be marked somehow. In any case, the exterior boundaries of the harvest area should be designated by signs, flagging, or marking on trees so that timber cruisers, potential buyers, and logging personnel can clearly see the layout. It may be advantageous sometimes to set out interior subdivisions also, especially when the logging should be done in a certain order. This type of exterior marking usually would be all that is necessary where clear cutting is going to be done.

Under the seed-tree cutting system, the seed trees are marked individually where they are scattered. When seed-tree blocks are employed just the boundaries are marked. If trees below a certain diameter are also to be left they need not be marked, because those trees can be readily determined by the timber fallers by estimation or measurement. However, trees below the minimum diameter in need of cutting for silvicultural reasons should be appropriately marked.

Under both the shelterwood and selection systems, the individual trees ready for harvest are carefully chosen. As discussed in Chapter II, this marking is primarily based on silvicultural and management needs. However, what species, sizes, and quality are acceptable on the current market should be considered too. Moreover, the tree farmer has to keep economics in mind in order to have a harvest that shows some profit. Within that restraint, for the purpose of forest improvement a person may elect to cut some poor trees that are not salable. In addition to profit opportunity for the forest owner, the proposed harvest should be made attractive to prospective buyers and operators.

Disposable pressurized cans of bright paint are convenient to use for marking purposes. Trigger-type spray guns are also handy in that a tree can be sprayed from a distance of a few feet (Figure IV-1). It is a good idea to mark trees to be cut both at breast height and at stump level; this gives a better record of what trees have been removed and helps prevent the taking of extra trees.

Advance Information Needed

Before a harvest can be planned and scheduled certain basic information is collected by the forest manager. Without it a timber cutting operation would not achieve the desired results in terms of the forest itself, efficiency, and economic gain. Interested buyers want knowledge about the forest in order to make offers.

Timber Cruise

Once the trees have been designated for harvest the area should be cruised by a competent person to find out what volume of timber by species is available for cutting. Cruising procedures are explained in the next chapter. This inventory can be made at time of marking to avoid going over the area another time. A general idea of the size range and

Figure IV-1
Marking trees with a paint gun.

quality of the timber is valuable to have. What existing roads can be used and what additional ones have to be constructed should be sized up and placed on a timber sale map. How the area should be logged, i.e., method and order, and the different logging conditions and problems should be noted during the cruise.

Timber Harvesting Plan

The State Forest Practice Act requires that a timber harvesting plan must be prepared, filed, and cleared for every commercial operation except for emergencies, conversion of timberland into another use, and certain minor harvests. This plan has to be prepared by a registered professional forester, usually at the expense of the operator, who also is primarily responsible for proper filing of it with the Department of Forestry. Since a forest owner has some responsibilities regarding implementation of the plan and conformance to state forest practice regulations, the owner or representative should at least monitor the preparation of the timber harvesting plan. Better yet, the owner should have a forester participate in developing the plan to protect the owner's interests in future forest productivity and management objectives. A lot of data is required, much of which can only be collected in the field. Therefore, as much of this information as possible should be gathered during the cruise. What exactly is required in the plan by the State is spelled out in a printed form and regulations, copies of which can be obtained from CDF offices.

Stumpage Appraisal

After the field work has been completed an appraisal of the value of the timber comes next. It is necessary to have an appraisal in order to establish the minimum sale price of the timber, or stumpage as it is called, which would be offered to prospective buyers. A modified overturn, or profit-ratio, method can be used to appraise stumpage. Simply stated, stumpage value is the difference between the market price less operating costs (including stumpage) with a certain allowance for profit. Expressed as a formula it is:

$$X = [S/(1 + \%)] - C$$

Where X = stumpage value in dollars per thousand bd. ft. measure (MBM)

S = selling price per MBM

C = operating costs per MBM

% = expected percentage of profit

Separate appraisals are made for each species or groups of species having the same value. The appraisal can start with the average mill-run selling price of lumber. However, if there is a local market for logs for which the general price is known, it is easier to start the appraisal there. Information is then needed on expected logging and hauling costs. This may be obtained from local operations or consultants. If not, one would get cost data developed by the U. S. Forest Service and other public forestry agencies from them or a CDF forest adviser and adjust those figures to fit the situation. The profit margin runs from 10 to 20 percent, depending on the risk involved.

To demonstrate this appraisal method, assume that price per MBM paid locally for average Douglas-fir logs delivered at the mill was $230, logging and hauling costs were $100 per MBM, and a 15 percent profit was expected. Then, stumpage value $X = [230/(1 + .15)] - 100 = 100$.

Before any values arrived by this method are accepted they should be compared with known prices for similar timber in the local area. This will serve as a check, and also in some instances comparisons may justify adjusting the values somewhat.

Logging Operations

The tree farmer should decide what logging methods should be used in any harvest. Logging has a big impact on the land and the trees, so methods that cause the least damage should be elected, providing they can do the job within the range of reasonable costs. To choose something that is especially expensive lowers stumpage returns to the forest owner and also affects the operator's potential profit.

Felling and Bucking

The felling and bucking (sawing) of trees into logs in California is still done by using power saws and hand tools like axes, wedges, and sledges. In other parts of the country, where the terrain is flat or nearly so, this operation is being increasingly done by mobile machines that sever the tree at its base with a scissor-like knife and then lay the tree on the ground. Some machines even delimb the tree, buck and bunch the logs, and haul them to a landing where the logs are loaded onto trucks for delivery to a mill. California's topography being as rough as it is, these kinds of all-purpose machines have limited use here, so felling and bucking will continue to be largely accomplished with chain saws.

Yarding, Loading, and Hauling

Getting logs to the loading area is called skidding or yarding. This is done in a number of ways. Most common is the use of track-laying (Figure IV-2) or rubber-tired tractors to drag the logs to the landing. A variety of special machines have been developed for this purpose: wheeled arches towed behind tractors that elevate the towing cable and chokers connected to the logs, machines that in effect have the arch as an integral part of the tractor, and tractors that have powered arms at the rear that bunch, lift, and hold one end of a few logs as they are skidded to the landing. Bulldozers are needed to build the skid trails as well as for road and landing construction and maintenance.

In general, to minimize damage and for sake of efficiency, the smallest yarding equipment that will do the job should be selected. Tractor logging requires a lot of roads and skid trails, which if not carefully constructed and tended can be harmful. However, generally this kind of logging is the cheapest method where the terrain and weather conditions are right.

Figure IV-2

Specially adapted track-laying skidder.

Cable yarding systems powered by stationary machines (donkeys) were once popular in California until they were largely replaced by tractors in the mid-1930s. These were big, complicated, heavy systems that were expensive to buy, install, and operate. These cable systems are finding favor again, but in the form of lighter and more mobile machines. This has been brought about because rougher and less accessible timber areas and smaller trees are being logged. Also, if properly used, cable logging causes less soil disturbance, so it is justified where soil and watershed values are of critical importance. Cable systems can be fairly complicated and require a great deal of know-how and skill, and they are not feasible for small volumes, scattered, or low-value timber.

Logging with balloons and helicopter is also possible in some cases. These methods are very expensive. So far they are mainly used to a limited degree on lands with difficult access, or where extra precautions have to be taken to avoid environmental damage. These areas include very rough topography, highly erodible soils, or those having exceptional watershed values. Being expensive to install and operate, the stumpage value of timber logged in this manner comes out quite low.

Contrary to these technological developments, using animal power for yarding should not be dismissed. Occasionally, horses and mules are still utilized in California forests, and because of increasing energy costs, draft animals may return more and more to the logging scene. They work well in smaller, young-growth timber, and cause the least disturbance.

Various kinds of mobile machines are employed to load logs onto trucks (Figure IV-3). They include front-end loaders, booms, cranes, and power-shovel types.

Figure IV-3
Front-end log loader.

Practically all the hauling of logs from the woods to the mill is done by large trucks. Logging operators often employ contract haulers for this rather than own and run the trucks themselves. In fact, some timber operators have sub-contractors or "gypos" to conduct all or part of the logging.

How to Sell

When one offers to sell some timber a list of potential buyers should be prepared. It may be advantageous to even consult some buyers to get an idea of what kind of timber they want, prices, and specifications. The more competition there is for a timber sale the better the prices for it will be. The public forestry agencies (e.g., USFS, CDF, Bureau of Land Management, Bureau of Indian Affairs) who sell timber are a good source of going price information for stumpage.

Sale Offers

Offers to sell timber must contain certain basic information. The location of the sale area is legally described with estimated acreage and shown on a timber sale map. A listing is made of the amount of timber by species that is being offered, along with the minimum asking price for each. The volumes should be developed from the cruise made during or after the marking of the trees to be cut.

Measurement

The timber owner should be the one to decide by what measurement method the timber will be sold, the log rule to use, whether to sell by cruise or tree measurement, and whether logs are to be scaled at the logging site or away from the woods, e.g., at the receiving mill. Scaling is the procedure for estimating the board feet content of logs by use of special tables called log rules (see Chapter VI).

The most popular log rule in California is the Scribner and its variant the Scribner Decimal C. A few other rules have also been employed such as the Spaulding table.

Selling timber on the basis of tree measurement is convenient. The sale is made for an agreed price payable usually in a lump sum. This method avoids the bother and expense of scaling and is especially adaptable to small, short-term sales of fairly sound timber. However, prospective buyers must have confidence in the cruise arranged by the seller, and should check it on the ground. Timber owners should never sell timber on the basis of a buyer's tree measurement cruise without having it checked by a competent person.

When sales call for scaling of the logs, the logs are measured in the woods after felling and bucking, as they are delivered to the landing, on trucks at a central point, or at the mill site. The timber buyer makes periodic payments to the seller based on the scale figures. Specially trained people called scalers are employed, because the procedures are exacting and estimates have to be made for defect in the logs to arrive at the net board-foot content. Therefore, the sale should be large enough to justify the extra costs of employing scalers, unless the job can be handled by the owner or forest manager. Care should be taken about accepting the scale of the timber buyer, operator, or mill as a basis for payment. In a few places in California the services of a non-biased private scaling bureau are available to both sellers and buyers.

Sale Contract

Regardless of the measurement methods above, it is very important that the timber is sold under a written contract rather than by an oral agreement. This protects both seller and buyer and minimizes disagreements about provisions of the sale. This document sets forth as clearly as possible the area (including map), time period of the sale, the amount of timber to be cut, rate and way of payment, measurement method, compliance with State laws and forest regulations, logging practices, utilization standards (stump height, acceptable defect, log lengths, trim allowance, and diameters), requirements for road construction and maintenance, treatment of snags and logging slash, and provisions for prevention of damage to the property, improvements, and the environment from the operations and wildfire. Other legal clauses like those on performance bonds and liability must be included also, so the advice of an attorney with experience in timber sale matters should be sought. A sample or a check list for a timber sale agreement that can be adapted to specific situations is available from CDF forest advisers. The agreement should be drafted ahead of time and used in making offers to sell and negotiating sales.

Bidding and Negotiation

Sales can be settled in two principal ways. One is by calling for competitive written bids. This requires the preparation and advertising or circulation of a sale announcement. Those used by the U.S. Forest Service, Bureau of Land Management, and the CDF can serve as samples. It should contain at least the following information:

    Location and size of area
    Volume and kind of timber by species
    Minimum bid prices and deposit
    Method of measurement (tree measurement, scale, etc.)
    Instructions regarding examination of timber and proposed contract
    Final date and place of filing of bids
    Reservation of right to reject bids

Using the same information as above, a less formal way to make a sale offer would be for the seller or his agent to visit or call timber buyers and mills to find out their interest and the prices they would be willing to pay. The sale could then be decided by negotiations with the most likely buyer and the contract agreed to and executed.

Supervision

A timber sale agreement is only as good as the supervision and follow-through that the tree farmer provides during and after the harvest operation. This insures that the owner is getting full value for his timber and that the job is being done according to contract and without unnecessary damage. Periodic inspections therefore are advisable. It may be advantageous that this be done by a registered professional forester in case problems result in disagreement or litigation. Also, having a qualified person present occasionally on the scene prevents problems from arising or growing into bigger ones. The forest owner should also request copies of reports of inspection from the CDF for compliance with state forest practice regulations (see below).

Legal Requirements

Many laws and regulations bear on the harvesting of timber. To protect oneself the tree farmer should have good knowledge about the legal requirements.

Forest Practice Act

Foremost of the legal requirements are the State Forest Practice Act and the forest practice rules and other regulations that have been adopted under the law by the Board of Forestry. The law and regulations are administered and enforced by the Department of Forestry which conducts periodic inspections. These legal standards are intended to not only protect forest values but also those relating to soil, water, fish and wildlife, recreation and aesthetics. The requirements are many and in considerable detail. First to keep in mind is that advance notices of any proposed timber operations must be filed by both the timber owner and operator with the CDF. Then, as mentioned earlier, before logging can commence the operator must file with the Department a timber harvesting plan and have it in approved form. In addition, the person conducting the harvest must have a timber operator's license.

The forest practice rules pertain to the timber operations and cover such subjects as silvicultural methods, stocking to be left after logging, timber felling, yarding, erosion control, logging roads, stream and lake protection, reduction of snag and slash hazards, fire prevention, and insect and disease protection. Where timberland is to be converted to another use the owner must first file for and receive an approved timberland conversion permit. Copies of the Forest Practice Act and the rules and regulations are available from CDF offices, and forest practice inspectors of the Department can comprehensively explain the requirements.

The penalties for violation of the law and regulations can be quite severe—a misdemeanor action in the local court, revocation of the timber operator's license, or injunction to stop operations. The State may require corrective action for some violations with charges levied against the person responsible, which charges also are placed as a lien against the property. While the responsibility for compliance is primarily directed at the operator, others like the timberland owner may also be charged, so it behooves the proprietor to do all that is possible by contract and supervision to see that the operator faithfully abides by the law and regulations. Of special note is that various reports on stocking may be required to be made to CDF for as long as five years after the harvesting, and this responsibility could ultimately fall on the owner.

Environmental Protection

Besides the protection of the environment provided under the Forest Practice Act program, there are a number of other laws and regulations that apply. The Fish and Game Code and related regulations prohibit obtructions in streams or deposits of materials that are deleterious to fish and their habitat. Where timber operations alter or disturb a stream a notice has to filed with the Department of Fish and Game.

Fish and Game also has laws to protect various species of wildlife. In addition, the Regional Water Quality Control Boards have adopted regulations to prevent and control deterioration of the streams, lakes, and other bodies of water. They have a keen interest in the erosion and transport of soils and debris into these waters.

Protection of other values like rare and endangered species and cultural-historical sites may be occasionally required as a result of the timber harvesting plan process. Concerned agencies like those above and others are notified of these plans and can participate in the review of the plans. Citizens organizations and individuals can also become involved.

Licensing of Foresters

As the reader has observed, the professional forester has a big role in forestry and timber harvesting in California. In order to practice forestry, by law one must be registered as a professional forester with the State Board of Forestry. This license requires seven years of professional forestry experience of which four years may count if the applicant has a college degree in forestry, and successful completion of an examination as prescribed by the Board. Registered foresters have to live up to certain standards and can lose their license if they fail to do so. Landowners are exempted from the licensing requirement if they personally practice forestry on their own lands, except that timber harvesting plans must always be prepared by registered professional foresters.

While registered foresters may run survey lines of various kinds for forestry purposes, they cannot practice surveying or civil engineering unless licensed in these fields. To avoid trespass upon a neighbor's land, in conducting a harvest, a tree farmer should have a duly recognized property line to go by, or engage a licensed surveyor or registered civil engineer to establish the boundary.

Taxation

Like any other person in business or farming, a forest owner is subject to various forms of taxation. It pays to have an understanding of what is involved in order to stay out of trouble and because these costs can be considerable. A timber property or business is subject to property and yield taxes, income taxes, social security tax, and sales tax. It is not the purpose of this handbook to go into detail on these matters because they are complex. However, enough explanation is given to alert the timberland owner on generally what one faces.

To operate a tree farm and to pay taxes one needs to keep many records. A timber grower may not wish to take the time and effort to develop and maintain a suitable accounting system. Because of its intricacies, this is a job that in many cases probably should be turned over to a specialist, preferably one who knows the timber business and who also handles income tax work along with accounting records.

Property and Yield Taxes

The taxation of forest products is covered by the Forest Taxation Reform Act of 1976 (popularly termed the Timber Yield Tax Law), which is jointly administered by the State Board of Equalization and the County Assessors. Under this law, non-federal timber-producing lands are classified by county zoning ordinances into Timberland Preserve Zones (TPZ) through a process involving the County Assessor, County Planning Commission, and timber owners. Such lands may be used for growing of forest products and compatible uses only, and the usual property or ad valorem taxes on TPZ lands are then based on those limited uses. Only the land is subject to the usual county property tax. Trees both within and outside of a TPZ are no longer subject to separate ad valorem assessment based on timber value, but trees outside a TPZ may be assessed on an ad valorem basis for their aesthetic or amenity value.

Instead of an annual ad valorem tax on timber, a special yield tax has to be paid to the State Board of Equalization for all forest products regardless of zone. This is payable at time of harvest at a rate of 6½ percent of the market value of the products, as determined by the taxpayer from schedules developed by the Board of Equalization. The sale price can't be used. The tax revenue, less some reserve funds, is allocated to the counties from which the products are harvested. The yield tax percent is subject to adjustment by the Board in accordance with criteria in the law and changing conditions.

The amount of products to compute the yield tax is the net measured amount when it is first definitely determined. The Scribner Decimal C rule is used for measurement of logs (see Chapter VI). The tax must be paid on a quarterly basis by the person responsible, who is defined as the owner of the trees immediately prior to felling. Usually, this would be the timber sale purchaser, but the forest owner can be held responsible for timely payment of the tax. The taxpayer is required to keep adequate records to support harvest reports and yield tax returns. Operators on public timber are also required to pay the yield tax. The law requires yield tax payers to register with the State Board of Equalization. More information about the taxation of forest products can be obtained from the assessors within timbered counties and the Timber Tax Division offices of the State Board of Equalization.

Income Taxes

Because of inadequate knowledge on the subject, many forest owners pay more income tax than the law requires—both federal and state. (The California income tax regarding timber is similar to the federal system.) A clearer understanding of the procedures would benefit the taxpayer financially and should at the same time encourage better forest management. The income tax laws contain a few features of advantage to the growing and selling for forest products.

With regard to expenditures, some are capital in nature and can be charged off (capitalized) so that the investment can be recovered proportionately as the timber is harvested. Capital expenditures consist of acquisition cost of the timber (not the land) and expenses for reforestation, stand improvement, and road construction, and may also include under certain conditions items like taxes and fire protection costs. These capital costs can be written off similarly to depreciation of equipment, except that in the case of timber the charge is called depletion.

Another important advantage in the income tax laws to the tree farmer is that concerning sale of timber. Income from wages, salaries, fees, investments, etc. is classified as ordinary income, and is taxed at graduated rates, according to the income bracket of the taxpayer. However, like the sale of property, income from any timber held over one year that is sold is recognized as capital gains. Such long-term capital gains are taxed under special provisions that usually are more favorable.

Special literature on the application of the income tax to timber can be obtained from the U. S. Forest Service and CDF forest advisers. Help is also available from the Internal Revenue Service, the California Franchise Tax Board, and tax consultants.

Other Taxes

Of course, there are other taxes that affect tree farmers. One is the federal social security or self-employment tax. It is payable when the income is above a certain level, and when 1) the timber was grown on a property that is agricultural as well as a tree farm, 2) the income from forest products is not considered capital gains, and 3) the timber operation is a part of and not separate from the farm business. Regardless of this, where a person has employees to conduct a timber operation, social security taxes must be collected and paid. Information and assistance on these matters are available from local Social Security Administration offices.

The state sales tax may apply to sellers of forest products if such sales are retail. Local offices of the State Board of Equalization can provide more information and issue the necessary seller's permit.

Forestry Organizations

In addition to public agencies, there are a number of private forestry organizations active in California that provide services of one kind or another pertaining to forest harvesting of interest to the tree farmers, forest managers, and timber operators. Depending on the organization, these private organizations are involved in representing their interests before legislative and regulatory bodies, providing professional and technical information through publications and other ways, developing and maintaining forest products standards, insurance programs, collecting and publishing forestry statistics, education of the public about forestry and the forest products industries, and in public relations. Qualifications for membership vary, but regardless of that, all of them can be helpful in some manner even to non-members, e.g., providing information and literature to interested parties. The organizations include the following:

American Forestry Association
Associated California Loggers
Association of Consulting Foresters
California Christmas Tree Growers

California Forest Protective Association
California Redwood Association
Forest Landowners of California
Society of American Foresters
Western Timber Association
Western Wood Products Association

More information about these organizations and their current addresses can be obtained from CDF forest advisers.

Besides the above, there are two others which deserve mention. These are the Redwood Region Logging Conference and the Sierra Cascade Logging Conference. They annually hold separate regional meetings early in the year at which practical topics on forest harvesting are discussed and where the latest machinery is displayed. Membership is open to anyone by paying a nominal registration fee. A lot can be learned at these conferences.

Chapter V

FOREST INVENTORY

To operate a forest business, the owner and manager should have a sound understanding of how land and timber are measured. The subject of forest measurement is known as mensuration. A working knowledge of both land surveying and mensuration is needed for land custody purposes, acquisition and sale of timberland, appraisal of the values, managing and regulating the forest, making timber harvests, and for administrative purposes like paying taxes of various kinds. While the subject may be rather technical, there's no reason why a tree farmer cannot get a good grasp of it, even to the point of personally being able to do some of the necessary tasks with the common tools used.

Land Subdivision

Except for some lands covered by grants made during the early Spanish occupation, all lands in California were once subdivided by the federal government according to a system of rectangular surveys. This system is used to legally describe land parcels and to settle questions of property boundaries. Figures V-1 and V-2 can be used to illustrate and explain the system.

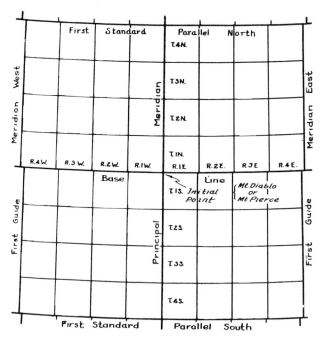

Figure V-1
Standard parallels, meridians, and townships of the U.S. land subdivision system.

Going to the first figure, three initial points were established in the state as bases for the network: Humboldt Base and Meridian (actually Mt. Pierce in Humboldt County), Mt. Diablo Base and Meridian in Contra Costa County, and San Bernardino Base and Meridian in southern California. Most of our timberland is tied to the Mt. Diablo Base and Meridian, usually written MDBM. In addition to the east-west base line, a principal meridian runs in a north-south direction through the initial point. There are guide meridians 24 miles apart that parallel the principal meridian. Similarly, there are lines called standard parallels every 24 miles north and south of the base line.

Within these guide meridians and parallels are additional lines spaced 6 miles apart to form townships. The north-south lines are called range lines and the east-west ones township lines. That means that a township is six miles square.

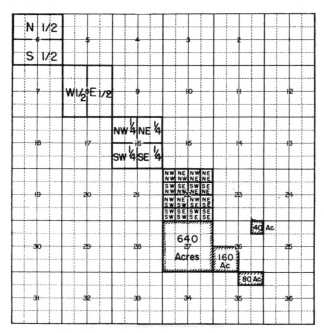

Figure V-2

Normal subdivision of a township and sections.

Now using Fig. V-2, each township was subdivided further into one-mile squares—36 in all, unless, due to original surveying errors, some sections were larger or smaller, or even missing. Section corner markers were originally established at the four corners, and additional markers were placed half-way between them to designate the quarter-section corners. Bearing trees were blazed or scribed nearby to reference the corners. Many of the original corner markings (stakes or rock mounds) and bearing trees have disappeared since the original surveys, most of which were made well before the turn of the century.

It is illegal to destroy, change, or deface a survey corner or bearing tree, and only a licensed surveyor or civil engineer can re-establish a corner or legal survey line. Copies of the original field notes on file with the Bureau of Land Management need to be used sometimes to find lost corners and to relocate lines. The local County Surveyor maintains records of resurveys and related data.

Within the township, each section is numbered in accordance with the scheme shown in the figure. The drawing also shows how each section can be further subdivided and described. Thus, the lone 40-acre parcel in Section 26 of the figure is described as the Northeast ¼, Northeast ¼, Section 26 (NE¼NE¼Sec.26), and the 80-acre parcel in Section 35 is the N½NE¼Sec.35. Identification of the township and the base and meridian is needed to complete the description. For example, N½NE¼ Section 35 T4S R3W HBM would mean that the parcel is located in the fourth horizontal row south of the Humboldt Base and Meridian and the third vertical row west of that initial point.

During these original surveys, distances were measured by a unit called a chain, which is equal to 66 feet. This unit is still in common use among foresters because it is a handy way to compute acreage. Here are some convenient numbers and conversions to remember:

$$1 \text{ chain} = 66 \text{ feet}$$
$$1 \text{ mile} = 5{,}280 \text{ feet} = 80 \text{ chains}$$
$$1 \text{ acre} = 43{,}560 \text{ sq. ft.} = 10 \text{ sq. chains}$$
$$1 \text{ section} = 640 \text{ acres}$$

Thus, a section is 80 chains by 80 chains, containing 6400 sq. chains, or 640 acres. And, a square 40-acre parcel (called a "forty") would be 20 chains on the side, or 400 sq. chains.

Table V-1. Map scale equivalents.*

Scale 1 to—	Inches per mile	Miles per inch	Feet per inch	Meters per inch	Feet per ½₅ inch	Acres per square inch	Square miles per square inch
600	105.6	0.0095	50	15.2	2	0.06	0.0001
1,200	52.8	.0189	100	30.5	4	.23	.0004
2,500	25.344	.0395	208	63.5	8.3	1.00	.0016
4,800	13.2	.0758	400	121.9	16	3.67	.0057
5,280	12	.0833	440	134.1	17.6	4.44	.007
10,000	6.336	.1578	833	254.0	33.3	15.93	.0249
15,840	4	.25	1,320	402.3	52.8	40.00	.0625
20,000	3.168	.3	1,584	482.8	63.4	57.60	.0900
24,000	2.64	.38	2,000	609.6	80	91.83	.1435
25,000	2.53	.39	2,083	635.0	83.3	99.64	.1557
31,680	2	.5	2,640	804.7	105.6	160	.2500
45,000	1.408	.7102	3,750	1,143.0	150	322	.5031
63,360	1	1	5,280	1,609.3	211.2	640	1.00
90,000	.704	1.4205	7,500	2,286.0	300	1,291	2.02
96,000	.66	1.5152	8,000	2,438.4	320	1,469	2.30
125,000	.507	1.9729	10,417	3,175.0	416.7	2,491	3.89
500,000	.127	7.8914	41,667	12,700.0	1,666.7	----------	62.3
1,000,000	.063	15.7828	83,333	25,400.1	3,333.3	----------	249
2,500,000	.025	39.4571	208,333	63,500.1	8,333.3	----------	1,556

* The acreage of an irregular area can be estimated from a map with a transparent overlay marked with 64 evenly-spaced dots to a square inch. The value of each dot can be determined by dividing the acres per square inch of the map by 64.

U.S.D.A. Miscellaneous Publication No. 225.

Maps and Aerial Photographs

Maps showing legal subdivision can be obtained from a number of sources. The U. S. Geological Survey (USGS) produces quadrangle maps for all of California; the maps also show topography by contours (lines of equal elevation). The interval between the contours, representing the height between them, varies among maps. Contour maps used in forestry usually have intervals from 40 to 100 feet. The maps can be ordered by mail from the agency or purchased in larger stationery, sporting goods, and engineering supply stores. Some plain maps (without contours) can be obtained or purchased from the CDF, U. S. Forest Service, and the Bureau of Land Management.

Maps have different scales. This is expressed as a fraction, e.g., 1:63,360, or in inches per mile, which for this fractional scale is 1 inch per mile. The scales of the public agency maps referred to above range from 1:24,000 to 1:126,720. Table V-1 shows map scales and their equivalents. The next to

Figure V-3
Vertical-view aerial photograph.

last column can be used to make a fairly good estimate of irregular areas by the procedure explained in the footnote. Instruments called planimeters are also used to determine areas by a tracing process.

In addition to maps, vertical-view aerial photographs are almost indispensable in forestry. Although they do not show some things like subdivision lines, name places, landmark identification, and features hidden by forest cover, photographs contain a wealth of detailed information not found on maps that is very useful to the forest manager. Without any instruments, these photographs quickly give the viewer a general picture of the land—topography, larger streams and water bodies, broad vegetation type, logged area, and other features discernible to the naked eye (Fig. V-3). They are a big help in preparing maps of the tree farm and for timber sales. Color aerial photography has advantages in some situations but the cost is higher than black and white.

By using a stereoscope to view paired photographs (Fig. V-4), the picture can be seen in three dimensions; this reveals much more to a trained person. Field foresters prefer pocket lens stereoscopes because they can be taken into the forest along with the photos of the area. Data on forest and vegetation type, stand density, age class, species composition, tree sizes, and logging conditions can be obtained by close stereoscopic examination. When properly used to minimize effects of distortion found in aerial photographs, especially near the edge, they can supply acreages of areas of interest. A general idea of where to locate roads to avoid rock outcrops and other difficult terrain can be had from the pictures.

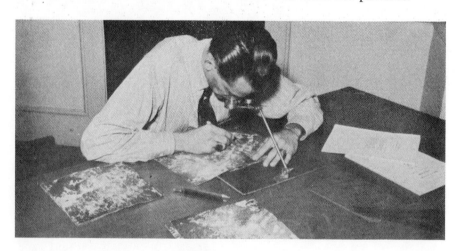

Figure V-4
Using a stereoscope.

Foresters can get fair estimates of timber volume by photo interpretation and field sampling. First, areas of similar timber are delineated on the photograph. Then measurements of trees on sample plots within these forest types are made to obtain the average timber volume per acre by forest type. From this average volume figure and the area within the forest types, the forester computes the total stand volume.

Photography scales in forestry range from 1 inch = 500 feet to 1 inch = 5,280 feet (one mile). Those of about 1 inch = 1000 feet are a good scale to use. However, most ready-made aerial photography that can be purchased is 1:20,000 (1 inch = 1,667 feet). Table V-2 gives vertical aerial photography scale relationships.

Table V-2.   Vertical aerial photograph scale equivalents.

Representative fraction	Inches per mile	Representative fraction	Inches per per mile
1:31,680	2.0	1:15,500	4.088
1:24,000	2.640	1:15,000	4.224
1:23,500	2.696	1:14,500	4.370
1:23,000	2.755	1:14,000	4.526
1:22,500	2.816	1:13,500	4.693
1:22,000	2.880	1:13,000	4.874
1:21,500	2.947	1:12,672	5.0
1:21,120	3.0	1:12,500	5.069
1:21,000	3.017	1:12,000	5.280
1:20,500	3.091	1:11,500	5.510
1:20,000	3.168	1:11,000	5.760
1:19,500	3.249	1:10,560	6.0
1:19,000	3.335	1:10,500	6.034
1:18,500	3.425	1:10,000	6.336
1:18,000	3.520	1:9,500	6.669
1:17,500	3.620	1:9,051	7.0
1:17,000	3.727	1:9,000	7.040
1:16,500	3.840	1:8,500	7.454
1:16,000	3.960	1:8,000	7.920
1:15,840	4.0	1:7,920	8.0

U.S.D.A. Miscellaneous Publication No. 225

Measuring and Running Lines

Land is measured by horizontal distance, not along the slope or ground. The latter distance is greater unless the terrain is flat. Two people are needed to accurately measure distance (called chaining), one forward and one to the rear. In forestry work, the lead person uses a compass (see later section) to keep the line going straight in the right direction (bearing). The one in the rear acts as the party chief, who also records the survey data, and makes corrections from slope to horizontal distance when that is necessary.

Horizontal Chaining

Engineers, surveyors, and occasionally foresters measure distances by using engineering tapes that are 100 to 300 feet long. They are graduated in whole feet, with the first and/or last foot graduated in tenths or hundredths of a foot. The tape has to be kept horizontal, so on slopes it is necessary to break chain, as it is termed. This means to horizontally measure with only part of the tape length each time, whatever the slope will allow. In effect, this process is like a staircase. A plumb bob or "eyeballing" is used to be sure to keep the points of measurement on the tape vertically over those on the ground.

Slope Chaining

Instead of direct horizontal chaining and breaking chain, distances can be measured along the slope, and this converted to horizontal values. If physically possible, the entire length of the chain is advanced and held parallel to the slope. An Abney level is used to determine the degree of the slope. The following formula can be used to calculate the horizontal distance.

$$D = S \times \text{cosine } A$$

where $D =$ horizontal distance
         $S =$ slope distance
         $A =$ degree of slope

Changes in elevation (V) between two points can also be computed by the formula: $V = D \times \text{tangent } A$. The tangent values are the same as the percent scale found on most Abney levels.

Table V-3 below gives horizontal conversion values for a 100-ft. tape up to 45 degrees of slope. One column gives the corrected horizontal distance. Where it is desired to set points at a given horizontal distance (e.g., 100 ft.) apart, the corresponding slope distance is approximately given by adding the correction shown in the next column. Values for the horizontal distances and corresponding corrections for degrees of slope not shown in the Table V-3 can be readily obtained from a table of natural cosines or some hand computers.

When running land lines, especially in rough country, foresters prefer special slope or topographic tapes that are about 2½ chains long. These tapes permit the correction of slope distance to horizontal distance without any computations or tables. This is done with the aid of correction

Table V-3.   Conversion of slope distance to horizontal distance for a 100-ft. tape.

Degree of Slope	Horizontal Distance	*Horizontal Correction	Degree of Slope	Horizontal Distance	*Horizontal Correction
0	100.00	0.00	23	92.05	7.95
1	99.98	.02	24	91.36	8.64
2	99.94	.06	25	90.63	9.37
3	99.86	.14	26	89.88	10.12
4	99.76	.24	27	89.10	10.90
5	99.62	.38	28	88.29	11.71
6	99.45	.55	29	87.46	12.54
7	99.26	.74	30	86.60	13.40
8	99.03	.97	31	85.72	14.28
9	98.77	1.23	32	84.80	15.20
10	98.48	1.52	33	83.87	16.13
11	98.16	1.84	34	82.90	17.10
12	97.81	2.19	35	81.91	18.09
13	97.44	2.56	36	80.90	19.10
14	97.03	2.97	37	79.86	20.14
15	96.59	3.41	38	78.80	21.20
16	96.13	3.87	39	77.72	22.28
17	95.63	4.37	40	76.60	23.40
18	95.11	4.89	41	75.47	24.53
19	94.55	5.45	42	74.31	25.69
20	93.97	6.03	43	73.13	26.87
21	93.36	6.64	44	71.93	28.07
22	92.72	7.28	45	70.71	29.29

* Slope distance minus horizontal distance (100 ft.)

graduations located on the underside of the tape beyond the one-chain mark and on the trailer part of the tape past the two-chain point. An Abney reading is taken of the slope in topographic units related to the tape. (Abney levels are available that have graduations in degrees, percent, and for use with topographic chains, all of which are useful in forestry.) The tape is moved ahead by the indicated amount, using the correction units on the tape. This then represents the true horizontal distance. If wanted, elevation can also be kept track of by the use of this kind of tape, because horizontal distance in chains times the Abney reading gives the difference in elevation in feet. A small metal mirror is handy in brush and timber to flash light towards the person reading the Abney.

Pacing

Many times in running land lines and especially in timber cruising, the accuracy of chaining may not be necessary, and the distances can be measured by pacing. It is faster and a person can do the job alone along with running a compass, conducting a cruise, and making a map.

On level terrain, an average-sized person while hiking takes two natural steps for every five to six feet, or about 12 double steps (called paces) per chain. To pace effectively one needs to determine what the natural pace is and practice pacing a measured course. Hand instruments called tally registers or whackers can be used to count paces or multiples of paces. Digital pedometers, which are attached to the waist belt, automatically give distance (slope) as you walk, but should only be used on easy ground, because the instrument moves every time a foot hits the ground, and adjustments to the given slope distances cannot be readily made by the user.

Some foresters and cruisers take 25 steps to a chain on the flat and mentally count 125 steps for five-chain units called tallies, which are recorded by notes on a tally register. Four of these tallies equal one-quarter mile, or the distance across a forty-acre parcel. The figures used depend on a person's natural pace. On slopes no attempt should be made to maintain a standard pace. Instead, experienced pacers allow for its shortening by only counting when judgment indicates that a truly horizontal pace has been covered. Also, in impenetrable brush or dangerous ground, they estimate by eye the distance ahead to some recognizable point, such as a tree or a rock, and offset around the bad area.

Measurement of Direction

Directions are measured by bearings, like North 45 degrees East (N45°E). Azimuth is more convenient to use; it is the clockwise angle measured from the north, 0 to 360°, Figure V-5 illustrates both of these methods. In forestry work, most lines are run in cardinal directions, that is north-south, east-west.

Foresters use either a hand compass or a staff compass graduated in degrees to maintain direction. To lessen the number of compass readings, sights as long as possible are made ahead on a tree, snag, or other landmark. Because magnetic forces do not correspond to a true north-south

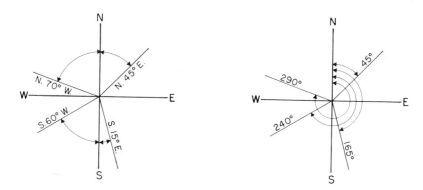

Figure V-5

Selective bearings and corresponding azimuths shown on the left and right, respectively.

direction, a compass needle in California points about 15 to 20 degrees east of the north pole. The difference in degrees between true and magnetic north is known as magnetic declination or variation. This value for your area can be obtained from local foresters, engineers, or surveyors. It can be also found on maps that show magnetic variation (isogonic) lines, like aerial navigation charts. Before using a compass, it should be adjusted to correct for magnetic declination.

On rare occasions compasses are affected by forces, called local attraction, caused by some iron ore deposits, objects of iron or steel, pipelines, electric lines, and wire fences. Iron or steel tools on a person may also cause the compass to deviate.

Measurement of Trees

In managing a forest, a tree farmer needs to measure standing trees in various ways—for site, growth, and timber volume. This requires getting data mainly on diameter and height to a certain top diameter. A number of different instruments are used to make these measurements.

Diameter Measurement

Tree diameters are measured at 4½ feet above the average ground level, except on steep slopes the diameter is taken on the uphill side of the tree. This is called diameter at breast height (dbh). The most reliable method to obtain dbh is with a diameter tape. Although it is placed around the trunk, the tape is graduated in units that represent the diameter in inches. This is derived from the formula where diameter equals circumference divided by pi (3.1416). Most tapes of this kind are 20 feet long and will measure diameters up to 76 inches. Some of these show feet divided into tenths or inches on the reverse side so the tape can be used for other purposes, like measuring plots or log lengths. Special tree calipers are also used to measure tree and log diameters in some situations.

The cruiser stick is quicker than a tape to measure diameter, although it is less accurate. It is an inexpensive, rugged rule about 39 inches long, whose four sides have graduations for inches, board feet of 16-ft. logs, log height of trees, and diameter. The diameter side is called the Biltmore scale. To measure diameter, the stick is held against the tree at breast height in a horizontal position 25 inches from the eye (Figure V-6). After the zero end of the Biltmore scale is lined up with the left edge of the tree, without moving the head, the viewer sights over the scale to the right side of the tree to obtain the diameter, usually to the nearest even inch. Most trees are not round, so more than one sighting on such should be made to get the average diameter.

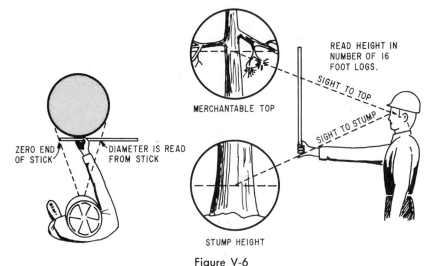

Figure V-6

Measuring diameter and height with a cruiser stick.

In timber cruising, diameters are obtained to the nearest inch or even-numbered inch, depending on the volume table to be used. After a lot of careful practice and with frequent checking with a cruiser stick or tape, a person can learn to estimate diameters by eye. However, since the accuracy diminishes with larger trees, they should be measured, prefera-bly with a tape.

Tree Heights

As explained in Chapter II, the total height of trees in feet has to be measured to determine the forest site. Because a reasonable degree of accuracy is required, Abney levels are often used for this purpose (Figure V-7). Either the percent (tangent) scale or the topographic scale can be employed. With the former, the height of the tree equals the percent reading times the horizontal distance between the tree and the observer. When using the topographic scale, the horizontal distance should be one chain, so the Abney reading then is equivalent to the tree height in feet. The Abney level is sometimes used in timber cruising to obtain the height of very tall trees.

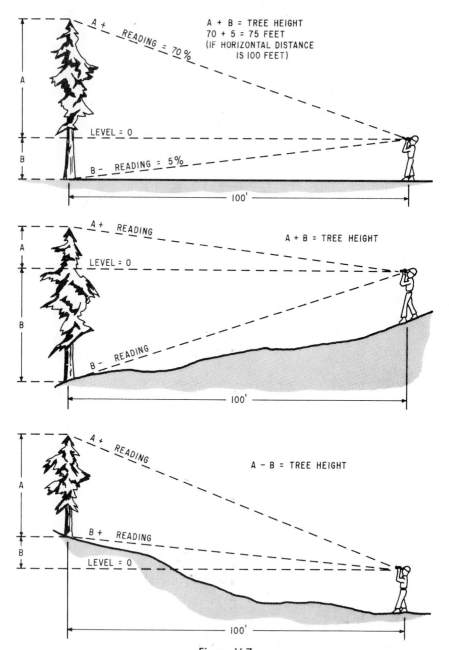

A + B = TREE HEIGHT
70 + 5 = 75 FEET
(IF HORIZONTAL DISTANCE
IS 100 FEET)

A + READING = 70 %

LEVEL = 0

B - READING = 5%

100'

A + READING

LEVEL = 0

B - READING

A + B = TREE HEIGHT

100'

A + READING

A - B = TREE HEIGHT

B + READING

LEVEL = 0

100'

Figure V-7
Measuring tree height with an Abney level
calibrated in percent

The number of logs is more conveniently measured by a cruiser stick. One edge of the stick has what is called the Merritt hypsometer scale, which gives number of logs for horizontal distance of one and 1½ chains. The estimater is stationed at either of those distances away from the tree. The stick is held vertical 25 inches from the eye, with the zero end lined up with the stump height of the tree. Simultaneously, a sighting is made to a point up the trunk where the diameter is that specified for the tables to be used for computing volume. This gives the number of logs in the tree. Other hand-held instruments called clinometers are available, but a cruiser stick and an Abney level are ordinarily adequate for general purposes.

Cruiser and foresters often make eye estimates of tree heights in logs. However, as in estimating diameters, practice and checking are in order.

Foresters have other instruments to measure trees than those described, some of which are quite sophisticated and costly. One such is the relaskop, which is an optical device that measures diameters of trees anywhere from stump to top and tree heights without a known horizontal distance. Another instrument is the dendrometer, a modified military range finder. These special tools are usually used only when exacting work is required, especially in large timber.

Volume Measurement

To convert tree diameter and height measurements into volume (usually in board feet), cruisers and foresters have a great variety of tables at their disposal. The more common ones are based on such factors as species, age-class (old- or young-growth), site, log rule, and minimum top diameter. Some of the more useful volume tables are reproduced in the Appendix. For an explanation of the board-foot measurement unit and log (volume) rules see Chapter VI.

These tables give the board-foot volume for trees usually by two-inch diameter classes and by number of logs or heights in feet, both to a specified minimum top diameter. Most tables are based on height in 16-ft. logs, but some for old-growth redwood and Douglas-fir may be for 20- or 32-ft. logs. Because large old-growth redwood trees frequently have a pronounced butt swell, some volume tables for this species are based on diameters 20 feet above the stump, instead of breast height. These diameters run from 6 to 20 inches less than dbh for trees from 24 to 92 inches dbh and have to be measured by a relaskop or estimated by a technique using a plumb bob and a long graduated stick held against and perpendicular to the trunk of the tree.

There are also other volume tables that have increasing use among professional foresters and more universal application, say between species and regions. These include form-factor, taper, and tarif volume tables. Also, local volume tables can be derived from various tables, where only the dbh needs to be measured, and heights ignored. Because of the variety and complexity of volume tables, a tree farmer should consult a local public or private forester to ascertain which is the best to use. The table must be selected before making a cruise, and the measurements and recording conform to that table's specific requirements.

Tree volumes of course can be obtained from formulas and even computer programs. Where volume tables are not handy, the following formula will give approximate values:

$$V = [(3H + 2)/10] D^2 - (H + 1)D$$

where V = volume in board feet
H = merchantable height in 16-ft. logs
D = dbh in inches

There are yield and volume tables showing volume in cubic feet of wood that are used in scientific work and to some extent where the trees are used for fiber rather than boards. They probably will have increasing use in the future. Also, tables in metric* units (cubic meters), now standard for most of the world, will begin to come into use as this country converts to the metric system.

Timber Cruising

Using these land and tree measurements described above, the volume of standing timber on an area can be developed by a sampling procedure called timber cruising. The resulting inventory gives reasonably good data on the species present, size classes, location, and amount of timber. Information also may be collected on grade of timber, defect, site, forest health, logging conditions, and topography. Cruise reports are valuable in buying and selling timberland, appraising the values, making forest management decisions, timber sales, and for financial and tax purposes. Tree farmers often employ registered professional foresters to conduct timber cruises in order to have reports acceptable to others.

Cruise Accuracy

Because cruising only samples a part of the tract and much judgment has to be exercised, the accuracy is variable. It depends on the size of the timber tract and the sample made, the uniformity of the timber, amount of defect, and certainly the skill and care of the cruiser.

The area sampled in cruising can consist of regularly spaced strips or special plots, whose acreage represents a certain percent of the total area. This percent ordinarily ranges from 5 to 20 percent. For a 10 percent cruise, the area of the strips or plots would be 4 acres for a "forty". On small tracts, or timber that is quite valuable or variable, a higher percent is necessary. The percent of area sampled should always be identified on a cruise report.

A cruise may be also selected by degree of accuracy desired. This is a statistical measure indicating the volume figures are within plus and minus a certain percent of being accurate, e.g., plus or minus 10 percent. This, along with the tract size and variability of the stand, determine how much area the sample plots should contain. This percent of accuracy measure is used mostly in plot sampling, as discussed in Chapter II and later in this Chapter under Plot Cruising.

Recording Data

Obviously, the measurements of trees during a cruise must be systematically recorded in a field book or on a form (Figure V-8). The data are

---

* See Tables A-1 through A-8 in the Appendix for various metric conversion factors.

customarily kept by forty-acre parcels. The sheet for each "forty" (or fractional "forties") should show:

Names of cruiser and compass operator (if any)
Number, size, area and location of strip or plot
Legal description of "forty"
Timber type (and site if necessary)
Date of cruise
Tally of trees by species, dbh, and height

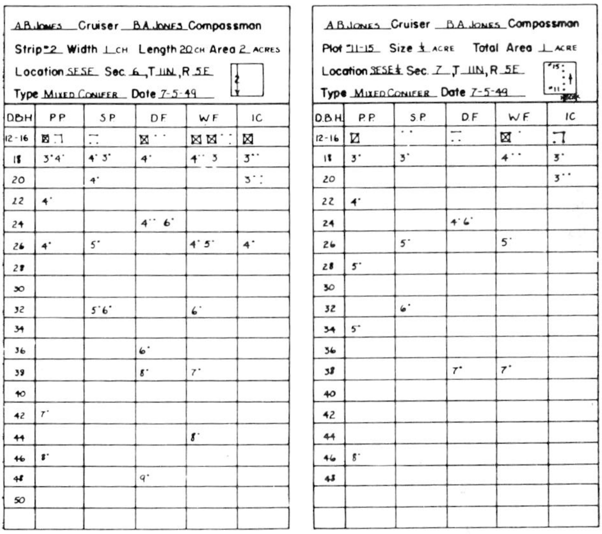

A.B.Jones Cruiser   B.A.Jones Compassman
Strip #2 Width 1 CH Length 20 CH Area 2 ACRES
Location SESE Sec. 6, T 1N, R 5E
Type Mixed Conifer Date 7-5-49

DBH	PP	SP	DF	WF	IC
12-16	⊠		⊠	⊠ ⊠	⊠
18	3'4'	4' 3'	4'	4' 3	3'
20		4'			3'
22	4'				
24			4' 6'		
26	4'	5'		4' 5'	4'
28					
30					
32		5'6'	6'		
34					
36			6'		
38			8'	7'	
40					
42	7'				
44				8'	
46	8'				
48			9'		
50					

A.B.Jones Cruiser   B.A.Jones Compassman
Plot 11-15 Size ¼ ACRE Total Area 1 ACRE
Location SESE ¼ Sec. 7, T 1N, R 5E
Type Mixed Conifer Date 7-5-49

DBH	PP	SP	DF	WF	IC
12-16	⊠			⊠	⊠
18	3'	3'		4'	3'
20					3'
22	4'				
24			4' 6'		
26		5'		5'	
28	5'				
30					
32	6'				
34	5'				
36					
38			7'	7'	
40					
42					
44					
46	8'				
48					

Figure V-8

Cruise tally sheets. One on left is for a strip cruise, sheet on the right side is for a plot cruise.

Trees are ordinarily tallied by two-inch classes and heights in logs (16 or 20 ft. as specified in the volume table to be used). To save time and space, the number of trees of the same height can be recorded by dots and lines as follows:

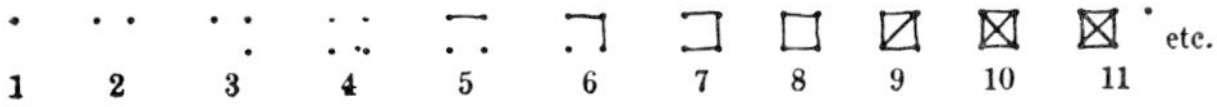

1 2 3 4 5 6 7 8 9 10 11 etc.

As will be seen later, using this method will also save time in calculating volumes. Reproduction, pole-sized trees under 12" dbh, and other special data may also be recorded, not for volume purposes, but to get information for management needs.

When cull or defect shown by a fire scar, fungus conk, or damage is observed, that is noted so that deductions from the gross volume of a tree can be made to get net volume. This takes a great deal of experience and judgement. Regardless of defect, a tree has to be always measured to a uniform top diameter and the defect deducted accordingly, because measuring a tree by log height to the point of defect or broken top will give inaccurate volumes.

To tally defect, the cruiser indicates the log(s) in which it occurs and the amount of cull next to the tree's number on the cruise sheet. A butt log of a 6-log tree that is one-half defective would be recorded as $6^{B\frac{1}{2}}$. If this amount of defect were in the third log of the same tree, the symbol would be $6^{3\frac{1}{2}}$. A 6-log tree with two top logs totally defective or missing would be tallied 4/6. A 7-log tree with a top log missing and completely defective third and fourth logs would be shown as $6/7^{34}$.

There are systems that are occasionally used to tally the logs by grade. However, this complicates the procedures. When a 100-percent cruise is being made along with timber marking in preparation for a timber sale, the figures have to be made in separate columns for the trees to be cut and left. Important information on the "forty" regarding forest health, logging conditions, road construction, presence of water and rock can be noted on the reverse side of the sheet.

Preparations for Cruise

The exterior boundaries and legal and intermediate corners of the tract are located and flagged before cruising commences. The acreage should be also determined ahead of time, if possible; otherwise it will have to be developed from a map drawn to scale while cruising. Remember that many "forties" do not contain exactly 40 acres. The accuracy of a cruise is dependent upon having good acreage figures for both the tract and the sample areas.

The next step is for the cruiser to select the proper direction and general spacing of the strips and plot lines so that the sampling is fairly representative. Usually, these lines run in cardinal directions that are most perpendicular to the contours on the tract, but access is also taken into consideration. After sizing up the area and timber, a cruiser decides the percent of the tract to be cruised and the width of the cruise strip or size and number of sample plots. For instance, a 10-percent strip cruise of a "forty" usually is made by two one-chain wide strips 10 chains apart and each located 5 chains from and parallel to the side of the parcel (Figure V-9).

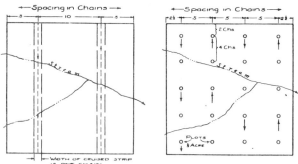

Figure V-9
Location of samples in strip and plot cruising.

In addition to cruising by the "forty" or some other sized parcel, cruises can be made by forest type for management reasons. That being the case, the area of those types must be carefully determined by field mapping. Aerial photos are helpful in delineating these types.

Strip Cruising

Cruising by strips can be done either by one or two persons, usually the latter, because more information can be collected during the work period and having two people in the woods is safer. In that case, one operates the compass, pulls the chain or does the pacing, and maps the area to show legal subdivision lines and corners, road and stream crossings, other prominent land features, non-timber areas, and sometimes even contours. The person in the rear acts as the chief of the party, handles the back end of the chain and makes the correction of slope distance to horizontal (if chaining is done), measures or estimates diameters and heights of trees on the cruise strip, records that data plus other pertinent information. Where only one person cruises by strip, that individual runs the compass, paces, estimates or measures the trees, and records the information.

The cruise may traverse a "forty" one or more times depending on width of strip and percent of cruise wanted. A 10-percent cruise could be obtained by running just one strip two chains wide through the middle, or two evenly-spaced strips one chain in width. Where the "forty" is truly regular, the sample areas in each case would be 4 acres. A 20-percent cruise could require two evenly-spaced strips two chains wide, or four evenly-spaced strips one chain wide, each case containing 8 acres. Ordinarily, one chain wide strips are the better, especially in dense timber or rough country, because its easier to cruise narrow strips, and also having more strips improves the sampling and aids the mapping process. Ten and 20-percent strip cruises are commonly made, and they give fair results in most cases, but bear in mind that smaller tracts, especially of irregular timber, require a higher cruise percent.

The cruiser controls strip width by pacing and occasional checking with the chain or pocket tape. The compass line runs in the middle so the horizontal distance to each side would be one-half the strip width. Trees are considered in the strip if they are more than half inside, and those falling exactly on the line are alternately included or excluded.

The exact total length of the strip(s) is very important, because the sample area is computed by multiplying that figure by the width of the strip. Also, when the parcel being cruised contains bodies of water, meadows, or pieces naturally without timber, as shown by the cruise map or notes, necessary deductions have to be made to obtain the net timbered area.

Plot Cruising

Some foresters in conducting cruises favor plots over strips. Because plots are uniformly and widely scattered, less sample acreage is required, but more lines must be run for a given accuracy. Exact lengths of lines are no longer important since sample area is controlled by the plots. This system is much easier to employ when the cruiser has to work alone.

As in strip cruising, lines are run through the "forty", but instead of measuring the trees enroute, the measurements are made within evenly-spaced plots (usually circular) as shown in Figure V-9. Cruisers generally use plots of one-fifth to one-fourth acre, although other sizes will do. Table V-4 following shows the dimensions of both circular and square plots of different sizes, and Table V-5 gives the number of one-fifth acre plots needed for certain conditions when one wants to adhere to statistical standards.

The number of plots can be also determined for a stated percent of cruise, like in the case of strip cruising. For example, when using one-fifth acre plots in a 10-percent cruise, four acres within a "forty" has to be sampled, or 20 plots that should be uniformly located as illustrated in Figure V-9.

While the lines are run, the cruiser locates the plot centers and marks them with a compass staff or in some other temporary manner. Measurements are then confined to the trees that are within the radial distance of the marked mid-point of the plots.

Table V-4. Size of selected circular and square plots.

Acres	Radius of circle	Feet on each side	Area in square feet
1/40	18.6	33.0	1,089
1/10	37.2	66.0	4,356
1/5	52.7	93.3	8,712
1/4	58.8	104.4	10,890
1/3	68.0	120.5	14,520
1/2	83.2	147.6	21,780
1	117.75	208.7	43,560
5	263.2	466.7	217,800

Table V-5. Number of one-fifth acre plots (evenly spaced) for three classes of accuracy.

Condition of Stand	Uniform			Average			Patchy	
Stocking*	Good	Medium	Poor	Good	Medium	Poor	Medium	Poor
area in acres	**Plus or minus 5% accuracy**							
40	57	109	160	89	133	171	160	185
160	73	185	400	133	267	480	400	600
640	78	223	640	152	356	873	640	1,371
5,000	80	238	775	159	394	1,145	775	2,190
10,000	80	239	787	159	397	1,172	787	2,290
100,000	80	240	799	160	400	1,197	799	2,389
area in acres	**Plus or minus 10% accuracy**							
40	18	46	100	33	67	120	100	150
160	20	56	160	38	89	218	160	345
640	20	59	188	40	97	274	188	505
5,000	20	60	198	40	100	291	198	586
10,000	20	60	199	40	100	298	199	593
100,000	20	60	200	40	100	300	200	599
area in acres	**Plus or minus 20% accuracy**							
40	5	14	40	10	22	55	40	86
160	5	15	47	10	24	69	47	126
640	5	15	49	10	25	73	49	143
5,000	5	15	50	10	25	75	50	149
10,000	5	15	50	10	25	75	50	150
100,000	5	15	50	10	25	75	50	150

* Good stocking is ⅔ to full stocking. Medium stocking is ⅓ to ⅔ full stocking. Poor stocking is less than ⅓ full stocking.
Two-thirds of cruises made will probably come within the indicated percentages of complete accuracy. One-third may exceed these percentages.
H. Coons—U. S. Forest Service.

Other Methods

A few other cruising methods are employed by foresters and forest scientists. Common is the variable plot system (see section below on Use of Prisms). A more recent system is called Three-P (Probability Proportional to Prediction Sampling); it makes it possible to combine conventional cruising techniques, a random selection of fewer than usual sample trees, and extra-careful tree volume determinations into a system that lends itself readily to electronic data processing. This very brief description must suffice because of space limitations of this book.

Calculating Volumes

In most cases of strip and plot cruising, the results of the cruise are tabulated after the field work has been finished. The entire timber volume of a tract, or a subdivision of it, like a "forty", is derived from:

1. Total board-foot volume by species on the sampled area
2. Total acreage of the sample
3. Average volume by species per acre
4. Total acreage of the tract, or subdivision

Using appropriate tables, the net volume for each tree recorded on the cruise sheets is first listed in columns by species. Then the total of each species is found and also noted at the bottom of the cruise sheets. Some tree farmers may wish to calculate defect volume as well to see how much it runs, or to get volumes by diameter classes for management purposes.

In the case of trees showing defect, this requires special treatment, because the volume of the log concerned must be known. This is obtained by using Table V-6, which shows the average volume (in percent) for each log in trees of various heights. For instance, the butt log of a six-log tree contains 29 percent of the tree's volume. So, if the tree was tallied as $6^{B\frac{1}{2}}$, one-half of that, or $14\frac{1}{2}$ percent of the tree's volume would have to be deducted. A six-log tree recorded as 4/6 would have to have its two top logs, which represent 14 percent (9 plus 5) of its volume, subtracted.

Table V-6. Tree volume distribution by log position.

Log position	Percentage distribution of volume for trees of indicated 16-foot logs per tree											
	2	3	4	5	6	7	8	9	10	11	12	13
Butt	67	50	40	33	29	25	22	20	18	17	15	14
2	33	33	30	27	24	21	19	18	16	15	14	13
3		17	20	20	19	18	17	16	15	14	13	12
4			10	13	14	14	14	13	13	12	12	11
5				7	9	11	11	11	11	11	10	10
6					5	7	8	9	9	9	9	9
7						4	6	7	7	7	8	8
8							3	4	5	6	6	7
9								2	4	5	5	6
10									2	3	4	4
11										1	3	3
12											1	2
13												1

The total acreage within the strips or plots is determined next from the cruise sheets and map. For strips, the sampled acreage is the actual length of the strips in chains, as measured by chaining or pacing, times their width divided by 10. The total acreage of sample plots is their total number times the acreage in each. You see here that distances are not needed.

The average volume by species per acre for the sampled area is calculated by dividing the total volume of each species by the acreage within the sample. This also represents the average volume by species for the tract or land unit being considered.

The total acreage of the tract or subdivision for which the cruise is being tabulated has to be carefully determined from notes on the cruise sheets or map. Gross areas have to be reduced by the acreage within bodies of water, meadows, and non-timber portions to arrive at the net area. This total net figure times the average volumes above gives the total volume for the tract or parcel. Usually, all the final cruise results are placed on a summary sheet showing at least timber volumes by "forty" or other parcel, species, and for the whole tract.

Use of Prisms

Foresters make good use of simple optical prisms in variable plot sampling for various purposes. The prism is an inexpensive, wedge-shaped piece of glass that bends light rays to a certain degree or critical angle, depending on what is called the diopter rating of the prism. One diopter represents an angle of 34.36 minutes. Prisms of different ratings are used according to timber types and sizes.

Instead of dealing with diopter values, the most convenient practice is to have prisms ground to a diopter rating that is exactly equal to a whole basal area factor (BAF), such as 10, 20, 25, 30, 40, etc. As explained later, the BAF is used in computing basal area of stands. Prisms with prescribed BAF's can be purchased from forestry and optical suppliers for a modest cost. Table V-7 below shows the relationships between diopters and BAFs.

Table V-7.   Prism diopters and basal area factor equivalents.

Diopter	BAF	Diopter	BAF
3.00	9.802	5.30	30.000
3.03	10.000	6.00	39.169
4.00	17.417	6.10	40.000
4.30	20.000	7.00	53.513
4.80	25.000	7.40	60.000
5.00	27.208	8.00	69.585

In using the prism, the observer holds it horizontally at eye level over the plot center and sights towards the dbh of a tree. Depending on the distance to the tree, the image through the glass of the tree trunk is displaced somewhat toward the thin edge of the prism (Figure V-10). Where the image through the glass superimposes the trunk to any extent, that tree is considered to be within the plot. If the image through the prism is displaced away from and separate from the trunk, the tree viewed is not in. The resulting sample plot is circular but not having a fixed radius. For small trees within the plot the radius of the plot is small and for large trees the radius is greater. This technique produces what is termed a variable plot, consisting of concentric circles, that is useful in forest sampling.

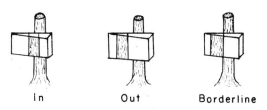

In   Out   Borderline

Figure V-10
Displacement of image caused by prisms.

The right prism should be used for the timber to be sampled. A BAF should be chosen that will provide a tree count of between four and eight trees per sample point. The prism ratings that foresters generally employ are as follows:

Timber Size	Diopter	BAF
Very large (48″ dbh +)	8	60–70
Large (32″–48″)	6	25–40
Medium (16″–32″)	5	20–25
Small (16″–)	3–4	10–20

The prism makes it possible to easily determine the basal area per acre of a stand. The basal area (in square feet) per acre at any sampling point equals the number of trees within the plot times the BAF. For example, in using a prism with a BAF of 10, you counted 12 trees within the plot, then the basal area per acre from that sample would be $10 \times 12 = 120$ square feet. In most cases, to have a representative sample, a number of scattered observations would be taken and the average number of trees in those plots computed, which then would be multiplied by the BAF to obtain the average basal area per acre.

As mentioned in Chapter II, basal area is a useful measure in forest management. It serves as an indicator of the degree of stocking or density of a stand—whether it is understocked, normal, or overstocked. The thinning of stands and even the harvests can be based on basal area standards. If a certain minimum basal area were prescribed, the forest manager can use a prism to quickly find out what areas should be cut.

Prisms work real well on flat ground, but where the slope is more than 10 percent, a correction is necessary, because the distances must be horizontal as they are in other forest measurement procedures. This correction can be made by rotating the prism in its plane by the slope angle. This rotation in effect reduces the critical angle of the prism gradually until it becomes zero at 90 degrees of rotation. What happens is that the prism reaches further away to pick up trees of a given diameter proportionately to the slope to horizontal distance relationships. An Abney level can be used to measure the slope and to also set the rotation angle of the prism. With the slope angle fixed on the Abney, the prism is placed on the Abney barrel and the bulb held level before the viewer sights through the properly rotated prism. Special clinometers are also available to make corrections for slope in prism sampling.

Sometimes a value called the plot radius factor (PRF) of prisms is handy to decide whether a tree, especially one that is not visible or borderline, is in or out of the plot. In those cases, the distance to the tree has to be paced or chained. The plot radius factor varies by the BAF. Every tree has its own plot radius, depending on its diameter and the prism, and a tree of that same size beyond that distance is not within the plot. Thus plot radius in feet equals PRF times the dbh in inches. The PRF for prisms of different BAFs are given in the table below:

Table V-8.   Plot radius factor for selected Basal Area Factors.

BAF	PRF	BAF	PRF
10	2.750	40	1.375
15	2.245	50	1.230
20	1.944	60	1.123
25	1.739	70	1.039
30	1.588	80	0.972

In addition to basal area measurements, foresters are increasingly using prisms and similar devices to determine the volume of timber stands. The method is called variable plot cruising. It is not the intent of this publication to cover this subject, because it is somewhat more technical than the traditional cruising methods. In essence, the volume per acre is determined by the use of volume tables converted to show volume per square foot of stem area. They are called V-BAR (volume-basal area ratio) tables.

Chapter VI

LOG SCALING

Another field of mensuration is the measurement of logs, or scaling as it is called in forestry circles. Scaling is the process of determining as accurately as possible the net volume of logs by the use of a log rule table, usually in board feet. This information is normally the basis of payment to timber fallers, contract loggers, log haulers, and timber sellers. The results of scaling are more accurate than timber cruising, because the tree in effect is more accessible and measurable.

Required Knowledge

To be a competent scaler, one must have a good basic knowledge about the units of measure used, required scaling equipment, the different log rules, and the procedures. And certainly, skills acquired by study, practice, and experience are a prerequisite, because much good judgement is need-ed to do a creditable scaling job.

Board-Foot Measure

In the U. S., the board food is the traditional and still most common unit of measure for the volume in trees and logs. This is because lumber is by far the leading forest product. Consequently, even though this unit was not designed to be a measure of non-lumber products, it is the predomi-nant measure in the forest end of the wood industry. Timber, logs, and lumber are commonly sold and bought by the thousand board feet. To avoid using the zeros, a thousand board feet is stated as MBF, or MBM (thousand board measure).

Nominally, a board foot, lumber tally, is one inch thick and one foot square. A piece of lumber of the same volume, e.g., 2″ x 6″ x 1 ft., is also one board foot. Whole inches are used as the standard to state thickness and width, regardless of the actual dimensions of the lumber. This came about when sizes in the rough stage were used to describe the same lumber after surfacing. The board footage of lumber can be calculated by this formula:

Board feet = [thickness (in.) x width (in.) x length (ft.)]/12

Because of losses in the sawing process, a cubic foot of wood in log form contains less than 12 board feet. Actually, the lumber yield per cubic foot depends on the diameter of the logs, ranging from 4 bd. ft. for logs of 5″ diameter to over 9 bd. ft. for 40-inch diameter logs. An average log of 10 inches in diameter has about 7 bd. ft. per cubic foot. The recovery is also dependent on the sizes lumber is cut; the smaller the dimensions are the less board feet there are in a cubic foot.

In addition to this factor, net board-feet scale rarely is the same as the board-feet tally of lumber produced. What the ratio is between the two depends on the taper of the logs, log rule used, mill efficiency, and sizes of logs and lumber that are sawn. In most cases of woods-run logs there is an overrun in mill tally over log scale, ranging from 5 percent to as high as 60 percent; the average is on the order of 10 to 20 percent. Sometimes, there may be an underrun if the milling process is inefficient.

Log Rules

There are many different log rules in this country, but only a few are used in California. The more common one in California is the Scribner log rule. Like most other rules, it gives the board feet in logs of various diameters (one-inch classes) and lengths by feet. An one-quarter inch wide saw-cut (saw-kerf) is assumed. The Scribner Decimal C rule is the same except that the board feet are rounded to the nearest 10 bd. ft. A more refined Scribner rule was developed cooperatively in 1972 by some West Coast users, and it is receiving wide acceptance because it is more adaptable to computer calculation (see Appendix).

The Spaulding rule, which is close to the Scribner for logs above 12 inches in diameter, has been used in the redwood-Douglas-fir region. Before the law was repealed in 1967, it was the legal rule for the state, meaning that when a log rule was not specified the Spaulding prevailed. The rule is based on an $1\frac{1}{32}$-inch saw-kerf. The Humboldt rule has been employed some for old-growth redwood; it is derived from the Spaulding rule, with those values being reduced by 30 percent to automatically allow for defect.

The International is the most accurate log rule, but its use has been restricted largely to scientific work. It makes allowance for taper of logs, which none of the above rules do, and has been prepared for both $\frac{1}{8}$-inch and $\frac{1}{4}$-inch saw-kerf.

The yield tax law (see Chapter IV) requires reporting by the Scribner Decimal C rule. This may gradually cause the other rules to fade out in California. However, as stated earlier, there is a slow trend in favor of cubic-foot rules, because so many more products are being utilized from logs besides lumber. And, someday we probably will have a cubic metric unit.

Like board-foot measure, there are a number of cubic-foot rules, all of which are based on formula, but of different accuracies. The Smalian's rule is fairly accurate and is used to some extent in the Pacific Northwest by the U. S. Forest Service and private companies. The diameters (inside bark) at both ends of the log have to be measured by this rule. Another cubic-foot rule is called the Huber (see Appendix); it is based on average middle diameter and it is considered to be the most accurate. Where cubic-foot measurement is practiced, a unit called the cunit, which equals 100 cu. ft., is used for ease of operations.

Both the Scribner and Spaulding board-foot rules were prepared by diagramming the lumber that could be cut from various size logs. The International rule is based on a mathematical formula. While log rule tables are more convenient, one could figure board-feet content of logs by formula, such as the one below:

$$V = (.79D^2 - 2D - 4) \times .0625L$$

where V = volume in bd. ft., approximately Scribner scale

            D = diameter inside bark in inches of log at small end

            L = length of log in feet

Scaling Equipment

In order to scale one need to measure both the diameter and the length of the log. A special tool called a scale stick with a hook or spud on the zero end is used most often by scalers. Up to 6 feet long, the stick is graduated into inches. Some sticks can directly provide the gross volumes for certain log lengths from special graduations on the stick in addition to the marks for inches.

Short log lengths can sometimes be estimated or marked off with the scale stick. A retractable tape of 20 to 50 ft. in length is commonly used, especially to measure longer logs.

Scale sticks are not absolutely necessary to measure diameter. One can use a stiff straight stick graduated in inches or even an 8-foot pocket tape. The cruiser stick will serve the purpose too; it has both an inch scale and graduations for board feet for 16-ft. logs by the Scribner Decimal C rule.

The scaler records the measurements and other data in a special scale book or on multiple-copy scale slips (see Figure VI-1). The latter have the advantage that copies of the scale can be provided to those having an interest, such as faller, contract logger, trucker, seller, and purchaser. The following information may be included on the scaling form:

Log seller	Species
Log buyer	Log number
Timber sale area	Diameter
Scaling location	Length
Load or truck identification	Gross volume
Scaler's name	Deduction for defect
Date	Net volume

Lumber crayon or canned spray-paint is used to mark the sale, log number, or any identification on the log ends, if that information is required. Branding axes are sometimes employed to designate ownership of logs.

Measurement Procedures

Scaling standards and procedures developed by the U. S. Forest Service are widely accepted in California. In general, the explanation of scaling herein follows that system.

Using the above equipment, to arrive at the gross board-feet volume of a log, the scaler essentially has to take two measurements—diameter and length. The former is done by placing a scale stick across the small end of the log and reading the diameter inside the bark (Figure VI-2). The diameter is read to the closest whole inch and recorded on the scale form. In case of logs that are not round, more than one measurement is taken to obtain an average diameter (to the next inch).

STATE OF CALIFORNIA
The Resources Agency

DEPARTMENT OF FORESTRY

FM-34 REV. 3-67

ORIGINAL

No. **90199**

STATE FOREST

SALES DESCRIPTION _____

AREA DESCRIPTION _____

SCALER _____ DATE ___ / ___ / ___

LOG NO.	LENGTH	DIAMETER	NET VOLUME BY SPECIES OR PRICE GROUPS							DEFECT DEDUCTIONS
1										
2										
3										
4										
5										
6										
7										
8										
9										
0										
1										
2										
3										
4										
5										
6										
7										
8										
9										
0										
1										
2										
3										
4										
5										
6										
7										
8										
9										
0										
TOTAL SCALE										
NUMBER OF LOGS										

Figure VI-1
Sample of a log scale slip.

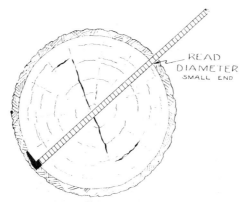

READ
DIAMETER
SMALL END

Figure VI-2

Diameter is measured inside the bark at the small end of the log.

Table VI-1.   Standard division of long logs for scaling with 20-foot maximum scaling length.

Length (feet)	Division of log—segment lengths in feet		
	Bottom	Middle	Top
21 [1]	11		10
22	12		10
23	12		11
24	12		12
25	13		12
26	14		12
27	14		13
28	14		14
29	15		14
30	16		14
31	16		15
32	16		16
33	17		16
34	18		16
35	18		17
36	18		18
37	19		18
38	20		18
39	20		19
40	20		20
41 [2]	14	14	13
42	14	14	14
43	15	14	14
44	16	14	14
45	16	15	14
46	16	16	14
47	16	16	15
48	16	16	16
49	17	16	16
50	18	16	16

[1] Scale overtrim 20-foot log as a 21-foot, 1-segment log.

[2] Scale overtrim 40-foot log as a 41-foot, 2-segment log.

In this table any log length and segment division will be used as the overtrim scaling length for the preceding length.

U.S.F.S., National Forest Scaling Handbook, 1974

The scaler then obtains the log length. Depending on the sale contract, the length is measured to the nearest foot or even two feet, with the specified allowance for sawmill trimming of 4 inches or more, depending on log length. In case the logger frequently exceeds this allowance, the scaler may apply a penalty scale by increasing the log length to the next foot. Where logs are primarily for lumber manufacture, the log lengths are usually in even-numbered feet. The scaler records the entire length of the log.

Logs longer than 20 feet should be scaled as two or more logs, with the longer one being the butt segment. For example, a 30-foot log would be scaled as a 16-ft. log (large end) and a 14-ft. log (small end) as shown in Table VI-1. This so-called short-log scale gives a higher volume than long-log scale by the common log rules, because they make no allowance for taper. In effect, the board foot-volume is that contained in a cylinder with a diameter at the small end of the log. Where long logs are converted to short segments for scaling purposes, the scaler can obtain the additional diameter(s) by estimation or by measuring both the large and small ends of the long log and pro-rating the taper accordingly. Thus, where a long log is converted into two segments of nearly equal length, the diameter of the larger one in most cases would be the average of the top and bottom diameters (Figure VI-3). Swelled butt logs may require assigned rates of taper because the taper is not uniform. The assumed additional diameters of the logs divided for scaling are not ordinarily recorded, because they are only needed to determine the gross volume of the log.

With these measurements, the scaler enters the gross volume of the log in the scale record. This is done by looking up the values in the appropriate log rule table. Some scalers obtain the volume directly from the scale stick if it is so graduated.

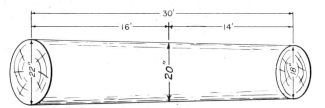

Figure VI-3.
Long logs are scaled as two or more logs.

Defect Deductions

After the gross volume of a log has been figured, the scaler must arrive at the net scale by making deductions for any defect that may be present. The procedure for this is not so precise as for gross volume and more judgement based on experience is necessary. The defects that are recognized in scaling include rot, insect damage, fire scar, shake (separation between annual rings), pitch ring or seam, splitting, checking, break, crook or sweep, crotch, and sometimes excessive number of large knots. If the logs are not for lumber or veneer purposes, only the first three kinds of defect may need to be considered.

As explained earlier, log rules of common usage, e.g., Scribner and Spaulding, do not make allowance for taper. This means that the gross volume of a log is that represented in a straight or right cylinder with a diameter the same as the small end of the log. Therefore, only defect within the confines of that cylinder should be deducted.

The standard method for reduction of scale for interior defects is accomplished by (1) boxing and measuring the defective area at the end of the log where it is the largest, (2) estimating the length of the defect, and (3) computing the deduction by the formula:

$$D = (W \times T \times L)/15$$

where   D = Deduction in bd. ft.

W = Width of defect plus 1 inch in inches

T = Thickness of defect plus 1 inch in inches

L = Length of defect in feet

If the interior defect is not visible at both ends of the log, the scaler has to judge what length it might be. Sometimes, exterior signs like conks, rotten knots, insect activity, and pitch indicate how far the defect extends lengthwise into the log.

Some interior defect such as shake and pitch ring may need special treatment. Logs with these defects often have good wood at the center which should not be deducted. Such a log of 16 feet in length is shown in Figure VI-4, where the outside limit of the shake or bad ring is 16 inches in diameter and the sound interior has a diameter of 12 inches. First the gross deduction would be 17 × 17 × 16 divided by 15, or 308 bd. ft. The sound interior would be the scale of a 16-ft. log of 12 inches diameter or 80 bd. ft. Therefore, the net deduction would be 308 minus 80 or 228 bd. ft. (rounded to 23 in case of Scribner Decimal C).

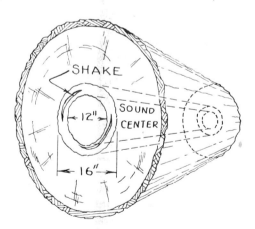

Figure VI-4
Defect caused by shake or pitch ring.

Side defects have to be approached differently. Deductions for them are made only when the defect comes within the right cylinder of the log, and any defect outside of that is ignored. To determine deductions for side defects, scalers have to apply logical reasoning and good judgment. For instance, in the case of a fire scar in a butt log shown in Figure VI-5, it is first estimated that about one-third of half the log is affected. Since the whole log contains 1,200 bd. ft., the deduction would be one-third of 600 or 200 bd. ft. The same method can be applied to crook or sweep.

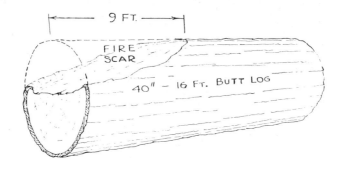

Figure VI-5
Fire scar defect.

There are a number of rules of thumb and special techniques used by scalers to make allowances for defect. Figure VI-6 illustrates some of the more common ways to handle deductions. The two excellent references that are listed in the Appendix contain much more specific instructions than those that can be included here.

Once the scaler decides on the deduction it is entered on the scale form along with the net volume of the log. Those logs that have excessive defect are labelled cull. To be merchantable, logs of high value (e.g., pines, Douglas-fir, redwood) should be one-quarter or more sound, and those of less valuable species like the true firs should be at least one-third good. In some cases cull logs that contain some chippable sound wood are sold for pulp purposes but for a lower price.

Weight Scaling

Instead of scaling individual logs, a system has been developed to obtain the volume by a weighing and sampling process. It is especially applicable to large operations in young or small timber, where it is inconvenient and costly to scale many low-volume logs. While this weighing method can be fairly cheap and accurate, it has such problems as the availability of precise truck scales, the great variation in log weights, the difficulty of understanding and accepting the system, and the statistical knowledge required to implement and control it.

The biggest difficulty is the great variability in weight of logs. Basically, this is governed by the specific gravity of the wood, its moisture content, and amount of bark and defect. Thus, the weight of logs is affected by such factors as:

Species
Locality, climate, and slope aspect
Season of year
Position of log in tree
Amount of defect and sapwood
Time since felling
Utilization of snags and windfalls

Because of these variables, before a weight scaling program is put into effect, it is necessary to develop data on what the relationship is between

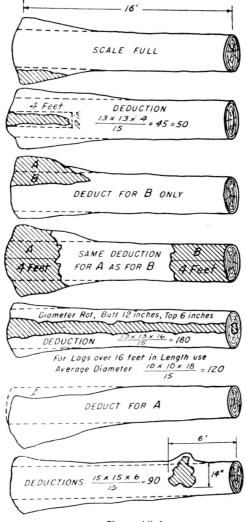

Figure VI-6
Deductions for common defect

the weight of the timber in the particular operation and the net log scale. This is called the weight-volume ratio, expressed as follows:

$$W/V = \text{gross log weight per load/net log scale per load}$$
$$= \text{pounds per board foot (net)}$$

First, enough logs have to be scaled and weighed to get a reasonably good ratio to start with. This may mean scaling and weighing all loads at the beginning of the operation. Then, this figure of pounds per net board foot can be used for a while to convert weight of subsequent loads to board feet without having to do any stick scaling. This ratio runs from 6 to 12 lbs. per bd. ft.

The ratio originally established should not be continued indefinitely. To maintain a high degree of accuracy, the ratio is adjusted periodically by scaling of sample loads. The number of loads to sample is computed by statistical methods, and what loads to scale are randomly selected. Ten percent or more of all the loads are sample-scaled, depending on size and variability of the timber sale. The minimum sample size to compute or adjust the ratio should be about 20 loads. When the W/V ratio is highly variable or the sale volume is less than two million bd. ft., the required sample percent becomes so large that the advantages of weight scaling are lost.

The result of this system is that all the loads from a logging operation are weighed at a convenient place and only part of the loads are scaled. The latter is usually done after the trucks are loaded and weighed, such as at the scales or a mill. To remove possibilities of bias in loading, what truck is to be scaled is kept confidential until arrival at the place of scaling. When sufficient number of loads have been scaled, the weight-volume ratio is re-computed by using a combination of the new and old data.

Other Forms of Scaling

Consulting foresters can provide or arrange for scaling on wood operations and at mills. The services of a private scaling bureau are also available on a contract basis. If a timber or log buyer is not willing to accept the scale of the seller, it is better to have a third party scaler rather than to agree to the scale of the buyer, because scalers and scaling practices are not regulated to any great extent.

The work of scalers should be checked occasionally. This check-scaling is necessary to be sure that the scaler is complying with the terms of the sales contract and standards of the trade. The values involved certainly are considerable and worth the expense of such checks. It is accomplished by the scaler and checker both scaling the same hundred or more logs and comparing the results. Volumes between scaler and checker should be within one percent of each other for sound logs and five percent for logs over 20 percent defective.

Where disputes arise over log scale, they can be settled by each party agreeing to arbitration by a competent third person, such as a forest consultant. The Division of Measurement Standards of the California Department of Food and Agriculture has been called upon occasionally to settle such differences, particularly between contract workers and employers. That agency also inspects and certifies weight scales.

Chapter VII

FOREST ROADS

The successful operation of a forest is dependent upon having a serviceable road system. It provides access to the property for silvicultural and management purposes, serves as a vital link between the harvesting of crops and the market, and it enables the tree farmer to better protect the forest from trespass, pests, and fire. The right kind and number of roads not only make these jobs easier but increases the financial return from the forest as well.

A system that is wisely planned, well constructed, and properly maintained saves money in more ways than one. Logging costs are largely affected by the location and quality of the roads and so are stumpage values. Good roads are cheaper to maintain and can be more easily kept in useable condition permanently. That means that once roads are in place they can serve future harvests besides providing ready access to the forest. Another saving in costs of roads that are laid out, built, and kept up properly is that they do less damage to the soil resource, water quality, and the landscape. No single part of a forest operation can cause as much soil disturbance and erosion as roads, so they need special attention in order to prevent such damage.

Road Planning

Before roads are actually located on the ground, some thought should be given to developing a general plan for the transportation needs of the forest. This might be in the form of a map to be incorporated in the overall management plan that was described in Chapter II. This planning should take into consideration location of markets, useable existing roads on and off the property, topography, management and protection needs, type and order of timber harvest, and other forest uses.

Rights-of-Way

Not all roads adjacent to the property, both public and private, may be available or suitable for use of the tree farmer. This should be determined ahead of time and the road plan developed accordingly. Encroachment onto public roads for access purposes may be regulated, and in fact, log-hauling on them may be even prohibited. Using private roads on adjacent properties may be advantageous to the tree farmer and this should be explored and assured by obtaining necessary right-of-way agreements. Reciprocal easements may be in order where adjacent owners can advantageously move timber or need access over each other's property.

For protection of both the grantor and the grantee, rights-of-way should be in writing and prepared with professional help. A non-specific or floating easement over a parcel without some description may lead to future trouble. The route should be at least described by land features, e.g., along a certain stream or ridge, existing road, or by general direction going through identifiable points. Some cases may justify a description based on a survey. The document should cover other points like compensation, purpose of right-of-way, width, rights and conditions of use by either party or others, responsibility for construction and maintenance, assignability, liability, time period, and amendment rights and procedures.

Routing

The usual pattern in tractor logging is to have the roads below most of the timber that is to be harvested. Typically, the main routes go up the principal drainages with laterals along side drainages, side ridges, and side slopes. The central idea is to avoid too much hauling uphill or adverse grade as it is called. Skidding distances are generally held to distances of 1,000 to 2,000 feet. Long ridges also are used for main roads where appropriate because of ease of construction and maintenance. Having roads on south exposure hastens spring snow melt and drying out of moisture from precipitation.

Cable logging is commonly done uphill. In such cases, the road system is designed to be the opposite of the above. Most roads are therefore above the timber to be logged. Generally, cable systems require less roads and yarding distances may be longer.

Large-scale contour maps, like the USGS quadrangle maps, are necessary in planning a road system. Aerial photographs, especially when viewed stereoscopically, and maps and notes made during a cruise are also useful.

A road system is not installed all at one time. Instead, it is constructed piece by piece to serve the planned harvests of the forest. Ordinarily, the roads necessary for harvest are constructed by the timber purchaser in accordance to the sale contract. It may take the entire cutting period for the forest to complete the network. Thus, road planning must consider contemplated location and timing of harvests, so that as each road segment is established, it becomes an integral part of the system. One example of this where a road will go through a timbered area that will not be logged until later. In that case, the road should be designed to serve that area later as well as the immediate area to be harvested beyond that point.

In some situations, where access to and within the property is inadequate, it may be necessary to develop enough roads ahead of harvests for purposes of silviculture, management planning, and protection. These can be lower standard roads. Preferably, their location should coincide with the planned logging roads and brought up to standard when the latter are established. However, some of these roads may be necessary just for administration and protection; they can be low-standard, 4-wheel drive roads, yet carefully built to prevent damage to the forest and the environment.

Road Location

When it comes time to build a road, the exact location has to be made by on-the-ground reconnaissance or surveying. This is needed to have the proper alinement and grade and to avoid costly construction and maintenance, hard rock outcrops, geologically unstable areas, highly erosive soils, too steep slopes, large cuts and fills, and potential streamside problems and damage. The main idea is to have the least costly road that serves the intended purpose and fits the terrain.

While engineers do a considerable amount of detailed engineering to locate and design roads, most foresters use less refined methods. In many cases this produces satisfactory results for forestry roads. Using a contour map, aerial photograph, or aneroid barometer (to get elevation readings), the locator first hikes the planned route to size up the situation and to fix control points, such as passes, saddles, favorable stream crossings sites, and places that should be avoided; e.g., rough or unstable areas.

The difference in elevation, or rise as it is termed, and the approximate horizontal distance (from map, photograph, or pacing) between adjacent control points is noted. Dividing the rise by the distance gives the approximate grade of the road segment in percent or the rise in feet for each 100 feet of horizontal distance. The grade in percent is also equal to the tangent of the slope angle expressed in degrees. Tables A-8 and A-9 in the Appendix show the relationship between degree of slope and grade percent. Depending on the class of road wanted, the maximum grade usually varies from 6 to 15 percent. If the computed grade percent is too high, then the length of the road segment must be increased in some manner, e.g., by carefully putting in one or more gentle switchbacks. Table VII-1 suggests grade and other standards for different classes of roads.

Table VII-1. Road standards by class of road.

Item	Class of Road *		
	I	II	III
Average Speed	30 mph	20 mph	10 mph
Maximum Sustained Grade	7 %	10 %	15 %
Maximum Pitch Grade	10 %	12 %	20 %
Minimum Radius of Curvature	100 ft.	60 ft.	40 ft.
Minimum Sight Distance	300 ft.	200 ft.	100 ft.
Minimum Width, traveled way * *	16 ft.	12 ft.	10 ft.

* I—main roads, II—laterals, III—spurs
* * One lane roads with intervisible turnouts

Once an acceptable approximate grade has been found, the road locator re-runs the line between the control points with an Abney level or similar instrument set on the right percent or its degree equivalent. The location is marked with colored flagging (not blazes) or stakes so that changes can be made as needed. One should be prepared to make many adjustments to the road location for good purposes, e.g. to:

1. Avoid sharp curves (see subsequent section)
2. Miss rock outcrops unless they are soft enough to cut or use as road base material.
3. Keep away from places having evidence of ground creep or slides. If they have to be crossed do so at or near the top so that they are the least disturbed.
4. Detour around erosive and expandable soils, e.g., those of the blue clay type. Use soil-vegetation maps and legends or other soil maps to the best advantage.
5. Stay clear of springs, meadows, and wet places.

6. Minimize the number of large cuts and fills on steep side-hills.
7. Have roads a safe distance from streams (100 feet or more, except at crossings) to prevent damage from high water and the movement of earth or debris from construction and maintenance into the streams.
8. Keep road away from residences and recreation sites to reduce safety hazards and nuisance caused by dust and noise.
9. Minimize areas that would have overly expensive clearing, construction, and mantenance costs—too heavy timber and wrong exposure.

Grade Considerations

Whenever practicable, forest roads should be built to a grade that is favorable (mostly downhill) to the log haul. Adverse (uphill) grades slow down the travel time, consume more fuel, and cause extra wear and tear on the equipment. Level roads don't have these disadvantages; however, they are more difficult to drain properly.

The grade percent of a road depends on such factors as class of road wanted, topography, soil type, and preciptation. Where possible, logging roads have a grade of two to eight percent favorable to the haul. Adverse grades should not exceed six percent except short pieces on spur roads may go as high as 10 percent. Occasionally these limits must be exceeded because of ground conditions. Keeping within these grade standards may increase road construction costs, but this is more than offset by lower road maintenance and haul costs. Erosion on unpaved roads exceeding six percent grade is likely to be significant and special prevention measures may be necessary.

Long sustained grades of the same percent are not the ideal as one would suppose. They too sometimes present drainage problems in that they offer no logical places to divert water from the bank side to the outside of the road. This can cause erosion and gradual deepening of the inside ditch.

Forest managers prefer a slightly broken or rolling grade, but one that is generally favorable to the haul. This will often permit better alinement without a corresponding increase in construction costs. Moreover, undulating grades provide more frequent places for diversion of water, faster water removal, and require less culverts. Changes in grade should be gentle and any adverse sections short and easy so that loaded trucks can maintain a reasonable speed without frequent shifting of gears.

Sometimes, short sections of steep or pitched grade may be justified because of terrain or economics. They can be compensated for by being straight and are preceded by a level stretch or slight downgrade. If used, pitched grades should be designed to control erosion and provide adequate traction.

Alinement and Curvature

The road locator must also consider alinement and curvature because they have an important bearing on efficiency and safety. Curves are circular, that is, arcs of circles connected by straight lines tangent to them; the connecting straight stretches are therefore called tangents. The sharpness of the curvature may be expressed in either of two ways; (1) by the length of the radius of the circle of which the arc is composed, or (2) by the central angle between two points on the curve 100 feet apart in a straight line. In the latter, the 100-ft. segment is called a chord and the angle subtending it at the center of the circle is termed the degree of curve. The relationship between these two is shown in the following formula:

$$D = 5730/R$$

where   D = Degree of curve (for a 100-ft. chord)

R = Radius of curvature

In forestry work curves are expressed by radius of curvature. Using the above formula, a curve having a radius of 100 feet would have a degree of curve of 57.3 degrees or 57 degrees and 18 minutes. Note that the relationship is inverse, that is, a gentle curve has a long radius and a small degree of curve.

Engineers employ a variety of mathematical methods and special tables to lay out curves. One is by measuring the deflection angle at the transit station between the tangent and points along the curve. Others include what are called the external distance, tangent offset, and middle ordinate methods.

Foresters occasionally use these same methods; however, ordinarily they employ a less time-consuming and simpler approach. With experience a person can learn to locate curves satisfactorily by eye with some checking and measuring with a staff compass and tape. The radius of curvature of roads is largely dictated by topography, but accommodations to fit the chosen standards can be made by the right positioning of a road at the middle of the curve, changing direction of the tangents somewhat, or planning more cut or fill. For example, in crossing a draw, if two tangents intersect at a sharp angle, the road could not be located close to the point of the intersection because the radius of curvature would be too short. Instead, to obtain a longer radius of curvature, the road would have to be placed further away from the point of the intersection. Providing these conditions are noted and planned for during the route location, most, if not all, of these kinds of adjustments can be made during the construction phase when it is more convenient to take necessary measurements.

Naturally, where curves are short and gentle they can be located by eye. However, long and complex curves require at least some simple surveying. One can use the following geometric relationship (Figure VII-1) to locate a turn of a road with a wanted radius of curvature:

$$T = R \text{ tangent } \tfrac{1}{2} CA$$

where   T = distance between intersection of tangents (PI) and where they touch the curve

R = radius of curvature

CA = Central angle of curve (also equal to the external angle between the two tangents at point of intersection)

To illustrate, assume that a 100-ft. radius of curvature is desired at a place where the central angle is 30 degrees. Then, T—the tangent distance—

would be 100 times the natural tangent of 15 degrees (.2679) or 26.79 feet. This distance can readily taped from the point of intersection of tangent along each to where the curve begins and ends. Table VII-2 shows these tangents distances for a radius of curvature of 10 feet and selected central angles.

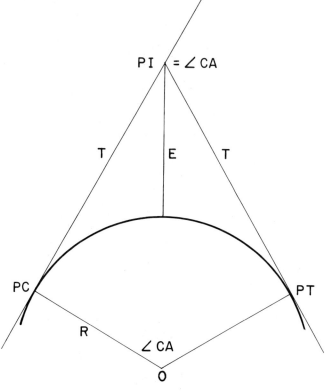

Figure VII-1
Road curve diagram.

Also, the table includes the external distance E from the intersection of the tangents and the mid-point of the curve; this is helpful to locate the middle of the curve on the ground. For the above example, the table would give an external distance of 3.5 feet.

The radius of curvature of logging roads varies by the class of road. Of course, curves should be as few as practicable, because they increase travel time and costs and reduce visibility and safety. Except for special situations the radius of curvature should not be less than 40 feet. Table VII-1 gives minimum curvature standards for different classes of roads.

Another critical factor in alinement of roads is sight distance (Table VII-1). This is the continuous length of road ahead visible to the driver. It is important to be able to safely stop a vehicle or to pass another. In addition to proper designing of curves, sight distances can be improved by adequate clearing of roadside obstructions and vegetation, and by a gradual change of upgrade to downgrade on hills. On a single lane roads intervisibility determines frequency of turnouts.

Table VII-2. Tangent distances T and external distances E for curves of radius 10 feet.*

Central Angle	T	E	Central Angle	T	E	Central Angle	T	E
10	0.87	0.04	56	5.32	1.33	101	12.13	5.72
11	0.96	0.05	57	5.43	1.38	102	12.35	5.89
12	1.05	0.06	58	5.54	1.43	103	12.57	6.06
13	1.14	0.06	59	5.66	1.49	104	12.80	6.24
14	1.23	0.07	60	5.77	1.55	105	13.03	6.43
15	1.32	0.08	61	5.89	1.61	106	13.27	6.62
16	1.41	0.10	62	6.01	1.67	107	13.51	6.81
17	1.49	0.11	63	6.13	1.73	108	13.76	7.01
18	1.58	0.12	64	6.25	1.79	109	14.02	7.22
19	1.67	0.14	65	6.37	1.86	110	14.28	7.43
20	1.76	0.15	66	6.49	1.92	111	14.55	7.65
21	1.85	0.17	67	6.62	1.99	112	14.83	7.88
22	1.94	0.19	68	6.74	2.06	113	15.11	8.12
23	2.03	0.20	69	6.87	2.13	114	15.40	8.36
24	2.13	0.22	70	7.00	2.21	115	15.67	8.61
25	2.22	0.24	71	7.13	2.28	116	16.00	8.87
26	2.31	0.26	72	7.26	2.36	117	16.32	9.14
27	2.40	0.28	73	7.40	2.44	118	16.64	9.42
28	2.49	0.31	74	7.54	2.52	119	16.98	9.70
29	2.59	0.33	75	7.67	2.60	120	17.32	10.00
30	2.68	0.35	76	7.81	2.69	121	17.67	10.31
31	2.77	0.38	77	7.95	2.78	122	18.04	10.63
32	2.87	0.40	78	8.10	2.87	123	18.42	10.96
33	2.97	0.43	79	8.24	2.96	124	18.81	11.30
34	3.06	0.46	80	8.39	3.05	125	19.21	11.66
35	3.15	0.49	81	8.54	3.15	126	19.63	12.03
36	3.25	0.51	82	8.69	3.25	127	20.06	12.41
37	3.35	0.54	83	8.85	3.35	128	20.50	12.82
38	3.44	0.58	84	9.00	3.46	129	20.96	13.23
39	3.54	0.61	85	9.16	3.56	130	21.44	13.66
40	3.64	0.64	86	9.32	3.67	131	21.94	14.11
41	3.74	0.68	87	9.49	3.79	132	22.46	14.59
42	3.84	0.71	88	9.66	3.90	133	23.00	15.08
43	3.94	0.75	89	9.83	4.02	134	23.56	15.59
44	4.04	0.78	90	10.00	4.14	135	24.14	16.13
45	4.14	0.82	91	10.18	4.27	136	24.75	16.69
46	4.24	0.86	92	10.35	4.40	137	25.39	17.28
47	4.35	0.90	93	10.54	4.53	138	26.05	17.90
48	4.45	0.95	94	10.72	4.66	139	26.75	18.55
49	4.56	0.99	95	10.91	4.80	140	27.47	19.24
50	4.66	1.03	96	11.11	4.94	141	28.24	19.96
51	4.77	1.08	97	11.30	5.09	142	29.04	20.72
52	4.88	1.13	98	11.50	5.24	143	29.89	21.52
53	4.99	1.17	99	11.71	5.40	144	30.78	22.36
54	5.09	1.22	100	11.92	5.56	145	31.72	23.26
55	5.21	1.27				150	37.32	28.64

* To obtain T and E for longer radius multiply values by appropriate factor, e.g. for 100 ft. multiply by 10.

Width, Cuts, and Fills

The width of a road and how much earth is moved affect costs of construction, maintenance, and use. And they have a significant impact on the forest and its associated values.

Except for large industrial tree farms where there is heavy traffic, roads of one lane should be preferred to those that allow passing anywhere. The vehicles have to move slower and cautiously on a one-land road, and this increases operating costs to some degree. However, a narrow road is much cheaper to build and maintain, and causes much less soil disturbance. The traveled width of a road depends on the number of lanes and class of road (Table VII-1).

To compensate for the narrowness of one-lane roads, either the traffic has be controlled or provision should be made to allow safe passing. The latter is the more common practice. This is accomplished by having special short sections of two-lane roads. These turnouts should be intervisible so that a driver can always see where the next turnout is. Where topography is light and grading is not heavy there may be some advantage to carrying the turnout width around the entire length of a blind curve.

Table VII-3. Volume of cuts and fills per 100 feet of road length and side slopes of 1½ to 1.

Average Height (ft.) of Cut or Fill at Road Center	Width of Base of Cut or Crown of Fill (ft.)		
	10	20	30
	cubic yards		
1	43	80	117
2	96	170	244
3	161	272	383
4	238	386	534
5	323	509	794
6	424	645	867
7	532	791	1050
8	651	948	1244
9	784	1117	1450
10	926	1296	1667
11	1080	1450	1820
12	1244	1615	1985
13	1420	1791	2161
14	1607	1978	2348
15	1806	2176	2546
16	2015	2385	2756
17	2235	2606	2976
18	2467	2837	3207
19	2709	3080	3450
20	2963	3333	3704

Logging roads usually require a considerable number of cuts and fills. To avoid wasting soil and to reduce costs the amount cut should equal the required fill volume, plus 10 to 20 percent to allow for shrinkage and settlement, except in the case of rock. Table VII-3 can be used as a guide to calculate volumes of cuts and fills. The cuts should be made so that the slopes are stable and have no overhanging banks or tree roots. Also, side-casting of the cut material over the road edge should be carefully done, especially on steep slopes above streams, so that it does not cause any harm. Table VII-4 shows cut slope ratios for various soil conditions. Where cuts are less than four feet or so, flatter slopes up to 3 to 1 are not too costly and will revegetate easier than steeper ones. To facilitate maintenance by a grader machine, and to have a safe road, the slope from the road to the bottom of the inside ditch should be flatter than the sidehill cut.

Table VII-4. Cut slope ratios (horizontal distance to vertical distance) for various conditions.

Soil Conditions	Natural Ground Slope	Slope Ratio
Normal soil	0–30 percent	1½ to 1
Normal soil	30–55 percent	1 to 1
Normal soil	55 percent plus	¾ to 1
Hard pan	All slopes	½ to 1
Solid rock	All slopes	¼ to 1

The stability of fills is especially critical since disturbed loose materials are used to form them. Care should be taken to not include stumps, slash, and other organic material. End hauling of fill material should be downhill and short as possible. Where practicable, earth fill should be placed in layers from 6 to 8 inches thick with each layer compacted by the staggered passage of construction equipment or by use of rubber-tired or sheepsfoot rollers.

In normal practice, the slope ratio of the fills is 1½ to 1. For most soils, this slope is considered the steepest that can be effectively protected from erosion, even when revegetated. In some clay and silty soils, slopes ranging between 2 to 1 and 4 to 1 may be available, especially on more shallow fills. Fills of clean angular rock may be on the order of 1¼ to 1.

Subgrade and Surface

Grading and preparation of the roadbed are important operations in road construction. The road is only as good as the subgrade on which it is located. The base has to be firm and stable, especially on fills or stretches of soft ground. Where suitable, only native material in or near the right-of-way is utilized. Sometimes it is necessary to haul in loose or crushed rock, decomposed granite, cinders, or gravel from nearby borrow pits or sources to strengthen weak subgrades. All-weather roads require such treatment for most if not all their entire length.

Plastic non-woven fabrics can also be used advantageously to stabilize roads, particularly over wet, unstable soils. A layer of the fabric is unrolled along the subgrade and covered by a course of rock or other base material. This technique reduces the amount of road base needed. The support membrane, which allows water to pass through it, keeps the aggregate and the subsoil from mixing, diffuses wheel loading forces, facilitates drainage and drying of the road, and keeps the bottom from dropping out of the road.

The wearing surface of a road does not have much capacity to carry loads but is of great value in protecting the road base from the traffic. A loose surface does not serve the purpose, nor does one where the surface material has been worn through or displaced. The serviceability of the road surface depends on its construction, the condition of the subgrade, drainage, and maintenance. A properly stabilized road has a smooth hard-wearing surface that will not wash or blow away. The surface needs to have enough abrasive resistance and shear strength to carry the expected traffic without breaking up under the weather conditions of use. Some roads or stretches of road require stabilization treatment. This is accomplished by increasing the compactness and density of the native soil through the addition of other materials. A stabilized surface is composed of a mixture of 1) well-graded, crushed rock or gravel of one inch or less in size, 2) fine aggregate of sand to fill the voids, and 3) an 8 to 10 percent clay binder, which contains and holds some moisture. When mechanically mixed the thickness is from 6 to 10 inches; this eventually compacts to a depth of 4 to 6 inches.

In addition to having a proper surface mixture, some heavily used and long-season roads are treated or paved with special materials to bind the surface, to reduce dust, and to control erosion. These include various forms of bitumen or asphalt, oils, and even chemicals like calcium chloride. The latter has to be carefully used because it is somewhat corrosive to equipment and leaching may sterilize adjacent soils or affect water quality.

Drainage and Erosion Control

Roads have to be drained well in order to keep them usable, to ease maintenance, and to prevent erosion of the adjacent land and fouling of nearby waters. Erosion caused by not having proper drainage can cause a lot of costly damage. While provision for the right facilities may raise construction costs considerably, in the long run it pays off for roads that will serve the forest in the future as well as the immediate present.

Surface Drainage

To provide for rapid surface drainage roads are cross-sloped. They may be outsloped, crowned, or insloped. Tangent sections of better class roads are commonly crowned in the center and sloped to both sides, and the curves are sloped in or out. Roads of light use and those with small cuts and fills may be outsloped most of their length.

The selection of the cross pitch is influenced by the local rainfall pattern, erodibility of the soil, type of road surface, and the gradient. For roads of 4 percent or less in grade, the following cross-slope pitches are used:

Natural soil or loose gravel—¼″ to ½″ per foot
Compacted mix   —³⁄₁₆″ to ⅜″ per foot

For gradients in excess of 4 percent the above values should be increased by 20 percent for each one percent increase in road grade. This will shed water to the side rather than have it run down the road. When the grade is more than 8 percent, cross sloping alone does not suffice and intercepting dips or drains should be used to prevent runoff along the roadway. Untreated shoulders of the road should be pitched 50 percent steeper than the traveled way.

For out-sloped roads exceeding 8 percent in grade or other situations, one can choose among three common methods to safely dispose of water from the road. For low standard roads so-called "thank-you ma'ams" may be constructed. These are shallow rounded ditches running across and at right angles to the road. This kind of dip is usually unsatisfactory because it impedes traffic, doesn't drain well, and wears out easily.

An improved dip (also called water break or water bar) is a smooth shallow ditch or depression of at least six inches in depth in the roadway that is at an angle of 45 to 60 degrees from the centerline of the road. These dips are installed on tangents, below outcurves, above incurves, seldom through fills, and elsewhere as needed on both out-sloped and in-sloped road sections. The spacing is governed by the road grade (see next paragraph). Figure VII-2 depicts a typical drainage dip installation.

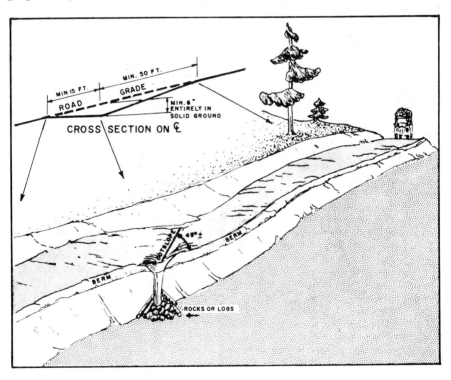

Figure VII-2
Typical drainage dip installation

A yet better method is to use an open-top box culvert made on the site from durable or treated lumber or poles, or pre-fabricated from corrugated, galvanized steel (Figure VII-3). The trough opening should be 3 to 4 inches wide and 4 to 8 inches deep. To clean out properly a flow-line gradient of ½ inch or more per foot of length is required. The usual distance between intercepting dips or open-top culverts are shown below. The spacing should be closer where rainfall is high and the roadbed is very erosive.

2– 5 percent road grade: 300–500 feet
6–10 percent road grade: 200–300 feet
11–15 percent road grade: 100–200 feet
16–20 percent road grade: 50–100 feet

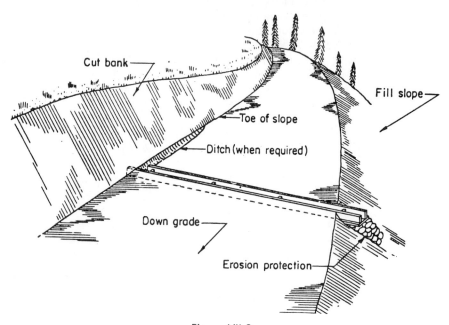

Figure VII-3
An open-top culvert installation.

Side Ditches

Except in case of out-sloped roads, water from the sidehill and from the surface must be transported by side ditches to a water course or a special drainage facility that allows the water to pass under the road. In addition, these channels provide subdrainage of the road and intercept undesirable intrusion of ground water from the sidehill.

The size of the ditch should be sufficient to carry any anticipated volume of storm water and prevent the heaviest flow from reaching the road surface. Ditches should have a grade of at least two percent. One that does not drain well may overflow or become a catch basin that can saturate the road subgrade. The side ditches should be relieved by occasional steeper pitches and frequent outlet ditches and culverts.

Cross-Road Drainage

Closed culverts are needed to move water from inside and under the road to the outside. These can be closed box culverts made from durable or treated wood, but metal corrugated pipe is preferable. While it may cost more, metal culvert is easier to place, does a better job, and lasts much longer. Metal pipe up to 6 feet in diameter is factory-built in various lengths. Larger diameter pipe is assembled on the job from prefabricated plates.

The length of the culvert is related to width of the roadway, its slope, and angle of the culvert to the centerline of the road. It should be straight except some installations may require a gentle or broken angled alinement horizontally or even vertically. The pipe should extend at least 1½ feet beyond the edge of the road at each end to prevent erosion, and the spill side should be protected with rocks, other non-erodible material, or special discharge aprons. Headwalls of concrete and wood or steel debris barriers may be necessary at the entry of the culverts to prevent washing and clogging.

Culverts should be large enough to carry the maximum flow expected. Where culverts are used to just transport water from the inside ditches to the outside of the road, they need not be large. Generally, the culvert grade should be at least one or two percent more than the entering waterway, but at least 6 inches drop in 100 feet of length. A 10-percent grade will ordinarily prevent sedimentation within the culvert, but grades over that may cause damage by scouring, and some inside paving may be required.

Large culverts—18 inches or more in diameter—are used where natural drainages and streams cross the roadway. These culverts should have the same alinement as that of the stream and they should be placed high enough to allow for some sedimentation at the entrance. They must also be cleared with the Department of Fish and Game.

Where the waterway is used by fish, the culvert should be installed so that their movement is not restricted. Things to watch are too steep a pitch, thin flows caused by oval pipe, precipitous drops, and no resting pool at the low end.

Sizes of these culverts must be designed to meet flood-stage requirements, rather than normal conditions. The factors involved include intensity, duration, and frequency of maximum rainfall, area and shape of the watershed drained by the water course, soil, and vegetative cover. Engineers have formulas, special tables, and other devices to compute the needed sizes. Table VII-5, which was derived from an empirical formula, gives culvert openings for various drainage areas. In addition to reviewing local rainfall records, clues as to the size of culvert needed can be obtained by looking at existing crossings of the same water course, other similar drainages with culverts, and evidence of flood runoff, e.g., water-deposited debris, bank cutting. Basically, the culvert opening should equal or exceed the cross-sectional area of the entering water course at high stage. In some cases, like shallow fills, it may be better to install two smaller pipes in parallel with well compacted earth separating them.

Extreme care must be taken in placing culverts in order to have them function properly. Also, poorly installed pipe can become severely damaged or possibly wash out. A common mistake is to place culverts too low, with no allowance for sedimentation and settling. Culverts should be put on a firm foundation of earth to prevent transverse bending or breaking due to uneven settlement caused by weight of the fill or clogging. The fill around and top of the pipe should be firmly tamped. The height of the fill above the culvert should be one-half the pipe diameter, and at the least 12 inches.

Fords can also be utilized to cross drainages, particularly where there may be flash floods, high seasonal runoff peaks, or frequent passage of debris. This type of crossing can be less expensive than a large culvert or a bridge. To protect water quality and to prevent stream damage a ford carrying a large amount of traffic should be paved. It consists of a reinforced concrete slab across the water course and a connecting discharge apron or energy dissipator on the down-stream side.

Table VII-5.   Culvert openings required for various drainage areas.

Drainage area		Waterway openings required (sq. ft.)			
Acres	Sq. mi.	Mountainous land	Hilly land	Rolling land	Flat land
1	0.0016	0.9–2.0	0.8–1.7	8.0–1.5	0.8–1.1
2	.0031	1.5–3.1	1.0–2.7	0.8–2.3	0.8–1.7
4	.0062	2.5–4.7	1.7–4.1	1.1–3.4	0.8–2.6
8	.0125	4.3–7.2	2.9–6.2	1.9–5.2	1.0–3.9
10	.016	5.1–8.2	3.4–7.1	2.2–6.0	1.2–4.5
15	.023	6.8–10	4.6–9.0	3.0–7.6	1.5–5.8
20	.031	8.3–13	5.7–11	3.8–9.1	1.9–6.8
30	.047	12–16	7.7–14	5.1–12	2.6–8.8
40	.062	14–19	9.5–17	6.4–14	3.2–10
60	.094	19–25	13–21	8.8–18	5.4–16
100	.156	28–35	19–29	13–24	6.4–18
150	.234	38–47	26–37	17–31	8.6–23
200	.312	48–59	32–44	21–37	11–28
250	.39	56–59	38–50	25–42	14–35
300	.47	64–79	43–58	29–47	16–38
400	.62	80–98	53–71	36–56	18–42
500	.78	95–116	64–85	42–64	21–48
600	.94		73–97	48–72	24–54
800	1.25		90–120	60–85	30–64
1000	1.56			71–98	36–73
1500	2.34			96–125	48–94
2000	3.12				60–112
2500	3.91				71–128
3000	4.70				81–142

Note: Within size ranges given above, use larger openings for factors contributing to rapid runoff of surface water such as high rainfall intensity, impervious soil, lack of ground cover. Use smaller openings for low rainfall intensity, open country, porous soil, sodded or wooded areas.
S.A.F., Forestry Handbook, 1955

Bridges are required on occasion to cross larger streams. Some timber operators construct bridges from large logs laid side by side and held together by cable straps or cross timbers. However, for safety purposes and to prevent rot, the end bearings should not be just the stream bank, nor should the deck be made of earth. Instead, substantial abutments should be constructed and the deck planked. Other types of bridges are also utilized but they should be of proven engineering design.

Revegetation of Slopes

Where soil and climate are favorable, erosion of disturbed roadside slopes can be controlled by seeding or planting of vegetation. Annual grasses like ryegrass are commonly employed in areas of mild climate. CDF forest advisers, Soil Conservation Service technicians, and county farm advisers can provide information on species to use, sowing rates, and application methods. Fertilization of non-fertile soils should be considered. Generally, what is wanted is a quick, temporary cover that eventually is replaced by the natural vegetation.

Some preparation may be necessary on steep or cut slopes. Furrowing helps hold the seed and plants. Mulching with hay, straw, duff, chips, special cellulose sprays, top soil, or brush improves revegetation results. Some mulches on steeper slopes have to be held in place by staking and jute or wire netting. Vines and cuttings (wattles) of sprouting species like willow are sometimes planted, but because it has to be done by hand labor the cost is high.

Roadside Treatment

In addition to revegetation control of erosion, there are other measures that could be taken to improve the appearance and protection of the forest (Figure VII-4). Most of this is done during the clearing of the right-of-way. Stumps that remain in position should be cut as low as practicable. Skidding away of uprooted stumps that cannot be burned will improve the looks of the roadside, as well as making the road more effective for fire control purposes. Non-utilized wood material, brush, and debris near the road should be eliminated or reduced. Debris left near the road increases chances for fouling of ditches, culverts, and drainage installations. Snags within 200 feet that are not nesting sites for important and rare birds should be felled and utilized or disposed of by some means.

Spoil or excess cut material can be an eyesore unless it is used somehow, spread, or placed properly. Excess rock can be used to good advantage to protect fill slopes and stream banks.

The appearance of the roadside should be considered during adjacent timber operations. A lighter cut, careful logging, more complete slash disposal, and cleaning up landings are some ways to do this. The accumulation of the litter should be prevented and controlled.

Road Maintenance

Regular maintenance of roads safeguards the investment in the road, protects the adjacent forest, and lowers operating costs. Its importance cannot be stressed too much, because many roads are lost or become inoperable for lack of maintenance, and the damage done to the surrounding land can be considerable.

Roads that are expected to be used intermittently, such as for custody and fire purposes, can be put to bed. First, they are graded, ditched well, and cross drainages cleaned out. The traffic on them is controlled by locked gates, especially during the wet season when they can become rutted. An inspection after heavy storms may reveal some necessary prevention measures.

Figure VII-4
Road nearing completion Latour State Forest.

When roads are being actively used they should receive constant maintenance. At the beginning of the season they should be graded and the ditches cleared. Some additional grading of dirt and gravel roads may be necessary during the logging season. Roads that are not oiled or paved which are undergoing heavy traffic should be sprinkled with water enough times per week to keep the surface bound and to reduce dust. It is a good idea to have the water truck equipped with a pump to draft from ponds or streams and a hose to transfer water to fire trucks and to operate a fire hose. At the close of the logging period, the roads should receive a final blading and the ditches and drainage facilities cleaned out in preparation for the winter storms. Traffic on them should be restricted unless they are designed as all-weather roads.

Chapter VIII

FOREST PROTECTION

A forest can be destroyed or severely harmed by fire, pests, and the weather. The first two forces are especially serious in most of California; but with good planning, the application of protection measures, and the use of special management practices, the losses can be kept to a minimum. Insurance coverage is not cheap, if available at all, so a tree farmer should take necessary precautions to prevent or lessen fire and pest damage. Assistance and services from the CDF and USFS are available to help with this important job.

Forest Fires

Fire is the most spectacular enemy of the forest. Besides killing timber, wildfire can burn people, destroy property, and deplete soil and water-shed values. Over 90 percent of the fires are man-caused, mostly through carelessness of the general public in smoking and using fire. Although forest fires resulting from timber operations account for less than five percent of the total, they too on occasion have taken their toll.

Prevention

Since people cause the bulk of the fires, much effort has to be put into trying to prevent fires from starting. A number of different approaches are taken, but prevention largely means education.

Since so many fires are caused by the general public, children included, the forestry agencies, the timber industries, and others individually and collectively publicize the need to prevent forest fires. Examples are the Smokey Bear and Keep California Green and Golden programs. The fire prevention message is freely communicated by the press, radio, television, posters, signs and other means.

There are a number of laws and regulations regarding fires. The fire laws applicable to timber operations are mostly contained in the Public Resources Code; a violation of them is a misdemeanor with penalties in form of a fine or imprisonment. Persons causing a wildfire may also be held liable for the costs of suppression and damages to the forest and improvements. Department of Forestry offices can provide copies of fire laws upon request.

One of these laws requires permits for using fire between April 1st and December 1st in and north of the counties of San Francisco, Alameda, Stanislaus, Mariposa and Mono. Permits are required year around in the rest of the state. The Forest Practice Rules also have certain protction requirements. The enforcement of these laws and regulations is a form of prevention. The investigation of the cause of fires is a necssary part of law enforcement and fire prevention.

Vehicles, industrial and logging equipment, and chimneys also can start forest fires. Therefore, they must have effective devices for arresting sparks that meet legal standards and specifications, and are periodically inspected.

Tree farmers and timber operators have a lot at stake so it is to their advantage to become personally involved in fire prevention. They can participate at least at the local level in fire prevention education and publicity. It is to their benefit to also be on the alert to report fires to the protection agency and to help in the investigation of fires. Some owners and operators cooperate in aerial patrols that supplement the detection of fires from forestry agency lookouts and after-work watch services on timber operations.

Attention should be paid to see that timber operations and workers on the property are conforming to laws, regulations, and contract provisions pertaining to smoking, fire tool requirements, and fire in general. The more important items include posting fire rules, regulation of smoking and lunch and warming fires, care in blasting and welding, watching cable lines and blocks (pulleys) for friction fires, caution in using chain saws and other spark emitting equipment, prohibiting uncovered glass containers, and inspection for fire for at least one hour after close of daily operations. During critical periods, thought should be given to closing the forest to public entry, conducting special patrols, restricting operations to the safe part of the day, or even shutting down completely.

Using existing and forecasted weather and other fire conditions data, protection agencies each afternoon during the fire season calculate a prediction of the fire danger rating for the next day for local ranger districts or other geographical units. The burning index is released daily by radio, telephone, or news media to all forest fire stations, timber operators, other forest users, and the general public in adjective form—low, normal, high, and extreme. It is posted also along roads by ranger or fire stations and on or near timber operations. In addition to alerting forest users about fire conditions, the index can be used to prohibit campfires and controlled burning, restrict forest use, and stop logging or other hazardous operations during bad periods.

Hazard Reduction

The elimination or reduction of fuels is really another means of fire prevention. Hazard reduction also has other benefits; it lessens the chance for a fire to start and it retards the spread and reduces the intensity once a fire is ignited.

Critical fire hazards within at least 100 feet of roads on logging areas require special attention. Fuels in the form of branches, tops, chunks, and similar materials should be treated by removal, safe piling and burning, chipping, or burying. Snags not being used for nesting by rare and important birds within the same road zone should be felled. They are dangerous because lightning strikes can start fires in them, and when aflame for whatever reason, snags can throw sparks out over a wide area. They can be bad from the standpoint of safety to workers and road travelers.

This roadside treatment is very important because that is where most fires start. Furthermore, roads are often used as firebreaks from which to fight fires and start controllable backfires. In some instances the roadside should be converted to what is called a fuelbreak, which is still better as a place to stop or fight a fire. In addition to the usual treatment of dead and down fuels and snags, an effective fuelbreak requires the elimination of shrubs, small unnecessary trees, and the pruning of all branches up to 8 feet high on trees, so that any fire within the fuelbreak zone travels slowly and burns less intensely.

Some abatement of slash resulting from logging operations away from the roadside may be also necessary. How much should be done depends on the forest type, topography, cutting system employed, the requirements of the Forest Practice Rules, and the fire and insect risks present (see following section on insect protection). Where the forest is only partially cut, the branches of unutilized portions of felled or knocked down trees can be severed so that they are in greater contact with the ground (Figure VIII-1). This lopping process, along with winter rains and snow, hastens the rotting of the limbs, eventually reducing this dangerous forest fuel. Nutrients from the decomposed slash are returned to the soil.

Figure VIII-1
Logging area where slash was lopped
Latour State Forest.

Careful burning of slash during safe weather conditions is substituted for lopping in some cases. An example is a clearcut where the heavy slash is not only a fire hazard but also impedes regeneration of the area. Either hand or bulldozer piling or windrowing is employed. Piles are sometimes covered with building paper so that they remain dry after the fall rains commence, after which they can be more safely burned. Long windrows of slash should be segmented to keep the fire under control and to allow ready passage of fire equipment. A few operators use broadcast burning to dispose of slash after clear-cuts, but the risk should be lessened by surrounding the area with effective firebreaks and restricting the burning to safe periods during the non-fire season. Depending on time and place, any kind of burning may require permits from both fire protection and air pollution control agencies.

Like slash, snags within logging areas should be disposed of where necessary for fire protection. Exceptions are snags that house eagles, hawks, owls, waterfowl or rare and endangered species. Snags should not be felled into streams or water bodies. In addition to roadsides, the felling of snags along strategic ridges is very important to control of wildfire.

Hazard reduction at landings and the surrounding area justify special consideration because of the concentration of workers, equipment, logging debris, and other fuels. The slash and snag hazards around landings should be abated before operations commence and not put off until later. As debris accumulates from operations it should be placed in a safe location surrounded by a firebreak. This should be then burned after the fall rains start and before the next fire season.

Dangerous materials like engine fuels and explosives should be safely stored and marked. Oily rags, used oil and engine filters, litter and other similar items should be carefully discarded.

Most of the hazard reduction and slash treatment is achievable through provisions of a timber sale contract, where the purchaser or timber operator does the work with the logging crews and equipment already on the job. The timber owner can obtain additional clean-up by personally making fuelwood from remaining dead and down material, or opening up the area to the public for the same purpose on a fee or free basis. Controls would be necessary for the latter operations to prevent fires and damage to the residual trees.

Fire Readiness

Both owners and operators should be prepared to suppress fires on or near the forest. A number of steps can be taken in advance that will make it easier and faster to control a fire. Ready access to a fire means faster control and less damage. Therefore, all roads in addition to those used for current operations should be opened for fire season. Besides providing access, roads generally can stop the spread of fire if they are cleared of flammable debris. Firebreaks and fuelbreaks should be also checked and maintained.

State law requires fire-fighting tools at certain places on logging operations. One key place is at active landings where a sealed cache of tools must be kept, plainly marked, and inspected periodically. In addition to the tool box at landings, there are other tools required for operating areas, vehicles and tractors used thereon, and logging camps or headquarters. Local rangers can advise you about specific requirements. Besides adequate spark arrestors, fallers with gasoline-powered chain saws must have an extinguisher or shovel handy to immediately put out a fire caused by the sawing operations.

It is good business to make dozers and water trucks available for fire duty when called upon. Some owners and operators have one or more pickup trucks like patrol and supervisory vehicles equipped with a small pump, water tank, hose, and fire tools. Water tanks or ponds should be developed and marked so those sources can be effectively used in fire-fighting.

All supervisors and employees of the forest owner and logger should be instructed to immediately report fires to the authorities and to promptly take control action. In addition, some training would be advisable; help in this can be obtained from the local protection agency.

A written fire plan is another requirement of the Forest Practice Rules. Every timber operator must file a plan by not later than April 1st of each year, or if the operation commences later, the filing has to be at the least 10 days prior to that time. Having a fire plan at hand when a fire is reported saves a lot of time.

Although only operators are expected to have them, non-operating owners will find such plans valuable; forms and assistance are available from the CDF. Fire plans should contain the following information:

> Name, address, telephone numbers, and fire duties of key personnel
>
> Frequency and call letters of the firm's radio network
>
> Location and number of available firefighters on operation
>
> Kind, type, and location of fire-fighting tools (Figure VIII-2) and equipment, including bulldozers and water trucks
>
> General procedure for detecting, reporting, and controlling fires
>
> Map and location description of current logging and hazardous areas
>
> Name, address, and telephone of nearest fire lookout and protection agency ranger

Fire Control

The California Department of Forestry has the responsibility for control of forest fires on private and state lands. The U. S. Forest Service and a few counties do this job under contract with the CDF in conjunction with their own protection responsibilities. Regardless of this governmental service, according to law every owner also has a basic responsibility to control wildfires. This must be done within the ability and means of the owner, especially by fast initial attack on a fire prior to arrival of the fire control agency. Remember that, in addition, where fires are caused or spread because of the violation of fire laws and regulations or negligence on part of an owner or operator, that person can be held responsible for both suppression costs and damages to others.

Forest fires mostly travel on the surface and these are called ground fires. Occasionally, with right conditions of weather, fuel, and slope, they flare up into the branches and tops of brush and trees to create a more dangerous crown fire. This kind is the more difficult to suppress.

The local climate and immediate weather conditions are important factors in the starting, spread, and crowning of fires. The wind speed and air humidity are critical elements—the stronger the wind and the lower

Figure VIII-2
Hand tools to keep handy in a cache for fire fighting

the humidity the faster a fire will ignite and travel. Winds of over 20 miles per hour combined with relative humidities of less than 30 percent can cause fires to burn briskly when forest fuels are dry enough to burn.

Fuel moisture is used as another indicator of burning. It is measured by weighing a wood stick of standard size and composition that is kept on a wire rack close to duff-covered ground at forestry weather stations. The weight of the stick varies with the moisture it contains and represents forest fuel conditions. A fuel moisture of less than 8 percent and low air humidity indicate that care about fire is in order. As mentioned previously, the fire protection agencies have a fire danger rating or burning index that combines all the factors involved that is used to advise the public and forest users what can be expected about fire. It is a good tool in planning daily timber operations, burning slash, and in fighting fires.

In the main, controlling a forest fire consists of two phases: 1) stopping the spread, and 2) putting it out, in that order and priority. The principle of fire control is illustrated by what is called the fire triangle in Figure

VIII-3. The sides represent heat, air, and fuel. Break anyone of them and the fire dies. This is done by cooling, smothering, or removing the fuel. Thus, flames can be extinguished by dirt, water, chemical retardants, beating, or cutting the fire off from the fuel supply. The traditional control method consists of firefighters or bulldozers constructing fire lines around and as close to the fire as possible. These lines are scraped down to mineral soil and made from a few to many feet wide, depending on the situation. Clean dirt may be thrown or placed to knock down the fire adjacent to the line. Water from backpack pumps or fire hoses connected to pumpers can be similarly employed. These control lines serve as places from which backfires are sometimes ignited to combat the main blaze. Where hazards and values are high, the protection agencies dispatch aircraft to drop water or retardants to directly attack a fire before protection forces arrive and to help them construct and hold fire lines. Firefighters are parachuted or delivered by helicopter into inaccessible areas.

Figure VIII-3
The fire triangle.

Effective fire control demands expert knowlege, skill, and specialized tools and equipment. Wildfires are often difficult to suppress and they can threaten the lives of firefighters and people in the vicinity. The protection agencies have the trained personnel, technology, radio communications, special equipment, and other resources to combat anything from spot fires to major conflagrations. The latter may mean a campaign of many days, employing hundreds of people, scores of pieces of big equipment, like bulldozers, a communications network, and setting up one or more fire camps to serve as a headquarters and a place to feed and keep firefighters. Therefore, the leadership and main job of attacking fires should be ordinarily left to the protection agency. However, the law expects that the personnel and equipment of the timber owner and operator of the land involved should be made available to combat the fire.

Once a fire is promptly reported to the authorities, tree farmers and timber operators should not hesitate to take immediate steps to control it.

This is where the fire plan described earlier goes into effect. Listed below are some guidelines for controllng a fire:

1. Size up the fire quickly and decide on the point(s) of attack, taking into consideration the wind, slope, fuels (slash, snags, brush, etc.), intensity of the fire, values at stake, ease of line construction, and natural or other breaks like streams, rock outcrops, and roads.
2. If possible, stop the main spread of the fire at its head by building a fire line or other means, and then work on the flanks and the rear to completely encircle the fire.
3. If the fire head is too hot to handle directly, attack the flanks from the bottom or rear and work rapidly toward the head.
4. Extinguish spot fires away from the main fire.
5. When the fire is surrounded by lines or otherwise contained, widen and improve the lines at the critical points, taking necessary steps to prevent burning material from rolling across the line by ditching or other methods, and extinguish or fall burning snags.
6. Take mop-up action by extinguishing burning stumps, roots, chunks, logs, and heavy fuels near the lines.
7. Patrol the fire to keep it under control until it is absolutely safe.

Prescribed Burning

Fire is not always an enemy; it can be a useful tool in certain situations. At one time in this state, broadcast burning (also known as light burning) was done periodically in open stands on easy terrain to reduce accumulated forest fuels. This is still done to some extent in the southern states to primarily assist in regeneration of stands. Boadcast burning of logging slash was also a common practice until the 1930s in California. This kind of burning was discontinued because of increasing value of the timber damaged or lost and the risk and liability involved.

Running a fire through an area still has a place in land management. It can be used to reduce forest fuels, prepare seedbeds and planting areas, and to remove brush from potential forest and range lands (see next chapter). However, because fires are dangerous, the procedures have to be carefully prescribed. This means consulting a fire control specialist, obtaining necessary permits, preparing good fire lines, selecting safe weather conditions, firing in the right manner, and having sufficient personnel and equipment to handle the burn.

Forest Insects

While forest insect epidemics are not as spectacular, they damage and kill more trees in California than fire. Besides the forest resource loss, dead trees in large numbers may increase the fire hazard and thereby threaten scenic and watershed values. Although some insect-killed trees are salvable so that the timber loss is ameliorated, prevention and suppression measures are a necessary part of forest management.

Insect Identification

Practically all of our bothersome insects are native to California forests. As in some gardens and agriculture, some insects in the forest are beneficial. Some prey on destructive species and others only work in dead wood, breaking down slash, snags, and windfalls. The bulk of the damage is caused by beetles of various kinds that attack the bark and stems of trees, but other species on occasion can injure or kill trees or parts of them.

The bark beetles are of most concern to tree farmers and forest managers. During the mating season in the spring and summer, these beetles bore into the bark of the tree trunks and mine many tunnels along the inner bark and cambium layer in which they lay eggs. The resulting hatch of larvae or grubs burrow new tunnels and grow in size. After a few weeks the larvae go into a pupal stage wherein they are gradually transformed into adult beetles. These adults bore out through the bark, fly away, and start a new life cycle. One or more hatches occur each year. The various bark beetles are selective as to the tree species they attack and their borings and tunnels have characteristic patterns enabling the beetles to be readily identified. The tunneling in effect usually girdles the tree; this leads to fading of foliage and death of at least part of the tree. Sometimes healthy trees resist the insects by exuding pitch that smothers the insect; this is called pitching-out.

The western pine beetle (*Dendroctonous brevicomis*) is probably the worst of these pests (Figure VIII-4). It primarily attacks the larger, mature or older, ponderosa pine, aggressively moving from tree to tree once an infestation has been established. The western pine beetle particularly hits trees which have had their tops killed by the *Ips* engraver beetle or trees damaged by lightning or wind, and those weakened by drought and for other reasons. A slightly different bark beetle known as the Jeffrey pine beetle (*D. Jeffreyi*) works on Jeffrey pine in a similar way. Both beetles may also attack overstocked areas of young growth.

The mountain pine beetle (*Dendroctonous monticolae*) is the main insect enemy of sugar pine (Figure VIII-4), but it also attacks western white, lodgepole, and ponderosa pine, and a few other less common trees. This species attacks both young and old stands, especially the former where excessive competition between trees may create stress.

The Douglas-fir beetle (*Dendroctonous pseudotsugae*) is a serious pest that prefers windthrown, felled, injured, or weakened Douglas-fir. It is a big problem in decadent, overmature stands of Douglas-fir.

The engraver beetles (Figure VIII-5) consisting of two different genera (*Ips* and *Scolytus*), work somewhat differently than the bark beetles. The engravers prefer thin-barked young trees, tops of older trees, and fresh slash from logging, wind, and snow breakage. Their attacks are similar to the bark beetles, consisting of borings and tunneling in the cambium layer and inner bark. They usually generate more hatches per season than the bark beetles. The pine engravers, consisting of a number of species within the genus *Ips,* infest all species of pines. Their attacks often lead the way to more lethal damage by the bark beetles. The fir engravers of the *Scolytus* genus attack true firs and Douglas-fir.

WESTERN PINE BEETLE
(Dendroctonous brevicomis)
Attacks mature ponderosa pine

MOUNTAIN PINE BEETLE
(Dendroctonous monticolae)
Attacks sugar, western white,
lodgepole, and ponderosa pine

LARVAE

LARVAE

PUPAE   ADULT

PUPAE   ADULT

Borings under bark of
ponderosa pine

Egg-galleries in beetle
killed pine

Figure VIII-4
Two principal forest insects of California pines.

PINE ENGRAVER BEETLES
(Ips confusus and Ips oregoni)

Attacks ponderosa, sugar, Jeffrey, coulter and lodgepole pine

 ADULT (Twice natural size)
(Ips confusus)

FIR ENGRAVER
(Scolytus ventralis)

Attacks true firs and Douglas fir

 ADULT (Twice natural size)

Ips confusus mines in inner bark of ponderosa pine

Ips oregoni larvae and borings in Jeffrey pine bark

Typical top of repeatedly attacked fir

Figure VIII-5
Pine and engraver beetles.

Sometimes, the fir flathead borer (Figure VIII-6) of the genus *Melano-phila* can be troublesome in attacking pines, Douglas-fir, true firs, and hemlock. Unlike the bark and engraver beetles, the adults do not bore into the bark; instead they deposit their eggs on the surface or in crevices. The grubs damage the tree by boring into the inner bark and destroy the cambial region. The borer attacks overmature trees, those on poor sites, or fire-damaged trees.

FIR FLATHEAD BORER
(Melanophila drummondi)

Attacks Douglas fir, the true firs, and hemlock

ADULT (Life size)

Flathead borer mines in sapwood (above) and inner bark (below). The larvae which have done the boring can be seen in the bark

Figure VIII-6

The fir flathead borer (*Melanophila drummondi*)

There are additional forest insects of economic importance (Table VIII-1); however, they do not cause near the damage that the above do. Defoliation like that caused by the Douglas-fir tussock moth and white fir sawfly can raise havoc on an extensive scale in true fir stands. As noted in Chapter II, other insects interfere with cone and seed production and consume seed. And there can be damage also from needle and twig insects of various kinds, especially in plantations.

Table VIII-1.   Other forest insects of economic importance in California.

Common Name of insect	Scientific name	Species attacked	Part affected	Remarks
Douglas-fir tussock moth	*Orgyia pseudotsugata*	White fir and Douglas-fir	foliage	One generation per year. Feeds on new foliage.
Black pine—leaf scale	*Nuculaspis californica*	Ponderosa and sugar pine	foliage	One generation per year. Scales weaken trees by sucking juices from needles. Bark beetles may kill weakened trees.
White fir sawfly	*Neodiprion sp.*	White fir	foliage	One generation per year. Larvae feed on previous year's foliage.
Pine resin midge	*Cecidomyia piniiopis*	Ponderosa pine	twigs	One generation per year. Lateral twigs fade in May and June. Attacks young trees of sapling size.
Douglas-fir gall midges	*Contarinia sp.*	Douglas-fir	foliage	One generation per year. Needles are infested as new growth begins. Current needles fall off Oct. and Nov. Attacks young trees.
Grasshopper	*Oedaleonotus enigma*	All pines	foliage	One generation per year. Hoppers destroy all needles. Attacks occur after grass is cured. Affects new plantations.

C.D.F., Hunt, 1978

Detection, Reporting, and Investigation

To preclude the possibility of an infestation getting a toehold, forest owners and managers should constantly watch for signs of insect activity. An attack on a single tree may not be significant, but when a group of trees show damage this is a danger signal. Early detection of insect activity means better chances for control and smaller losses.

Symptoms of insect attack vary considerably, depending on the insect and tree species involved and the time of the year. In case of the more common beetles described above, the first sign is the appearance of faded or red-topped trees. The foliage changes from green to straw color, then to reddish brown as the girdled tree dries out. Other clues are found on the trunk. Bark beetles in pines cause pitch tubes; these are whitish or brownish masses of boring dust and pitch on the outside of the bark at points where the beetles have entered the tree. Bark beetles in Douglas-fir, and the engravers, do not make pitch tubes as such so the only outward evidence consists of some streaming pitch on the bark, entrance holes, and boring dust. Positive proof of attack for most beetles can be obtained by chopping out a section of the bark to see if there are any tunnels or galleries on the inside.

The Forest Practice Rules require timber owners, operators, and registered professional foresters to assist the State in locating and reporting pest outbreaks. The report can be made to CDF forest practice inspectors or forest advisers, who will investigate the situation to determine the cause. They have access to state and federal entomologists when needed to check the infestation and decide what control measures, if any, should be taken.

The public forestry agencies usually conduct an aerial survey each fall to detect and locate pest attacks. This information, including data received from ground observations of owners, operators, and foresters, reveals existing or potential epidemics. The compilation is reviewed by the California Forest Pest Control Action Council, an organization of interested private and public agencies and organizations, to decide what action should be undertaken. A report of the pest conditions and recommendations is then published by the CDF and widely distributed.

Some situations may need more investigation. The forestry agencies with the help of the owners conduct a biological evaluation to obtain the necessary information. These findings are particularly helpful to make pest control decisions.

Prevention

Much insect damage can be prevented or lessened by good forest management practices. Trees become weaker as they grow older or when their vigor is affected, e.g., by site, weather, competition, mechanical injury, and disease. The risk of insect attack varies according to conditions of tree age, vigor, health, and timber management.

One measure of risk of bark beetle attack is Keen's classification system for ponderosa pine shown in Figure VIII-7. The high-risk trees should be harvested as early as possible. The principles of this system can be applied to some extent to other trees; that is, the degree of insect risk is shown by the health of foliage, twigs, and crown. High-risk trees rarely recover their ability to resist insects.

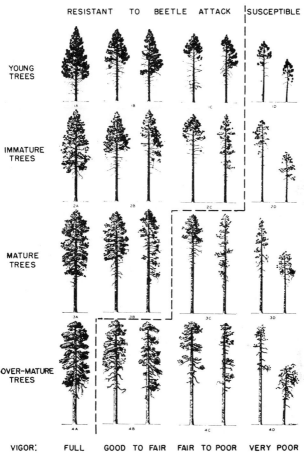

Figure VIII-7

Keen's ponderosa pine tree classification.

In addition to early harvest of high-risk trees, the following practices will reduce and avoid damage from insects:

1. Make periodic light sanitation cuts of trees of poor thrift and declining vigor to prevent the development of high-risk trees, thus keeping the forest in a healthy, vigorous, growing condition.

2. Eliminate breeding places by prompt salvage of recent fire-weakened or killed trees, those struck by lightning, infested trees, and fresh windfalls. Insect damage cannot be reduced by disposing of old windfalls, chunks, or forest debris, because tree-killing insects do not live in dead wood.

3. Do not leave cut green trees in the woods during spring and summer; prevent damage to residual trees during logging.
4. Treat slash by immediate lopping or other safe methods, especially during the spring and summer, so that it will not become a breeding ground for some insects.
5. Through other silvicultural and management practices promote vigorous, thrifty growth of the forest.

Control

Once it has been determined by forest entomologists that an insect epidemic exists, consideration has to be given by the owner and the authorities as to whether direct control action is possible and necessary in order to reduce damage. While a few insects may not be controllable, there are means to suppress the more common and serious insects like the bark beetles. This requires the joint efforts of the forest owner and the state and federal forestry agencies.

Under state law and policy, every owner has a responsibility to initiate control measures, but the state and federal governments are also involved. When an epidemic occurs and control is justified and possible, the Director of Forestry declares a zone of infestation. Upon approval of the Board of Forestry, this declaration authorizes control of the insects where the costs are shared between the land owners and the CDF, and sometimes local government and the USFS. The state agency operates the project where mostly private and state lands are included; however, the project may be a cooperative one where federal lands are also being treated, or the entire job done by the USFS under a contract with CDF.

Depending on what insects are causing the epidemic, the control methods vary. The usual procedure in the case of bark beetles requires the felling and bucking of infested trees and the burning of the bark, or ground-spraying it with a safe insecticide. To be effective, the treatment must be done as soon as the needles fade while the insects are still in the tree. Normally, beetles spend the winter under the bark so this is the best time to act.

Logging of infested trees at the right time is another way to control insect damage. Salvage logging yields utilizable wood and reduces the control costs considerably. There should be no delays in removing the felled trees from the woods, because the beetles can emerge and re-infest new trees. For the same reason, the logs should be utilized quickly if the mill is in or near a forested area.

Aerial sprays have had to be used a few times in California to suppress outbreaks like the Modoc budworm and Douglas-fir tussock moth. More selective spraying by hand and from the ground is done in the case of plantations, seed orchards, and Christmas tree farms.

Like other chemicals in forestry operations, insecticides have to be used with great care. Experts must select the correct spray, determine the formulation, and prescribe application rates and methods in order to prevent injury or damage to workers, other people, domestic animals, fish and wildlife, and the environment. The use of certain chemicals has to be under the supervision of a state-licensed pest control applicator and under permit issued by the county agricultural commissioner. Neighboring owners, forest users, and agencies concerned with fish and game and water quality must be notified.

In addition to the indirect approaches covered under Prevention (consisting of silvicultural and sanitation measures), other possibilities appear to have some promise. These consist of various biological approaches, e.g., using scents to attract and concentrate insects where they can be treated in some manner, infesting insects with bacteria and viruses, encouraging predator insects and birds, and reducing reproduction of insects through introduction of individuals that have been sterilized by radiation. As these new methods develop they will be preferable to insecticides that may be harmful.

Forest Diseases

Diseases constitute another major destructive agent in California forests. They kill trees outright, predispose them to attack by insects, and decay wood. Most of these pests are various fungi or plant parasites.

Kinds of Diseases

Heart rots are the leading cause of wood decay. The causal fungi enter the tree through the roots, fire and lightning scars, trunk and other wounds, and open knots. They spread by spores shed by fruiting bodies or conks growing on the trees. Under moist conditions, these tiny spores germinate and send filaments into the wood, exuding substances as they travel that cause the wood to decay. Ordinarily, the amount of decay increases with the age of the tree.

A few root diseases are also troublesome. Mortality from the root fungus *Fomitopsis annonsus* especially is more common than is realized, particularly in some pine stands. Spread occurs from one tree to another through overlapping roots. Killing of young growth around old, infected stumps is not uncommon, as the fungus will live in the roots of harvested trees for years. Besides death of surrounding trees, pines may be weakened to the extent that they are ready prey for bark beetles. Table VIII-2 lists the principal timber decays of California conifers.

There are 20 or more tree rusts (genus *Cronartium*) in this state's commercial forests. The most serious one is the white pine blister rust (*C. ribicola*) that infects sugar pine and other 5-needled pines. It is an invader that originated in Europe. The rust enters through the needles, grows into the twig, and gradually forms a spindle-shaped swelling there. In late spring the bark on the canker cracks and liberates orange spores. These air-borne spores cannot infect other pines directly, but cause another form of the rust on currant and gooseberry bushes. Then new colorless spores from the underside of rusted leaves are released and infect pine needles during the damper fall months. Pine branches are killed after two years or more and the rust can grow into the main trunk, eventually killing the tree. The rust is most damaging on smaller trees in the northern and moister part of the state.

Sometimes, gall rusts damage California hard pines. They form round, persistent cankers or galls on twigs, branches, and occasionally on trunks

Table VIII-2.   Principal timber decays of California conifers.

Common name of decay	Causal fungus	Type of decay	Part affected	Tree species attacked	Occurrence of conks	Remarks
Red ring rot	Phellinus pini (Fomes pini)	Small white pocket rot	Trunk	Douglas-fir (Occasional in pines and other conifers)	Frequent	Common. Decay often extensive
Brown stringy rot	Echinodontium tintorium	Light brown or reddish stringy rot	Trunk	White fir and red fir	Frequent	Common. Decay often extensive
Pocket dry rot	Polyporus amarus	Brown, cubical pocket rot	Trunk	Incense-cedar	Occasional	Common. Decay extensive
Red-brown butt rot	Phaeolus schweinitzii (Polyporus schweinitzii)	Brown cubical rot	Butt	Douglas-fir and pines	Fairly common, usually on ground	Common. Decay usually ending in butt log
Brown trunk rot	Phomitopsis officinalis (Fomes laricis)	Brown cubical rot	Trunk	Douglas-fir, sugar pine, ponderosa pine	Occasional	Occasional. Decay sometimes extensive
Redwood pocket rot	Poria sequoiae	Large brown pocket rot	Butt and trunk	Coast redwood	Occasional, usually hidden	Fairly common in old stands
Fomitopsis (Fomes) root rot	Fomitopsis annosa (Fomes annosus)	Light brown spongy rot	Roots and butt	White fir, red fir, ponderosa pine, sugar pine	Occasional, usually hidden	Most common butt rot of white and red fir. Kills pine on eastside
Shoestring root rot	Armillariella mellea	Light brown spongy rot	Butt and roots	White and red fir	Fairly common, short-lived	Common. Decay usually ending in butt log
Red ray rot	Dichomitus squalen (Polyporus anceps)	Reddish pocket rot	Trunk and top	Ponderosa pine	Almost never on living trees in California. Occurs on slash.	Occasional. Mostly in N.E. California

U.S.F.S., Wagner, 1949, Revised C.D.F., Hunt, 1978

of both mountain and coastal species. Orange spores are produced in crevices of the bark of the swelling in spring or early summer and can spread directly to other pines, without going through an intermediate host as blister rust does. Infection takes place on tree growth of the current year, and the galls appear from 6 months to 2 years later. The twig or branch carrying the infection is dead within a few years. These rusts are serious in pine plantations, including those for Christmas trees.

Dwarf mistletoes (genus *Arceuthobium*) affect pines, firs, and Douglas-fir. Infection starts in twigs and the resulting parasite lives indefinitely, causing swellings or irregular growth called witches brooms on branches and trunks. Swellings on tree trunks develop into cankers, through which decay may enter. The female plants produce sticky seeds that are forcefully shot out when ripe in early fall to adhere to new infection sites. It takes from 3 to 5 years after germination for new plants to be readily visible. Heavy infection can ruin young trees, and the growth of older trees is frequently impaired, sometimes followed by rot. Bark beetles as part of the pest complex will attack and kill trees infected with mistletoe.

There are other trouble-causing diseases that tree farmers must face occasionally. An example of this is the *Elytroderma* needle disease; it infects ponderosa and Jeffrey pine in cold locations, killing needles and dwarfing twigs. Diseased needles turn red in spring before the new tree growth commences. Repeated infections will kill trees and cause them to be susceptible to insect attack. Some other needle diseases damage young Douglas-fir and red and white fir, thereby reducing their value as Christmas trees. Table VIII-3 lists a few additional diseases affecting California forests.

Table VIII-3. Additional diseases affecting California forests.

Common name of disease	Scientific name	Species attacked	Part affected	Remarks
Black staining root disease	*Verticicladiella wagenerii*	All pines and Douglas-fir	Roots and butt	Brownish-black stain in outer sapwood. Fungus acts like Dutch elm disease. Will move through soil via roots.
None	*Cytospora abietis*	Red fir	Branches	Disease enters dwarf mistletoe infections. Dead branches turn dark red.
Phloem necrosis	*Dermea pseudotsugae*	Douglas-fir	Tops and branches	Attacks plantations and young natural stands. Sunken cankers girdle tops and branches.
Red band needle blight	*Scirrhia pini*	Monterey and Bishop pines	Foliage	Pine plantations within 15 miles of the coast in Humboldt, Del Norte and Mendocino counties are subject to attack. Entire plantations have been killed.

C.D.F., Hunt, 1978

Forest nurseries, plantations, and seed orchards have unique problems with plant diseases. They justify special attention and treatment because losses can be sudden and severe.

Detection, Reporting, and Investigation

The same general procedures as for insects should be followed to detect, investigate, and report damage resulting from forest diseases. At the first signs of any abnormal disease attacks, the forest owner or manager should notify the CDF and ask for help. These incidents and investigations are compiled yearly similar to those about other pest losses to keep track of disease conditions in the state, and this is combined in the same annual report.

Prevention and Control

Very few direct control techniques for forest diseases have been developed. Instead, control has to be achieved mainly by instituting prevention and indirect practices. Basically, this means making a forest healthy and vigorous by silvicultural, management, and sanitation measures such as the following:

1. Harvest old, diseased, weakened, or damaged trees that are declining in vigor.
2. Prevent fire and logging damage to trees.
3. Where rusts have formed on trees in plantations and Christmas tree farms, prune out the galls before they become too numerous, and remove old gall-bearing trees nearby.
4. In case of dwarf mistletoe, harvest all infected trees of merchantable size and remove smaller trees that are heavily infected. Prune out branches bearing the parasite only when practicable.
5. Reduce competition by control of unwanted brush or hardwoods.
6. Through other silvicultural and managment practices promote vigorous, thrifty growth of the forest.

At one time California had an extensive program of blister rust control. Forestry crews would locate and destroy by grubbing or herbicides all currant and gooseberry plants within and near stands of sugar pine. This attempt to suppress the alternate host was discontinued because costs of eradication and maintenance rose too high, and the disease continued to spread despite the containment efforts, especially in the wetter northern parts of the state. Some sugar pine trees have demonstrated a natural resistance to blister rust, and cuttings and seeds of these select trees are being used to grow seed orchards. Eventually, the disease may be checked by planting resistant trees as the original ones are harvested or destroyed.

Prevention measures may be appropriate where *Fomitopsis annosa* root disease is a threat to valuable pine and fir forests. Infection starts by spores landing and germinating on freshly cut stumps, followed by the disease moving down into the roots. Then, the infection is largely spread underground from the roots of infected stumps and trees to those of adjacent trees. Centers of infection in high-risk areas may be prevented by quick killing of the roots of harvested trees by treating the surface of fresh stumps with a dry mixture of commercial borax. However, treatment of this kind will not suppress an existing heavy infection center. The only alternative is to clear-cut the area and reforest it with the more resistant species.

Animal Damage

There are some animals that can damage young trees by feeding on them, trampling, and in other ways. These mammals range in size from small rodents to elk, and include both domestic and wild animals. Most of them are valuable to us or the ecosystem from the overall standpoint so any damage caused to forests has to be prevented or controlled on a rather selective basis.

Animal Pests

In addition to the depredation on seed and seedlings mentioned in Chapter II, rodents injure small trees of all species. Losses can be serious when they occur in plantations, seed orchards, and Christmas tree farms. The damage is caused by chewing, bark-stripping, or cutting by gophers, beaver, chipmunks, squirrels, mice, woodrats, and rabbits. A large rodent, the boomer or mountain beaver, is a serious pest in young redwood and Douglas-fir stands in Del Norte County.

The porcupine feed on the inner bark of ponderosa pine, usually in the late summer, fall, and winter. In doing so, they may cause extensive damage in young stands by girdling the tops of the trees. They live in dens and rest trees; the rest trees usually range from 4 to 20 inches dbh.

In some cases, deer can be a big problem in young forests. When more preferred browse becomes short, deer will feed on the foliage of Douglas-fir and occasionally other species. This browsing does not ordinarily kill the tree, but it retards the growth until the tree outgrows the reach of the animals. Elk do similar damage in northern parts of the redwood region on Douglas-fir and redwood. Some tramplng by deer and elk occurs in recently seeded or planted areas.

Another animal pest in the northern redwoods is the bear. It climbs young trees to strip the bark and feed on the inner parts. Because of its size, the bear also breaks branches and tops of the trees during the feeding process.

Domestic animals like sheep and cattle can be destructive at times. Trampling and breaking of trees cause the most damage, but feeding on the foliage also happens, especially by sheep.

Checking Damage

Some animal damage is easy to identify, especially that from the large hooved species because of distinctive tracks. Identifying damage by smaller mammals, such as rodents, is more difficult. They are elusive, often nocturnal, and do not leave much sign, except for the burrowing kind like gophers. Teeth marks and other peculiarities of the animal are used as clues.

It is important to know what animal species is involved, because prevention and control measures vary. Local CDF and other foresters can be helpful in diagnosing animal damage. Sometimes, it may be necessary to obtain the expertise of animal biologists from the Department of Fish and Game or the U. S. Fish and Wildlife Service. The latter agency has specialists that can identify damage from non-game as well as game species.

The annual forest pest conditions report mentioned earlier in this chapter also contains data on animal damage throughout the state. This is based on reports submitted by biologists, foresters, and tree farmers. Keeping tab on the situation is necessary to locate trouble areas, to plan prevention and control measures, and to identify research needs.

Prevention and Control

Where animals are injuring forests to an intolerable degree consideration should be given to taking steps to prevent or reduce the damage. The nature of the problem varies greatly because of the many kinds of animals, tree species, and habitats. Therefore, each situation requires selective analysis and treatment.

The damage caused by wildlife should be investigated by a competent biologist before any prevention or control is prescribed. The control of rodents may be possible by various means: chemical retardants, lethal baits, or trapping. Rodenticides of any kind have to be very carefully handled; their use is strictly regulated and has to be cleared by the county agricultural commissioner. Moreover, the application of most of them has to be under the supervision of a licensed pest control applicator.

The harvesting of a forest greatly changes the habitat, often resulting in an early invasion of plants that are quite attractive to deer and elk. This may lead to an overpopulation of animals and serious depredation on young trees. There are a few compounds available that are sprayed on the foliage to deter feeding, but the method is costly and considered temporary. Plastic netting has been effective but also costly. Another solution is an indirect one—to bring about a better balance between the animal population and the habitat by applying wildlife management principles and through game regulations (see Chapter X). The animal numbers may be reduced by adjusting seasons, special hunts, and the taking of either sex. Bear damage can be reduced by similar programs of hunting and trapping. Tree farmers can relieve a problem by allowing these activities by the public on their properties.

The prevention and control of damage by livestock is basically a range management matter (see Chapter IX). The browsing and trampling may be due to trespass; it should be controllable by complaints to the offending parties or legal action, if necessary. Stocking the forest with too many animals is another source of trouble. Permanent or drift fencing may be helpful in both preventing trespass and keeping livestock out of sensitive reproduction areas.

Other Tree Losses

Natural events, like the weather, sometimes cause tree losses of various kinds. Occasionally, windstorms cause severe blowdown. Some windfall may be prevented or lessened by cutting practices that do not expose the residual stands too much to strong prevailing winds. The borders of clear-cuts and ridges are critical places. Not much can be done in instances of more devastating storms. Wind-downed timber should be quickly salvaged to utilize the material and to reduce insect and fire hazards.

Besides wind, lightning is a tree destroyer. It breaks and splits trees and ignites fires in dead tops and snags. Strikes on live trees may kill them or make them more susceptible to insect and disease attack. Where practicable, damaged or dead trees should be cut or harvested as soon as possible.

Extremes in soil moisture lower tree health and sometimes kill trees. Too much water by flooding will do this; so will drought. Logging and road construction may alter natural surface drainage which may lead to flooding. Excessive soil disturbance and root cutting may bring about drought conditions to a tree or a group of trees.

Extremes in temperature likewise affect tree health. Sudden drops in temperature to well below freezing following a mild period can kill tops of fast-growing conifers. This quick freezing injures the inner bark of the tree. However, only vigorous tops that are exposed to the sun are affected. If the tree is not an insect hazard it may recover or grow a new top. Hot temperatures during the growing period before new foliage and twigs harden may cause some dessication and burning, especially when accompanied by strong, dry winds, but usually the consequences are not serious. Air pollution also affects tree health in some areas.

In addition to protection from fire, pests, and weather, forests and residual stands need to be guarded from damage that may be caused by human activity. Public access should be controlled to prevent indiscriminate travel by vehicles, cutting of trees, and vandalism. The productivity of the site is at stake as well as the future value of crops to the landowner.

Chapter IX

FOREST-RANGE MANAGEMENT

As pointed out in Chapter II and elsewhere in this handbook, a forest has other important resources besides wood that deserve attention of owners and managers. Some of these non-wood values have tangible uses that are marketable. A good example of this is forage that grows within and adjacent to forests. It's fairly common to find forested properties that produce both timber and grazing income.

Multiple Use

Before discussing range management and other forest uses (Chapter X), the concept of multiple use needs to be explained. Multiple use is a popular term in conservation and forestry. It is defined as a practice that fulfills two or more objects of management, particularly in utilization of a forest. This is a desirable objective because there is an opportunity to include it in most management programs, at least to some extent. Single-purpose forestry has little place in modern land management. Multiple use does not mean that each acre is managed intensively for more than one purpose. Instead, it embodies the principle that a forest is composed of a number of values that occur in varying mixes. In parts of the forest, wood or any other resource may be the dominant value and is treated accordingly. An example is a meadow within a forest that logically would be utilized for grazing, but a meadow also stores an immense quantity of water, provides feed for certain wildlife, and is an excellent visual asset to a property. Thus, the concept of multiple use is to manage a forest as a whole for all its potential uses and to stress certain ones in those parts where biological and other natural factors so dictate. Compatibility is the key to multi-purpose management.

In addition to timber growing, other main uses of a forest include grazing, water yield, fish and wildlife production, and recreation. Associated with these are the aesthetics or beauty and the environmental attributes of a forest. Although these values are immeasurably important, this book cannot cover these subjects in as much detail as for timber production, because each of them is a big topic in itself. To do justice to them would really require separate handbooks. Nonetheless, our purpose is to emphasize that a forest has a number of resources and all of them should be wisely managed.

Forest-Range Use

A significant amount of the land being grazed by domestic livestock in California is forested range. On many forests the earnings from grazing are substantial and second only to timber growing. While some damage may be done to trees and the site by domestic animals, if properly done, forests can provide both wood and forage without impairment of either or any other resource. In fact, the right kind and amount of grazing can benefit tree growing.

Proper utilization of these two resources requires the practice of forestry and range management together. The latter is an art and science separate from forestry that is involved in the procurement of maximum sustained use of the forage crop without jeopardy to other values or uses of the land. Range includes many kinds of grazing lands—uncultivated pastures, prairies, natural grasslands, some brushlands and deserts, and areas having a mixture of forage plants and trees. We are primarily concerned here with the last of these broad types of range.

Because it is an integration of plant ecology, soil technology, and animal husbandry, range management is a profession in itself. Many foresters have a working knowledge of this subject; however, much of the range lands are managed directly by, or with the advice of, range specialists. Tree farmers wanting assistance in this field can obtain it from county farm advisers, the Soil Conservation Service, the U. S. Forest Service, private consultants, and brush-range improvement specialists of the California Department of Forestry.

Range Plants and Types

Grazing animals consume many kinds of plants, from small forbs to woody vegetation. Most range areas contain a mix of grass, forbs, and shrubs. What livestock feed upon and how a desirable forage cover can be maintained need to be understood in order to manage a range resource.

Kinds of Plants

Overall, grasses constitute the most important forage for livestock and for many wild animals. There are a great number of grass species. The more desirable ones are the perennials, especially some fescues, because they are excellent feed, provide a more dependable forage supply, and add more stability to the ecosystem. However, annuals have a place also, especially to provide winter or early spring forage in milder, lower-elevation areas. Table IX-1 lists the more common grasses, palatable forbs, and browse species found on forest-ranges.

The forbs are next in importance. They are low growing, non-grasslike annual or perennial broadleaved plants, the top growth of which dies each fall. The many species of forbs exceed those of grasses; they range from highly valuable clovers to weeds and poisonous plants.

Many shrubs and a few broadleaved trees are another source of feed to livestock and big game animals. Browse, as it is called, includes deciduous or evergreen shrubs or trees, the sprouts, twigs, stems, vines, and leaves of which are cropped. These plants are valuable, because the seasonal nutritive content tends to vary less than in grasses and forbs, and they add variety to the diet and enhance the nutritional intake. Sheep, goats, and deer usually prefer browse and forbs over grass.

Table IX-1. Common forage plants of California forest-ranges with comparative grazing values.*

Grasses		Forbs		Browse (shrubs)	
G	Perennial bromegrasses	G	Bur-clover	G	Deer brush
G	Perennial fescues	G	Filaree	G	Bitter brush
G	Needlegrasses (*Stipa sp.*)	G	Clovers	G	Winterfat
G	Oatgrass	G	Cow parsnip	G	Service berry
G	Bluegrasses (*Poa sp.*)	F-G	Mules-ears	G	Mountain mahogany
G	Soft chess	F	Yarrow	G	Aspen
G	Wild oats	F-P	Lupines †	F-G	Oaks
G	Wild-rye	F-P	Vetches	F-G	Willow
F	Ripgut brome	P	Tarweed	F	Chamise
F	Red brome	P	Turkey mullein	F	Fireweed
F	Foxtail fescue			F-P	Sagebrush
F-P	Downy chess			P	Manzanita
F-P	Wild barley			P	Rabbitbrush
P	Nitgrass			P	Cherries (Prunus sp.)

* G—Good, F—Fair, P—Poor
† Many species poisonous
CDF, Dodge, 1978

Range Types

Ranges can be broadly classified by their vegetative composition and potential grazing value or carrying capacity. The main broad groupings found in or adjacent to forested lands in this state are described below:

Meadow types have the best carrying capacity, but they are limited in area and have to be handled carefully to maintain their productivity. Overgrazing can not only decrease the valuable forage plants, but it can cause erosion, gullying, and resulting draining of the huge amounts of water stored underground. Some meadows are wet and others are dry on the surface.

Wet meadows are found in valleys and even on slopes where water is abundant, such as at high elevations. Usually, the forage, consisting of sod-forming herbs, sedges, and rushes, and some grasses, stays green throughout much of the summer. Bluegrasses, bent grasses, and clover grow on the drier sites of the meadow.

East of the Cascade and the Sierra Nevada, there are dry meadows on flats and small valleys, where spring snow-melt provides water. The plants in these meadows, which dry out by midsummer, include bunch grasses, like the Nevada bluegrass. Another dry form is the sedge meadow found on flats and benches on the eastside and high in the mountains. There, sod-forming sedges grow profusely, independently or along with bunch grasses and other plants.

Prairies, or natural grassy glades, which are interspersed within forested areas of the north coast region, are another good forage producer. The dominant plants are such perennials as oat grass, tufted hairgrass, fescues, reed grass and some annuals and a variety of forbs. These prairies are located on natural grassland soils.

Foothill ranges and woodland-grass areas within and adjacent to the lower-elevation conifer forests, especially bordering the Central Valley, are extensive and provide a large amount of grazing, mostly during the rainy season. In the early days these ranges included highly prized perenial bunch grasses accompanied by various forbs. The dominant plants no longer are these valuable species; they have been replaced in large part by annuals, many of them invaders from abroad. A few of these, like wild oat, soft chess, filaree, and bur-clover, have good value as forage, but some of the species present today are poor to worthless or even damaging to livestock.

Brushfields or chaparral also contain feed for livestock as well as wildlife, but it takes many acres to support an animal. In addition to the browse, grass and forbs grow in openings and along margins. These brush stands are characteristic of dry sites on slopes and ridges in the foothills and mountains. The composition of the brushfields varies considerably according to soils and climate. They are mostly evergreen and many will sprout when cut or burned. The common dominants include various forms of chamise, manzanita, ceanothus, sagebrush, and scrub oak, accompanied by other shrubs. Some chaparral areas are the result of old wildfires in timber, and others are caused by brush invading overgrazed areas of former grassland and woodland-grass types.

Intra-forest ranges are composed of conifers and a wide selection of intermingled grasses, forbs, and browse plants, including some hardwood trees. While they have low carrying capacities, some commercial forests supply forage during the critical dry season. The pine and the mixed conifer types are used quite a bit for grazing. Douglas-fir stands have less forage potential, while redwood and red fir produce little range feed. However, all timberlands after harvest form a better range type temporarily, because of the modification of the forest canopy and logging disturbance. Grasses, forbs, and shrubs usually multiply for a few years, providing an increased amount of forage until new trees become established and shade out the understory plants.

Subalpine weed-grass type occurs above the commercial timber zone, generally on steep slopes. Where located on lava soils, it is an important forage type. Plant composition is quite variable, but usually includes some bunch grasses, sage brush and other browse, forbs like wooly mules-ears and lupines, and scattered trees.

Burned types are transient variations of brush and forest-ranges. They are the result of wildfires, slash burning, or fires set to try to improve the range where little or nothing was done to get a complete burn or to control subsequent woody plants. Burning can adversely affect timber and watershed values and can alter the site markedly. Intense fire can reduce the protective humus, change the chemical and physical properites of the soil, and will expose the surface directly to the sun and rain. The value of the resulting forage is highly variable—some bad, some good.

In the case of brushfields, for a few years after a burn there is a temporary flush of grasses, forbs, and sprouts that offer fair grazing. Much of this is caused by the ash nutrients. The original shrubs become re-established by seed or sprouting, and these plants while young have some browse value. However, depending on the site, forage capacities for livestock are generally low, and the wildlife that are attracted to the area reduce the available feed. Fire as a range improvement tool is explained in a later section.

Burned timber areas are invaded mostly by fireweed and other forbs and shrubs. Some grasses may appear also. These plants, especially some of the more desirable shrubs like deer brush and other ceanothus species, provide considerable forage for a few years. Careful grazing of these areas during this period can be helpful in checking competition from these plants to conifer reproduction.

Range Evaluation

In order to properly manage any forage the manager must know its biological potential, condition and trend, and carrying capacity. Range scientists and practitioners have developed various procedures for making this evaluation.

Basic Site

The basic quality of the site should be determined first. Soil, climate, slope, density of existing forest cover, and other factors affecting the quality of forage growth need investigation to determine the potential of the site. Some open forests and associated lands present an immediate opportunity for range management while others, like wholly dense forests, may not.

Using data on the basic qualities of the site and the condition of the range, a manager can decide whether a grazing program would be feasible for a forest property. Economic factors such as costs of fencing, water development, herding, and necessary range improvements along with prospective income must be considered too. Grazing fees on nearby public lands can be used to judge market value of grazing leases; this information is obtained from the U. S. Forest Service and Bureau of Land Management. When the returns will be of little consequence it may be better to keep the forage for wild game. In some situation, where forage is in short supply, reducing grazing competition from domestic animals may lessen the possibilities of wildlife damage to trees.

Range Condition

Next to be examined is the current condition of the range resource. Composition, vigor, and density of the forage plants are key indicators of range condition. This is important because management will be governed by it. The trend in the condition, whether it is improving or worsening, indicates what present grazing practices are doing to the range resource. What is happening to the soil as to packing and erosion, the tree crop, and other values should be checked also.

The evaluation is made by one or more of the following:

1. Noting the condition of big game animals and livestock, both during and at the close of the season, but keeping in mind that they may be getting enough food by depleting the range.

2. Observing the general appearance of the range—forage cover, soils, and associated tree and other values.

3. Looking for certain indicator plants.

4. Studying in detail key plants or areas.

With adequate forage, both domestic and wild animals will look healthy. However, this criterion should not be used alone, because animals can be in good shape, especially from early to midseason, when overall the range may be deteriorating.

Western false-hellebore (skunk-cabbage) increases rapidly on meadows where the water table is lowered by gullying; these meadows can be restored by erosion control and conservative use

On bunchgrass ranges a marked increase in woolly mules-ears indicates overuse of the grasses. (Photos by L. T. Burcham.)

Figure IX-1

Two common indicators of range conditions.

Table IX-2.   Some indicator plants of range conditions.

Plant names	Characteristics	Indicates	Remedial action
Downy Chess (Bromus tectorum); also called downy brome, cheatgrass.	Grass; low annual, with hairy leafage and drooping seedheads.	Overuse of range	Adjust range use to favor perennial grasses.
Red bromegrass (Bromus rubens).	Grass; annual, with distinct purple to reddish color when dry; seed heads compact, with rigid awns.	Repeated burning or severe overuse accompanied by (sheet) erosion.	Adjust range use; erosion control measures.
Western false-hellebore (Veratrum californicum); also called skunk cabbage, corn lily.	Tall robust herb, with unbranched leafy stem; leaves parallel-veined; showy white flowers in terminal clusters.	An increase in this plant on meadows and moist stringers shows drying of soil from lowered water table; decrease shows improvement in range.	Erosion control structures to raise water level; very conservative use or non-use until range begins to mend.
Tarweed (Hemizonia wrightii).	Annual weed of sunflower family; sticky, pungently-scented leaves; yellow flowers.	On perennial grass ranges indicates overgrazing.	Adjust range use to capacity of perennial grasses; graze early to remove tarweed when young.
Turkey Mullein (Eremocarpus setigerus).	Annual herb; prickly gray leaves, with three main veins.	When abundant in annual grass types it indicates over-use.	Rotation grazing to permit annual grasses to set seed and rest range area.
Buttercup (Ranunculus spp); also called crowfoot.	Annual or perennial herb; solitary yellow or white flowers; extensive root systems; usually in wet meadow types.	Overuse of sedges and rushes; drying out of meadow type.	Adjust grazing to favor re-establishment of meadow vegetation; erosion control to maintain water table.
Woolly Mules-ears (Wyethia mollis); also called big sunflower, gray dock.	Perennial herb of sunflower family; large leaves with white woolly hairs; bright yellow flowers.	On bunchgrass ranges increase of this plant indicates deterioration of bunchgrasses; decrease indicates improvement of range.	Adjust season of use and number of animals to favor perennial grasses.

L. T. Burcham, 1949—C. D. F.

A better measure of range conditions, especially in connection with the above, is through general observation of the range. This includes looking at soil compaction and erosion, quantity and vigor of forage plants, availability of water for livestock, rodent activity, and damage to trees and the watershed.

The presence of certain plants are good indicators of environmental range conditions (Figure IX-1). These indicator plants invade areas that are overused or abused in some manner. Table IX-2 lists some of these indicator plants and their characteristics.

The replacement of one kind of plants by others under changing environmental conditions is called plant succession. It is a natural phenomena in the development of permanent or climax plant types that can be affected by man and animals. Successional trends up and down this scale of development are schematically shown below for California annual range (left), and for perennial range (right).

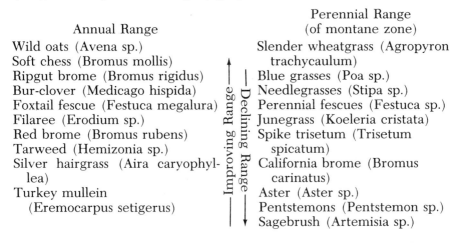

Annual Range	Perennial Range (of montane zone)
Wild oats (Avena sp.)	Slender wheatgrass (Agropyron trachycaulum)
Soft chess (Bromus mollis)	
Ripgut brome (Bromus rigidus)	Blue grasses (Poa sp.)
Bur-clover (Medicago hispida)	Needlegrasses (Stipa sp.)
Foxtail fescue (Festuca megalura)	Perennial fescues (Festuca sp.)
Filaree (Erodium sp.)	Junegrass (Koeleria cristata)
Red brome (Bromus rubens)	Spike trisetum (Trisetum spicatum)
Tarweed (Hemizonia sp.)	
Silver hairgrass (Aira caryophyllea)	California brome (Bromus carinatus)
Turkey mullein (Eremocarpus setigerus)	Aster (Aster sp.)
	Pentstemons (Pentstemon sp.)
	Sagebrush (Artemisia sp.)

(center arrows: Improving Range — Declining Range)

U.C., Sampson, Chase, Hedrick, 1951

Another sign of range condition is the extent to which key species are grazed, especially the more palatable and abundant plants. For example, a dry meadow is properly used when about a quarter of the bunchgrasses is ungrazed, the soil between plants is only slightly trampled, and the grazed plants have at least 1"–1½" stubble. In addition, some critical range localities may provide worthwhile information for management purposes. These key areas represent the various types that range technicians study in a more formal, detailed way to evaluate the effects of grazing.

Carrying Capacity

After an area has been determined suitable for grazing land and its condition evaluated, the manager needs to know what numbers of animals on the average it can support without deterioration of the range and other resources. Setting the correct carrying capacity maintains a good balance of desirable species and sustains forage production. The capacity of a range is related to climatic conditions and management practices.

Grazing capacity can be expressed in number of animal unit months (AUM) a range can sustain in the course of an average year. An AUM is the amount of forage needed to feed a mature cow, or its equivalent (five sheep) for one month. It equals 300 pounds of total digestible nutrients or 3/10 tons of hay. The AUM is a measure of how many stock to put in an area; it is used also by public land agencies as a unit for grazing fees. The acreage required per AUM varies widely by kind and condition of the range—from less than one acre for productive meadows, one to three acres for annual and grassland types, 30 or more acres for chaparral and coniferous forest types. As an example, a 900-acre property exclusively of the latter type would support perhaps 30 cows during the month(s) that the range plants are flourishing.

Management Practices

The production of ranges can be increased by a number of practices. They seek to obtain better distribution of the livestock, equalize utilization of the forage, increase the forage plants, control poisonous plants, other unwanted species, and rodent damage, and safeguard the soil and watershed resource. Where the forest owner does not personally use the range, the costs of some practices can be borne by or shared with the range lessee.

Watering Facilities

Of high priority is the need to provide adequate water supplies for the livestock. This allows more stocking of animals, and if spaced properly, they are distributed better and utilize the forage more evenly. If possible, water should be available so that cattle do not have to travel more than one-half mile for it in rough country, one mile in rolling terrain, or two miles on gentle ground. For sheep, the water should be within 1½ miles in rough topography to three miles in easy country. Table IX-3 gives the daily water and salt requirements for livestock.

Table IX-3.   Water and salt requirements for range livestock.

Class of stock	Water requirement per head (gallons per day)	Salt requirement per head (pounds per month*)
Cattle	10 to 12	1.0 to 2.5
Horses	10 to 12	3.25 to 3.75
Sheep	.25 to 1.5	.25 to 1.0

* Includes an allowance for weathering losses.

Salt Needs

Salting is another effective practice of encouraging proper distribution of stock and utilization. It also promotes good weight gains. Because it leads to excessive concentration and range damage, salt should be placed away from watering facilities and meadows, such as on accessible ridges, benches, and openings in the forest, where the area is large and level enough for stock movement. It should be also placed to draw animals away from sensitive areas into lightly used or hard-to-get areas. Salt should be distributed throughout the range at intervals of about one mile for cattle and horses and with more spacing for sheep.

Control of Stock Movement

Fencing, or other means, may be necessary to keep livestock within bounds and to prevent trespass on other property. However, in a few counties or parts thereof (Lassen, Modoc, Shasta, Siskiyou, Trinity) open range is still practiced and stock cannot be considered in trespass unless the lands strayed upon are fenced. Therefore, except in those places, it is the livestock owner's responsibility to keep grazing animals off lands for which there is no lease or permit.

In addition to property line and other permanent fencing, temporary or moveable drift fences are useful to distribute livestock properly. Herding the animals about may be necessary occasionally for the same reason.

Seeding and Fertilization

Broadcast seeding and fertilization by hand or aircraft can improve forage growth where it is needed on some ranges. Selective hand-seeding in forested areas on skid trails, landings, and roadsides prevents erosion as well as furnishing some forage. Seeding sites and conditions are highly variable and each project should be studied by a range technician beforehand as to species to use, timing, sowing rates, methods, and rodent control needs. Large areas should not be seeded in total until some field tests have demonstrated probable success. The same caution applies to fertilization.

Poisonous Plants

There are many plants that are noxious or poisonous to one or more domestic livestock. The more common ones are listed in Table IX-4. Some plants can be lethal; others cause sickness, growth loss, or malformation of offspring. Stock do not eat these plants by choice. Heavy injury or loss is the exception where wholesome forage is in adequate supply. Thus, the control of these plants depends largely on proper range management. Some practices to reduce stock damage are:

1. Avoid too early use or overuse of the range.
2. Delay placing stock in poisonous plant areas until stock have become adjusted and the forage is in good condition.
3. While moving stock, travel slowly through areas of poisonous plants so that the animals will have time to select the right forage.
4. Withhold grazing of poisonous plant areas to allow re-establishment of better plants.
5. Eradicate the worst poisonous plants by grubbing, frequent cutting, or chemicals.

Table IX-4.   Common noxious or poisonous plants of California forest-ranges.

	Animals Affected		
Plant	Cattle	Horses	Sheep
Bracken fern (*Pteridium aquilinum*)	X	X	X
Waterhemlock (*Cicuta sp.*)	X	X	X
Poisonhemlock (*Conium sp.*)	X	X	X
Larkspur (*Delphinium sp.*)	X		
Lupine (*Lupinus sp.*)	X	X	X
Locoweed (*Astragalus sp.* & *Oxytropis sp.*)	X	X	X
Death camas (*Zygadenus sp.*)	X	X	X
Klamath weed (*Hypericum perforata*)	X	X	X
Milkweeds (*Asclepias sp.*)	X	X	X
Skunk cabbage (*Veratrum sp.*)		X	X
Western azalea (*Rhododendron occidentale*)			X

C.D.F., Dodge, 1978

Control of Rodents

The control of rodents, such as the ground squirrel, may be necessary where they are a problem. Their depredation may reduce from one-fourth to one-half the forage, besides causing other damage like soil erosion and feeding on tree seed and reproduction. Rodent populations are sometimes kept in balance by hawks, other raptors, and preying animals. The advice of county farm advisers, agricultural commissioners, soil conservation technicians, fish and wildlife authorities, and licensed pest control applicators should be sought.

Erosion and Watershed Repair

Erosion depletes many ranges, especially meadows and prairies. Over-grazing of these valuable forage areas reduces protective plant cover leading to sheet erosion of the topsoil. Sometimes, gullying follows; it causes a lowering of the water table and allows invasion of less desirable plants like conifers, brush, and unpalatable species. Better regulation of grazing and clogging gullies with brush, debris, and rocks can stabilize or improve the situation.

Controlled Burning

As stated previously, controlled burning can be used to improve and convert brush ranges into better forage. Fire should be employed very discriminately and in a safe manner. To obtain the best results, only sites that have the basic capability to respond satisfactorily should be chosen. Examination of the soil or study of soil maps will indicate what areas have a reasonable chance of success. In addition to preparation of secure fire-lines, the selected areas preferably should be carefully prepared by bull-dozing, crushing, chaining, or chopping to place the fuel into manageable form. The burning should take place under the required permits (fire and air pollution control) during the right weather conditions. This is after the treated fuel has dried to some extent. The firing method should be one that will safely consume most of the woody material. The success of the project will be enhanced greatly by follow-up seeding and especially regulated grazing. Safe, selective herbicides can be effectively used to control post-burn woody sprouts. Literature, advice, and assistance on brush range improvement and controlled burning are available from the CDF and county farm advisers.

Grazing Systems

Livestock operators and range scientists have devised a number of different grazing systems. The purpose of the system is to promote the most efficient land management practicable. It should conserve or improve the forage production, and other resources, and yet allow an optimum level of livestock production. The chosen system should be one that can be integrated and compatible with the overall management of the property and still protect the timber, water, wildlife, and recreation values.

Grazing can be either continuous throughout the grazing season or year, or it can be based on partial use. The system must be picked specifically for each range by considering growth and maintenance requirements of the forage plants and livestock, the grazing habits of the animals, and the quantity and location of the feed. There are five main grazing systems that one can employ.

Continuous Grazing

The traditional grazing system allows livestock to graze a range throughout the year in mild climates, or throughout the season when the area is growing accessible forage. The use pattern is generally the same each year, except for adjustment because of weather factors. Uniform grazing is achieved by the management practices described earlier in this chapter—watering, salting, fencing, and herding.

Continuous grazing is convenient. It requires the least investment in range improvements, less handling of livestock, and generally, it utilizes the different kinds of forage when they are most nutritious.

There are disadvantages to continuous grazing. Livestock tend to concentrate too much in the better areas, thereby damaging the forage and soil. Poor distribution of the animals and uneven utilization of the plants waste forage in some places.

Deferred Grazing

Grazing is delayed on some ranges or areas to favor reproduction, early growth, and physiological needs of forage plants. Deferred grazing is often selected for ranges where the grazing period would otherwise include all or part of the growing season. The system generally is best adapted to ranges in need of rehabilitation. This is accomplished by promoting firm establishment of new growth and full development of the reproductive organs of the plants. Usually, deferment of grazing is combined with rotation grazing.

Rotation Grazing

This system provides for the orderly rotation in the grazing of two or more parts of a range. The use of these parcels is alternated within the grazing season, the year, or between years with no-grazing periods in between in order to rest the range. The purposes of this system are to keep the forage on the entire property in good condition, utilize the range evenly, and to avoid damage to soil, the watershed, or tree crops. It is best adapted to ranges in fair and better condition.

Fencing or herding is usually required for rotation grazing. This alternate use might be obtained to some degree also by change in yearly location where livestock begin grazing and controlling livestock distribution by herding, salting or watering.

Deferred-Rotation Grazing

This is a combination of the above two systems. Under this method, grazing is deferred for awhile on part of the range during the growing season for one or more years. Then, the use of the other parcels are deferred in rotation. Grazing takes place on the entire range for at least part of each grazing season or year.

On ranges with summer grazing about one-third the season remains after forage seed has matured. Three different grazing units are needed to practice a deferred-rotation season. Use is delayed in each parcel for two-thirds of the season at least every third year. As in rotation grazing, fencing or other means to distribute the stock according to the plan are required.

Rest-Rotation Grazing

This is a more sophisticated system that is a further refinement of the deferred and rotation grazing systems. This plan has the additional feature of having complete rest on certain parts of the range during certain seasons or years. The long rest period restores the condition of the forage by allowing the more desirable species to grow and reproduce.

Choosing the System

The system to employ on a property depends on its soil, vegetation, climate, and livestock involved, and the objectives of the management. The plan of use should be developed cooperatively between the owner, manager, range adviser, and the user.

No management practice—season of use, rate of stocking, distribution of livestock, range improvement, or grazing system—will by itself materially improve any range. All must be combined into a management plan to be successful in achieving the most effective and efficient use of the range and other resources. Investments often have to be made to secure the best results and to provide reasonable returns to the landowner and livestock operator.

Regardless of the grazing system, the guiding principle of proper range management is that conservative use is necessary to maintain the right kinds and amount of forage species. The chief causes of rangeland depletion are too early grazing and too close cropping during the normal grazing period. A range long overgrazed has usually lost most of its best forage plants. A substantial percent of the current amount of palatable vegetation and seed stalks need to be left at the end of the grazing season to maintain a range in good condition.

Protection of Timber

Historically, there has been a serious conflict between grazing and timber production. This doesn't have to be; studies have shown that usually damage to trees from livestock is due to faulty grazing management. Other problems have arisen from unwise attempts to convert timberlands to range and range improvement burning that was not properly controlled.

There are a number of contributing factors in the damage of trees by livestock, namely:

1. Where proper forage is limited or unsuited to livestock, trees are harmed by browsing and breakage.
2. Too early grazing, prior to full development of forage plants, results in excessive browsing of trees and trampling of young tree seedlings. Grazing during periods when snow covers part of the ground forage in early spring and late fall also leads to browsing and trampling.
4. Poor distribution of livestock is another reason for trampling and browsing of trees.

Despite these dangers, range utilization has benefits besides those of an economic nature. The right kind of grazing can increase reproduction of trees by planting of seeds by the hooves of the livestock. The competition to tree seedlings is decreased by animals feeding on herbaceous plants. Similarly, browsing on hardwoods keep those species in check in conifer stands. Another benefit to forests from grazing comes from reducing forest fuels in the form of grass, forbs, and shrubs. Moreover, some livestock trails can be used to start fireline construction.

The key to achieving compatability and mutual benefits between range and forest production is wise management. If each resource is handled correctly, the impact of one on the other is lessened and the total output is better than by not having an integrated management plan.

Chapter X

WATER, WILDLIFE, RECREATION

In addition to timber and range, the other valuable uses of forests are watershed management, fish and wildlife production, and outdoor recreation. These resources may not offer much in the way of a saleable, physical product like wood and forage; nonetheless they provide many benefits to both forest owners and society in general. In many situations, the tree farmer can personally utilize these resources and even market a service based on them within the framework of a multiple-use program.

Watershed Management

Water is a necessity for all living things. It is especially critical here in California because of our large population, irregular geographical distribution of precipitation, and its seasonal nature, marked by occasional severe drought years. Consequently, California has spent more on water development, transport, and protection of quality than any other state in the U. S.

The annual average yield of water from California lands is 67,788,000 acre-feet. Besides this native water, additional amounts are imported. Most of this water has its source in the wildlands, about 60 percent coming from the commercial forests alone. Because of the importance of wildlands to water production, forest owners and managers have a vital role in the protection and management of watersheds.

The Hydrologic Cycle

To carry out this responsibility, one should have an understanding of the hydrologic cycle (Figure X-1) and the various factors involved. Some of them can be manipulated and thereby affect quantity and quality of water yield, flood runoff, erosion, and sedimentation.

The natural distribution and transport of water in its various forms (solid, liquid, vapor) follow the hydrologic cycle. It can be expressed by the formula:

$$RO = P - E - T - (or +) S$$

where   RO = runoff or water yield

      P   = precipitation

      E   = evaporation

      T   = transpiration

      S   = storage of water in ground

Precipitation by rain, sleet, snow, hail, fog, mist, dew, and frost is the principal source of water on the earth's surface. All are derived from the atmosphere where moisture exists as vapor, particles of water, and snow or hail. These forms are created and precipitated to the ground by various weather phenomena.

Evaporation is one process by which water from the land and water bodies returns directly to the atmosphere in the form of vapor. The rate is a function of 1) solar radiation, 2) temperature, 3) wind, 4) atmospheric

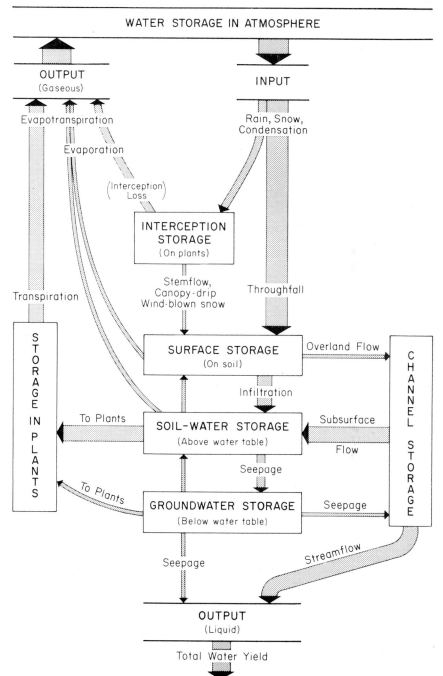

Figure X-1
The hydrologic cycle.

U.S.F.S., Pacific Southwest Forest and Range Experiment Station, 1978.

pressure, and 5) humidity. It is affected greatly by the interception and holding of precipitation by vegetation or surface objects. The result is a sizeable reduction in the water reaching the ground. For instance, studies have shown that a ponderosa pine can intercept from 22 to 40 percent of the precipitation. However, occasionally the interception is temporary and the water still gets to the ground from flow down the plant stems and fog drip.

Transpiration is the release of water vapor into the air from vegetation. The amount is related to vegetative cover, the growth activity of the plants, and weather conditions, varying by hour, day, and season. It is also affected by the available ground water.

Although plants do not consume much water in the absolute sense, they do take water from the soil, use it in their physiological processes, and release it as a vapor so that it is not readily available. A single tree can extract hundreds of gallons of water per day from the soil. In general, on a per-acre basis, transpiration from brushlands and forests is from 5 to 25 inches per year, or more. Certain plants whose roots reach the water table (phreatophytes) and riparian or stream-bank plants like alder and willow are notorious users of water. Transpiration is the primary source of water use in forests, in contrast to evaporation from the soil, since the canopy intercepts most of the solar energy.

Storage of water in the ground consists of soil moisture and as free water below the water table in porous strata or formations known as aquifers. Because of variations in amount of stored water and the nature of the geological structure, the runoff from a watershed may not equal the input less evapo-transpiration losses. When the watershed is saturated and the ground water table is at its highest level, the outflow is at a maximum. However, some watersheds leak because of their geological structure, so the runoff is less than would be expected. Conversely, some watersheds yield water from deep underground storage by artesian springs, in which case the runoff is increased.

Water moves from the land surfaces into the soil mantle by infiltration. The rate is high when the soil is dry and low when the soils approach their capacity to hold water (field capacity). Moreover, infiltration is affected by amount and kind of plants, ground litter, soil structure and texture, turbidity of the water, and character and depth of frozen soil. Movement of water deeper into the soil and below is called percolation.

Effects of Soil and Vegetation

Obviously, soil and vegetation affect the functioning of a watershed. This needs to be understood by forest managers and users because management activities change the amount and composition of the plant cover and the accompanying soil resource to a significant degree. However, these effects can be altered by land management.

Vegetation has minimal effect on precipitation, most of which is caused by cyclonic and convective storms. However, forests improve the microclimate and bring about a little precipitation from fog drip and by interception of moisture-laden clouds at high elevations. Most important is the amelioration of high temperatures, low humidities, and wind movement at ground level that are often destructive to young seedlings and unfavorable from the standpoint of wildfire.

Interception and transpiration cause some water loss, but this is offset by other benefits. One gain is that this movement of water into the air also improves the local climate by cooling the air and increasing the humidity. Interception of precipitation by plant foliage breaks the impact of raindrops on the ground and prevents puddling and erosion of the soil.

The infiltration capabilities of soil and vegetation are especially valuable to watershed management. Good infiltration prevents or decreases flood runoff and extends the time of water yield. Both the amount and rate of infiltration into the soil are governed by a number of factors. One of these is the porosity of the soil that can be decreased by compaction. The kinds and combinations of particles in a soil—clay, silt, sand, rock—largely determine porosity. Soil texture and depth also affect water-holding capacity. The vegetal litter and humus form organic matter in the soil that makes it more porous, binds small particles into aggregates, holds moisture, and adds nutrients.

Much of the erosion and flood runoff damage is caused by surface flow of water. Some erosion is natural or geologic and some is accelerated because of human activity. Soil is moved by sheet, gully, and channel or streamside erosion. The rate is related to the gradient and water velocity; for instance, doubling of the velocity increases erosive power four times. Mass movements also occur sometimes in form of slips and slides, especially in unstable areas. Erosion is also materially affected by the kind of soil (see Chapter II—Site). The more erodible soils of California forest areas are listed below:

Redwood–Douglas-Fir Region	Pine Region
Atwell	Chaix
Casper	Corbett
Empire	Chawanakee
Hely	Heitz
Larabee	Lytton
Mendocino	McCarthy
Modesty	Shaver
Tonini	Tish Tang
	Windy

(C.D.F., Stone)

Vegetation may decrease erosion in three ways: 1) the canopy reduces dislodgement of soil by rain drop impact, 2) plants and humus facilitate infiltration and thereby reduce surface flows, and 3) the velocity of overland flow of water is greatly decreased by the vegetation and its debris. Generally, the denser the cover the more the water flow is held back with the peak discharges correspondingly lowered. Vegetation along roads and streambanks particularly deters erosion at those critical places.

Water Utilization

Because water is such a valuable commodity in California, its use and protection are strictly regulated. Moreover, the laws and regulations on water rights are quite complex. Basically, water is a public resource and people's individual rights to it are limited. An owner has rights to water that can be tapped by springs and wells on the property without much restriction. The use of surface water from streams and lakes, however, is controlled by the State. To assure continuance of these riparian rights, an owner should file for a permit from the State Water Resources Control Board. That agency can also supply literature on water rights and the various regulations.

The quality of water in streams, lakes, and underground sources is also protected by laws and regulations of the above agency. This control is administred by local Regional Water Quality Control Boards. Similarly, as noted in Chapter II, the Department of Fish and Game has laws and regulations to prevent damage to streams, lakes, and fish habitat. Besides protecting these resources because of legal mandates, water and water-sheds have a personal value to an owner for domestic and land-use reasons.

Some landowners find it worthwhile to impound water behind dams or in ponds to increase and extend supplies for domestic, agricultural, and livestock purposes. Assistance in the design of such facilities is available from the State Department of Water Resources and the Soil Conservation Service. Dams of more than six feet in height that store more than certain acre-feet minimums must be built under a permit from the Department of Water Resources and meet strict safety standards. Dams on streams used by migrating fish need a passage structure.

Water is measured in a number of ways. In addition to inches (precipitation) and gallons, water is measured by such units as 1) acre-feet, 2) cubic feet per second (cfs) of flow, also called second-feet, and 3) miners inch. An acre-foot is water one foot deep over one acre; it equals 43,560 cu. ft. or 325,851 gallons. A cubic foot of water equals 7.48 gallons or 62.4 pounds. The miners inch, a carryover measure from the early mining days, is still used in mountain areas. It is a flow of water through a one-inch square notch with the incoming water level 6½ inches above the bottom of the notch, and is equivalent to 1.53 cubic feet per minute. The Appendix contains other measures and conversion factors useful in forestry.

Impact of Forest Land Management

Forests and other vegetation provide positive benefits for water production. Land-use activities can alter those benefits, easily in a negative, or less so in a positive way; it all depends on the attitude and actions of the land manager. If the manager accepts the concept that soil and water resources have value like trees and forage, much can be accomplished to conserve watersheds.

It is not a simple job to protect the watershed values while timber is being harvested and the forage grazed. To do so the tree farmer should adopt a program of wise use of these crops with appropriate limits on watershed damage. To achieve this goal, the land manager must know these limitations, the basic cause of damage, and what protective methods need to be applied. Some areas remain relatively stable under rather intensive use while others are much more sensitive. The differences in susceptibility are due to variations in geology, soil, climate, topography, and cover.

A number of the impacts on watersheds from timber harvesting and grazing are clearly recognizable from experience and scientific studies. Water storage and yield are affected by some timber operations. The effects can be positive if more water is produced or if the flow can be extended over a longer period. On the other hand, peak flows may be increased and cause damage in some cases.

Both timber harvesting and grazing can compact the soil and expose it to erosion. The consequences of some erosion may be serious to the property owner, neighboring lands, downstream improvements, and water users. It's well recognized that excessive erosion lowers the site quality and can damage road systems. Agricultural lands and improvements of various kinds on and off the property may be impaired by deposition of eroded materials. Sediment from erosion spoils fish habitat in streams and water bodies, reduces storage capacity of reservoirs, and lowers water quality.

Perhaps a more widespread impact is that soil disturbance can lower the quality of water in streams, lakes, and reservoirs. The addition of soil particles, organic material, nutrients, and debris degrades the water; this limits its use, lowers potability, impairs waterways and facilities, and increases treatment costs. Disturbance of the sides and channels of streams adds to the problem. Removal of vegetation along streams increases erosion and water temperatures so that fish life and other aquatic populations may be reduced or even eliminated.

Different impacts on the watershed are caused by the various forest operations. The cutting of trees by itself probably has the least effect. Some cutting techniques improve summer water supplies by increasing snow deposition and slowing snow melt. More commonly, removal of trees reduces transpiration losses; this may be good or not, depending on the circumstances. Water yield is increased, which may be desirable, but not so when the cutting takes place on poorly drained, slide-prone areas, because the greater amount of water left in the soil may increase likelihood of mass soil movement. The eventual decay of the tree roots reduces the anchoring and binding of the soil. While many slides occur in undisturbed areas, their frequency may be increased by timber cutting and the road development and yarding that accompany it.

Physical damage or increased hazard of surface erosion from yarding comes about in three ways: exposure of the soil, deep disturbance, and compaction. Exposure of the soil is usually of least consequence unless extensive or on highly erosive soils. Some light disturbance of the top soil may enhance the germination and establishment of a new tree crop. However, deeper disturbance resulting from bulldozer cutting of skidroads and landings, skidded logs plowing the soil, and heavy equipment activity, especially during wet weather, can lead to erosion problems. Compaction damage varies enormously according to kind of soil, its moisture content, kind of logging equipment, and frequency of traffic. Severe compaction adds to the likelihood of faster runoff and erosion; it also may retard subsequent establishment and growth of reproduction. Compaction depends on degree of harvesting, and is greatest with tractor logging and least with off-the-ground cable or aircraft methods.

The construction and use of roads create a very large share of the watershed damage associated with management activities, as much as 90 percent in many cases. Roads on gentle to moderate slopes on stable terrain have small impact except through careless construction and maintenance practices. Difficulties and hazards multiply where roads are built on steep topography, cut into erosive or unstable soils, encroach on streams, or when constructed during wet weather. The resulting disturbance that is not localized or revegetated causes soil and debris movement, deteriorates the site, lowers water quality, and clogs water courses. Mass soil movement is a frequent risk with mountainous roads. Poor road maintenance also harms watershed values in much the same way.

Slash disposal operations may have a negative effect on watershed values. Some treatment of slash is favored in many situations because it lowers fire hazards and improves the site for regeneration of a new tree crop, and in doing so contributes to retention and establishment of a protective cover. If properly done, slash burning does little damage to a watershed, but if uncontrolled or too hot, soil cover and structure may be degraded. This can lead to more water and wind caused erosion, reduction in infiltration, and the introduction of ash, soil sediments, and nutrients into nearby streams.

Aside from timber harvesting, watersheds can be harmed by other forest uses. Heavy feeding by livestock, wildlife overpopulation, and concentrated recreation use can increase surface runoff by reducing plant density and by increasing soil compaction from trampling. Plants lose their vigor by continual too-close cropping and heavy trampling; productivity drops, tops and roots die back, and protective cover and litter dwindle. Original cover is often replaced by plants less efficient in staving off erosion, and continued overuse exposes dangerous high proportions of bare soil.

Prevention and Control of Damage

It has been demonstrated that the way land-use is conducted has immediate and long-term impacts on watersheds. Well planned operations will keep watershed degradation to a minimum level. Although careful operations may add significantly to the costs of forest management, it is an expense that is necessary to protect personal and public interest in watershed values. Forest owners need to recognize this cost and to balance it, together with other resource expenditures, against the benefits and returns.

Principal measures aimed at prevention and control of watershed deterioration resulting from timber harvesting, grazing, and other operations are as follows:

1. Avoid or modify timber cutting on unstable areas to prevent mass soil movement, because of geological disturbance by logging, reduction in soil anchorage by roots, and lowered transpiration losses that can result in oversupply of soil moisture on the area.
2. Adapt equipment and methods of logging to reduce gouging and deep soil disturbance. Consider using cable systems on sensitive areas.

3. Prohibit or reduce use of tractors on erosive, steep slopes and sloppy (saturated) ground. As a rough guide, 30-percent slopes approach the desirable maximum for tractor operations on non-rocky soils.

4. Keep skid trails and landings well drained by diverting surface water to areas where sediments can filter out and erosive energy be safely dissipated. The installation of diversion ditches or water bars after logging is important, and these should be checked during the wet season to see that they are functioning properly.

5. Do not yard logs along, across, or in stream channels. Instead, skid logs away from streams and suspend them fully at necessary crossings. Keep logging debris out of streams and carefully remove any that gets into streams that may cause damming, obstruction of fish passage, diversion of flow, bank cutting, and lowering of water quality.

6. Plan road, landing, and skidtrail locations in advance of construction to reduce soil disturbance and to lower construction, maintenance, and use costs (see Chapter VII).

7. Learn to recognize and avoid trouble spots for roads from the standpoint of geology, soils, seeps.

8. Avoid steep road grades and provide adequate drainage facilities.

9. Locate roads and landings at a safe distance from streams, and leave a margin of protective trees and vegetation. Keep roads on benches and ridges and away from swales and depressions.

10. Minimize earth movement during road construction.

11. Provide regular maintenance to prevent road and watershed damage.

12. Where slash or other burning is necessary, it should be carefully prescribed and controlled (see Chapter VIII). Avoid slash burning adjacent to streams.

13. Graze forage moderately under a carefully prepared range management plan (see previous Chapter).

14. Manage wildlife populations and recreation use wisely to avoid watershed damage (see subsequent sections).

Fish and Wildlife

Forests and the associated atmosphere, soil, vegetation, and water are natural homes for a vast number of species of the animal kingdom, such as birds, rodents, fur bearers, game, other animals, and fish. Many species that live in and around forests are found nowhere else, and when woodlands are harmed, some creatures become fewer or disappear. To save the beautiful and useful kinds of fish and wildlife, their habitats must first be protected, because that is the source of their food, water, shelter, and a place to breed, hide, and live.

Forests and Fish

Like the raw water resource, streams, lakes, and the fish belong to the public regardless of who owns the land. As pointed out earlier, laws exist to protect these resources. The inland fisheries resource ranks high in terms of economic value; it supports a valuable salmon industry in California and provides much sport fishing that has both recreational and monetary value. The streams in the forests not only have resident fish like trout, but some also produce migrating or anadromous species such as salmon, steelhead trout, sturgeon, and shad. Some small streams are important producers of salmon and trout even though they may intermittently dry.

Many physical, chemical, and biological conditions affect fish life—oxygen, carbon dioxide, minerals, alkalinity, food, shade, temperature, drought, and flood. Many kinds of fish, especially salmon and trout, require clean, cool water with adequate levels of dissolved oxygen and mineral nutrients. The gravelly stretches and riffles are of special importance for reproduction and food production, and these need to be relatively free of sediment. Natural reproduction is more efficient and desirable than expensive and less effective planting of hatchery-reared fish.

Food for trout and young salmon is supplied from both land and water, about 10 percent from the former and 90 percent by the water itself. A myriad of insect larvae of many sizes, shapes, and varieties that cling to objects under water are the dominant food. Waters that drain soils from forests and ranges are rich in this insect life. Also fed upon are crayfish, small snails, clams, small fish, and other life forms.

The fisheries can be materially affected by forestry and range practices. In general, the same factors that are involved in watershed protection covered in the first section of this chapter pertain to fish.

As noted, surface erosion and mass soil movement perhaps have the greatest influence on both the fish and their habitat. The resulting debris and sediments block streams and smother spawning beds, fish eggs, and young fish. The quality of the water is lowered by the addition of soil particles, ash from burning, and organic material. When the latter decomposes it consumes the oxygen in the water and releases carbon dioxide and other harmful gases; this can kill fish. The effects that timber cutting and grazing have on water yield may be damaging at times. Less vegetal cover causes faster runoff, higher peak discharges, more erosion, and lower stream flows during the late dry season. The removal of streamside shade can raise water temperatures to lethal levels for fish; this puts portions of the stream out of production and creates thermal barriers for passage of resident and migrating fish.

It was stated earlier in this chapter that by far the greatest potential for watershed damage is from roads. This is equally true for the fisheries resource. The major causes of damage to fish and fish habitat from roads are:

1. Roads located too close to streams.
2. Siltation from unstabilized slopes and road damage.
3. Landslips triggered by poorly located, constructed, or maintained roads.
4. Removal or disturbance of too much tree and other vegetative cover along streams, causing higher water temperatures, bank erosion, and diminished food supply.

5. Disturbance of beds and banks of streams during construction of crossings—bridges, culverts, and fords.

6. Improperly installed or maintained culverts that inhibit or prevent fish passage.

Chapter VII on Forest Roads also discusses standards and practices for protection of watersheds and fisheries.

Terrestrial Wildlife

Terrestrial wildlife constitute another valuable public resource that is a source of beauty, biological study, recreation, and income. Animals also contribute to the natural woodland balance; e.g., birds and mammals that prey on insects and rodents that are harmful to forest and range resources. As other resources are protected and managed so must wildlife be, in order to fully realize these benefits; they accrue to the forest owner and society alike.

A main element of wildlife management is vegetative habitat. It has most of the things wildlife need for living—food, cover, water, and living space. Each species eats specific foods, some vegetative and some animal, which in turn are derived directly or indirectly from plants. Vegetation and other natural features form the cover and ecological niches that protect animals while they feed, sleep, breed, play, and travel. All wildlife need water; it is obtained from surface sources, dew, snow, and succulent plants. The last habitat requirement is enough space to preclude overcrowding and too much competition.

A given habitat can only support a certain number of each species of wildlife. This carrying capacity of the habitat is related to the arrangement and availability of food, cover, and water. One good arrangement is where these components occur in close, mixed blocks with a lot of transitional edges between different types of vegetation (called edge effect). Many wildlife benefit from this because they commonly live on the edges, not the centers, of different types of cover. There are many types of wildlife habitat and each requires certain management to provide the greatest benefits to the animals it supports.

Each species resides in the biotic community (all the plants and animals together in the immediate area) that best meet its needs, or in several communities. These communities are subject to slow successional changes because of weather, soil development, plant growth, and other factors. Resultingly, the plants and animals are replaced over time by other species that are better equipped to survive in the changed habitat. Natural succession can be disrupted by land-use disturbances, for example, burning, grazing, and timbering. Many wildlife species benefit from some disturbances that hold back plant succession to intermediate stages. However, some wildlife species need a stable or climax habitat (e.g., a mature forest) to survive.

The riparian habitat is perhaps the most productive and vital of all the plant communities for wildlife. Most species are very dependent upon this cover and are sensitive to its disturbance. Hardwoods (particularly oak) and brush in combination also rank high as wildlife habitat. This is followed by mixed types containing conifers, hardwoods, and brush. A few animals are peculiar to just pure plant types like conifers and brush alone.

Wildlife Management

Wildlife are managed by skillful treatment of the animal populations and the habitat. The tools used to manage populations include regulation of hunting and trapping, refuges, stocking with native or exotic species, habitat protection or improvement, and predator control. The regulation of hunting and trapping must be flexible and based on biological principles in order to be effectively applied by wildlife managers. The habitat approach is the real key to wildlife management, because without a suitable environment animal numbers and health cannot be maintained regardless of other methods.

Various land-uses change the cover and habitat for wildlife. The effects can be either good or not; it all depends on how it is done. Woodland that is intensively grazed is usually a poor place for most wildlife. Overgrazing and trampling destroy the more desirable forage plants and young trees. Thus the habitat becomes deteriorated to the point that wild animal numbers and even species are reduced.

While selective, controlled burning may improve some habitats, indiscriminate burning and wildfire may cause damage. Intense fires can burn animals and seriously impair the habitat by reducing cover for shelter and decreasing food and water supplies.

Timber harvesting can have a dramatic impact on wildlife habitat. If correctly planned and executed, it can serve wildlife purposes. Forest practices can be used to produce or insure diversity and stability of both plant and animal communities, or to provide better habitat for selected animals. These practices offer the most practicable broadscale approach to alteration of the forest habitat that is available to wildlife managers to achieve their goals. However, no single forestry practice or system is a panacea for wildlife, and management must be both appropriate and flexible to accomplish the desired overall results. Some forest practices to consider for protection and enhancement of the wildlife resource are:

1. Choose a cutting system that favors variety of habitat. Group selection cutting, small clearcuts that are well spaced, and fairly heavy single-tree harvesting result in diversity of wildlife habitat.
2. Retain streamside cover and protect meadows.
3. Harvest trees in ways that create most edge effect.
4. Reserve some patches of brush within or adjoining the forest for edge effect and habitat diversity.
5. Save live trees with hollow trunks and limbs for such animals as raccoon, opposum, squirrel, chipmunk, wood duck, owl, sparrow hawk, woodpecker, and insect-eating and song birds of various kinds. Hollow windfalls also are homes for some animals.
6. Save some hardwoods, especially oaks, as a source of food for many birds and mammals. Black oak acorns (mast) alone provide feed for 45 species, including woodpeckers, pigeons, jays, raccoons, squirrels, wild pig, and deer.

7. Keep snags that are not hazardous for fire and safety reasons, or any snag that contains nesting birds of valuable species, e.g., eagle, osprey. Snags house countless species of birds, mammals, and insects that decompose wood and provide food for wildlife.

8. Protect and develop water sources for wildlife.

Biologists of the Department of Fish and Game, U. S. Fish and Wildlife Service, U. C. Cooperative Extension, and the U. S. Forest Service can provide literature and advice on wildlife protection and enhancement. In fact, the first agency will help forest owners assess their properties from the standpoint of managing them intensively for wildlife. Some private wildlife consultants are also available in California.

Species Protection

Most native wildlife were abundant during the early days, but this has changed mainly because of land development and use, and to some extent by hunting and trapping. However, some species that fell to a low level due to humans have recovered because of various wildlife protection measures. On the other hand, some species that once were widespread now have much smaller populations and ranges, and a few are extinct. Elk, antelope, bighorn sheep, marten, fisher, wolverine, some fox, and some raptors have become fewer. Contrary to popular belief, such predators as coyotes and raptors are not necessarily bad and shouldn't be exterminated, but they may need some control where they cause damage to domestic animals.

To prevent a virtual disappearance of declining wildlife, both the federal and state governments have officially recognized some species within California as endangered, threatened, or rare. Protection programs for these species have been jointly developed by the public agencies concerned with help from private wildlife organizations. Laws, regulations, and environmental impact processes are utilized to give special attention to the preservation of these critical species, and their habitat. At this time of writing, the critical species associated with California's forest and associated lands are as follows.

Endangered	Threatened	Rare
California condor	Lahonton cutthroat	Bighorn sheep
Bald eagle	trout	Wolverine
Peregrine falcon	Paiute cutthroat	Siskiyou Mt.
San Joaquin kit fox	trout	salamander
Owens River pupfish		Kern Canyon
		salamander
		Modoc sucker
		Rough sculpin

Less critical than the above, yet of real concern, are unique species like prairie falcon, spotted owl, tule elk, Little Kern golden trout, and redband trout. Certain raptors—golden eagle, hawks, owls—and waterfowl deserve special consideration also.

Forest Recreation

Recreation is the last, but certainly not the least important, of the various forest uses covered in this handbook. As its name implies, recreation means to recreate, revive, divert, amuse, and gratify the human body, mind, and spirit. To fill these needs there is a broad range of recreational opportunities within and near forests. They encompass sight-seeing, resting, picnicking, camping, hiking, photography, bird-watching, trail riding, snow sports, boating, swimming, fishing, hunting, berry-picking, second homes, and studying geology, botany, zoology, archeology, and history.

Parks, forests, and other lands in public ownership provide most of the outdoor recreation, and they contain fairly elaborate facilities to handle the expanding use. Some of these public lands, like parks and wilderness areas, are dedicated to recreational use of one kind or another while others are based on the multiple-use concept. In most cases, timber and range management can be compatible with recreation. Industrial tree farmers are increasingly allowing public use of their lands and some have even provided facilities for that purpose on a free or fee basis. Other forest owners may wish to consider implementing a recreational program, or at least taking steps to conserve aesthetic or recreational values for personal, moral, or social reasons.

Protection of Recreational Resources

Where recreation of one or more kinds is to be integrated into overall property management certain steps are necessary to protect and even improve natural features. The treatments may be necessary only on part of the forest. Some of these entail costs, but this may be at least partially offset by economic returns and pride of accomplishment.

The basic drawing power of wildlands for recreation is the natural landscape and its varying characteristics due to terrain, vegetation, water bodies, topographic features, and cultural past. The impressions are mostly visual, but sound, smell, and touch also play an important part. Visual perception may be broad, sweeping or panoramic vistas or localized on special features of contained settings. The effects may be ephemeral, changing by weather, season, light on water, and animal occupancy. Variety and deviations add to the richness of the landscape. Another main attraction of forests is that in this pleasant setting there is something to do that can be hardly done elsewhere.

How we manage timberlands has a big effect on the visual resource and the potential recreational activities. Some measures that a tree farmer should consider are:

1. Determine where special precautions are justified—along main roads and trails used by the public, at vista points, adjacent to streams and water bodies, around meadows, at known or recognized Indian campsites and other archeological and historical sites, and near habitation, parks, and campgrounds.

2. Cut trees conservatively in high-priority areas, removing dangerous trees and snags that may be a liability or safety hazard. Where clearcuts are made in areas visible to forest users keep them small, irregular in shape, and well spaced.

3. Make special cuttings to improve vistas along main roads, trails, and places where people congregate.
4. Cut trees and vegetation near road curves to open the view and in the interest of safety.
5. Carefully harvest the important areas to avoid unnecessary damage to residual trees, other vegetation, soil, and valuable features.
6. Abate slash hazards and clean up debris in high-use areas by crushing, chipping, or careful burning. Fuelbreaks along main roads will reduce fire risk and hazard and facilitate control of wildfires. Control public access to active logging and hazardous fire areas.
7. Adopt and post rules about public use, road and trail travel, trail bikes, snowmobiles, fire prevention, property and resource damage, firearms, and sanitation.
8. Protect and enhance fish and wildlife habitat as explained earlier in this chapter.
9. Widen roads near streams and other key places to provide parking for recreationists and people wanting to fish or hunt.

Recreation Programs

Besides protection of recreational resources, forest owners may wish to adopt public use programs. The minimum that could be done is to open the forest to free use for sight-seeing by road or trail, fishing, hunting, berry-picking, and unimproved picnicking or camping. To control these activities some landowners post informational signs or require permits subject to regulations. Use without some logical controls is not advisable, because continual free access may give prescriptive rights to the public, meaning that the owner would have difficulty in keeping people off the property once that right had been established.

In situations where recreational values and use are high, tree farmers may choose to implement more intensive recreation programs. These involve considerable expenditures, management time, and risk so charges would be in order. There are a number of different projects that one could undertake. All of them require special knowledge, skill, and experience to put into effect and to stay within resource and legal requirements.

One paying recreational program that may not require too much investment or expenditures is the use of the property for hunting. The acreage has to be productive and substantial enough to support wildlife in sufficient numbers to attract hunters. The size of area needed varies by species and the habitat that is available.

Two methods are used to charge for the service. One is to collect a daily fee per hunter, and the other is to lease exclusive access or hunting rights on the property to a club. The latter method is common for large properties, especially for the hunting of game species, e.g., deer and quail. All kinds of arrangements are possible to accommodate unattached hunters, e.g., rustic campgrounds, simple cabins, and more elaborate facilities where food and lodging services are provided by the owner or a concessionaire. Clubs may provide their own facilities under the hunting lease.

It is a good idea to have a wildlife improvement and management plan where intensive hunting will take place. To initiate such a program, one should have the property examined by a qualified biologist. Game managers of the Department of Fish and Game are helpful in making such assessments, and the services of private wildlife consultants are likewise available on a fee basis. These experts can estimate existing wildlife populations, appraise the habitat, and recommend positive steps to improve the property for hunting.

Sporting activities similar to hunting may be possible with respect to fishing. Here it may be just charging a modest fee to allow a person to cross the property to get to native fishing waters. Fish ponds are another possibility, but this would require technical assistance and capital expenditures. See Water Utilization section in this chapter for state regulations on dams.

The biggest recreational use of forest property is for outings that involve diverse activities. Forests along highways are especially adaptable for picnicking areas and campgrounds. Places near streams, lakes, or other natural features are most popular. In addition to accessibility and location, the more important factors are water, sanitation, and space.

As the public recreational agencies have learned after many years of experience, the development and operation of campgrounds take careful planning and administration. Facilities have to be installed to accommodate the camper—camp roads and trails, signs, parking, camp sites, fireplaces, tables, water systems, garbage disposal, and sanitation. The last three are regulated by law, usually by the county health department. The development and maintenance costs can be considerable so the whole operation should be well planned to avoid costly mistakes and pitfalls. Fortunately, standard designs and specifications have been formulated through the years and these are available at least for inspection at National Forests, State Forests, National Parks, State Parks, and similar agencies. Visits to nearby campgrounds also would reveal much information of value.

How to charge for use of developed recreation areas is another matter to investigate. Two general methods are employed—manual and mechanical. The former is handled by a person collecting fees at an entrance gate or doing daily patrols. A cheaper and more flexible way is by self-registration. The camper obtains a combination registration form and envelope from a central point, fills in the necessary information, and deposits it with the fee into a strong-box. Part of the registration form is posted at the chosen campsite.

Mechanical collections can be made by coin-operated gates, ticket-vending machines, or parking meters. The first two require electricity. Mechanical systems are not foolproof, they require maintenance and repair and are subject to vandalism.

Precautionary Measures

In addition to the many considerations explained above, there are a number of other important points that a forest owner should fully realize when embarking upon a recreation program, especially one of intensive character. The exposure to liability is definitely increased. This requires keeping the property and facilities in a safe condition. Felling or pruning of unsafe trees within campgrounds is a good practice. Insurance coverage should be sought to supplement prevention measures.

An income-producing recreation program affects the owner's property taxes. As described in Chapter IV, commercial timber is ordinarily covered by the yield tax law, but another use, such as recreation, will increase the basic land tax. The effect of this added cost has to be recognized in making decisions on recreational developments.

As any other use, recreation can have an impact on forest and associated values. Overuse compacts soils, causes erosion, destroys vegetation, reduces wildlife, deteriorates beauty, and pollutes waters. The cutting of firewood around campgrounds can be harmful unless regulated. Therefore, recreation has to be managed in a way that the environment is not adversely affected. Some forms of recreation in the forest, such as motorcycle and jeep travel, have to be rigidly controlled. An ever-present danger is wildfire, so slash and other hazards in or near public areas must be abated, campfires contained by stoves and fireplaces, and rules adopted on fire use and smoking.

Forests can continue to be the most important force in outdoor recreation, providing many and varied opportunities for a vast number of people, as well as providing other goods and services. It is all a question of balancing the multiple uses that forests offer so that no values are seriously impaired. As repeatedly stated in this handbook, this takes good planning and management.

A P P E N D I X

PAGE

Terminology in Forestry 161

Various Conversion Tables 174

Basal Area Table 179

Various Volume Tables 180

Various Site Curves and Yield Tables 214

Log Rules (board and cubic feet) 224

List of Tables in Handbook 229

Some Practical References 232

Terminology in Forestry*

Advance Growth. (or Reproduction). Young trees that have become established naturally before harvests are made.

Adventitious Bud. One that develops on any part of a stem, leaf, or root outside the usual order of time or position, and lacks vascular connection to the pith.

Afforestation. Establishment of a tree crop on an area from which it has always or very long been absent. See also Forestation and Reforestation.

Age Class. One of the intervals, commonly 10 years, into which the age range of trees (and sometimes other vegetation) is divided for classification or use.

All-Aged. Of a forest, crop, or stand that contains trees of all or most age classes. Also called Uneven-Aged. See also Even-Aged.

Allowable Cut. Amount of forest produce that may be harvested, annually or periodically, from a specified area over a stated period, in accordance with the objects of management.

Aneroid. Portable barometer used in the field to determine differences in ground elevation.

Animal Unit Month. Amount of feed necessary to maintain one mature cow (or five sheep) properly for 30 days.

Annual (Growth) Ring. Growth layer of wood produced in one year.

Aquifer. A deep rock or geological horizon holding water or permitting its passage.

Area Ignition. Simultaneous or quick successive firing of all parts of an area to be burned in order to produce a fast, hot spread, and clean burn. See also Controlled Burning and Prescribed Burning.

Aspect. Direction or exposure of terrain towards which a slope faces.

Azimuth. The horizontal angle or bearing of a point, measured clockwise from true north. The azimuth plus 180 degrees is termed the back azimuth.

Back Cut. In felling, the cut made on the backside of the tree, after, and a few inches higher than the front undercut.

Backfire. Fire set along the inner edge of a control line to consume the fuel in the path of a wildfire, or change the direction of the fire's convection column.

Backpack Pump. A portable sprayer with hand-pump fed from a tank fitted with backpack straps, used in fire control and pesticide applications.

Barber's Chair. High slab-like splinters, resembling a chair-back, left standing on a stump above the undercut as a result of faulty felling or heavy lean of a tree.

Bare-Root Stock. Planting stock with naked roots. See also Container Stock.

Bark Gauge. Instrument for measuring the bark thickness of live trees in making growth studies.

Barron Tool. Long-handled combination hoe and rake used in building fire line in light fuels. See also McLeod Tool and Pulaski Tool.

Basal Area. Cross-sectional area of a tree stem, including bark, generally at breast height.

Bench Mark. Marked point on the ground whose elevation has been determined and officially recorded.

Biltmore Stick. Graduated stick used to measure tree diameters. See also Cruiser Stick.

---

* Adapted from Terminology of Forest Science, Technology, Practice and Products, Society of American Foresters, 1971 (amended 1977) and other various sources.

Block.   (1) a pulley used in cable logging, (2) a forest management unit or logging area (see also Compartment and Working Circle).

Blue-Stain.   Common form of fungal stain of sapwood and light-colored wood of improperly stored logs and lumber, principally the pines.

Board Foot.   Nominally (not exactly) a board 1 in. x 12 in. x 1 ft., or equivalent, used in measuring logs and lumber.

Bole.   Trunk of a tree past the pole stage.

Bolt.   Short piece of round or split wood cut for fuelwood, shakes, shingles, veneer, etc. Also called billet or block.

Borrow Pit.   An excavation away from the construction site to provide road material.

Broadcast.   (1) Burning—controlled fire over an entire designated area, (2) Seeding—sowing seed more or less evenly over a whole area.

Broadleaved.   Trees or shrubs of a botanical group, usually having conventional leaves, in contrast to needle-leaved, cone-bearing trees (Conifers). Broadleaved trees are also called Hardwoods.

Buck.   To saw felled trees into shorter lengths.

Burl.   Protuberance of abnormal growth on a tree trunk composed of a mass of buds, some of which may sprout, particularly the coast redwood.

Butt.   Base of a tree, or larger end of a log.

Butt Rigging.   Various combinations of swivels, shackles, links, or straps to permit connections between cable lines or logging chokers.

Cambium.   Layer of cells just beneath the bark of woody plants from which new wood and bark cells develop.

Canker.   Definite, relatively localized necrotic gall with lesion, primarily of the bark and cambium of trees and shrubs caused by pests. See also Gall.

Canopy.   More or less continuous cover of branches and foliage formed collectively by the crowns of adjacent trees or other woody growth.

Cant Hook.   Stout wooden lever, fitted with a gripping lip at the end and a hinged hook, used in turning logs and cants. See also Peavey.

Carrying Capacity.   Maximum stocking of animals on a given range or wildlife area without diminishing the forage crop in either amount or quality, or the value of related resources. The same concept can be applied to recreation use.

Catface.   Defect on the surface of a tree or log resulting from a fire or other wound where healing has not re-established the normal cross section. See also Fire Scar and Goosepin.

Cellulose.   Carbohydrate that is the principal constituent of wood and forms the framework of cells.

Chain.   Length measure used in land surveying divided into 100 links, and equal to 66 feet.

Check.   Lengthwise separation of wood, which usually extends across annual rings, commonly resulting from drying stresses.

Cheese Block.   Wedge-shaped moveable wedge-block set on a bunk of a truck or railroad car to hold logs in place. Also called chock.

Choker.   A noose of wire rope by which a log is pulled or lifted in yarding.

Clearcutting.   Removal of the entire standing tree crop, sometimes done in patches.

Climax.   Culminating stage in plant succession for a given environment, the vegetation being conceived as having reached a highly stable condition. See also Succession.

Clinometer.   Simple instrument for measuring angles of elevation or depression. See also Hypsometer.

Codominant.   One main crown class of trees with their tops in the upper canopy but lower than the dominant trees. See also Dominant, Intermediate, and Suppressed.

Cold-Trail.   To build a Fire Line right along the edge of a wildfire when it is burning slowly or very little, taking advantage of favorable burning conditions.

Compartment.   Unit of a forest designated as a basis for management, commonly a subdivision of a Block or Working Circle in a large forest.

Compression Wood.   Abnormally dense wood that often forms on the lower side of branches and of leaning trunks of conifers.

Conifer.   Tree that bears cones and in most cases have needle or scale-like leaves. Also collectively called Softwoods. See also Broadleaved and Hardwoods.

Conk.   Projecting fruit-body of a wood-destroying fungus.

Container Stock.   Young trees grown in pots, tubes, or other receptacles. See also Bare-Root Stock.

Controlled Burning.   Planned application of fire to natural fuels, including brush and slash, with intent to confine it to a predetermined area. See also Area Ignition, Light Burning, and Prescribed Burning.

Coppice Forest.   Forest originating from sprouts or root suckers.

Cord.   Measure of pulpwood, roundwood, or fuelwood representing a stack 4 ft. x 4 ft. x 8 ft. or 128 cubic ft. See also Tier.

Crook.   Defect in logs, poles, or piling, consisting of an abrupt curvature. See also Sweep.

Crown.   Upper part of a tree or other woody plant, carrying the main branch system and foliage.

Crown Fire.   Intense forest fire burning and spreading in the crown of trees.

Cruise.   Survey to determine the kind, quantity, and quality of timber on an area, commonly including the collection of topographic, logging, and other pertinent data.

Cruiser Stick.   Graduated stick to measure diameter and heights of trees and to occasionally scale logs. See also Biltmore Stick, and Scale.

Cull.   1) Trees, logs, or lumber of merchantable size rejected because of defect(s), 2) Deduction from gross volume of trees or logs to adjust for defect(s).

Cunit.   Measure of solid wood content equal to 100 cu. ft.

Cutting Cycle.   Planned, recurring lapse of time between successive cuttings under the selection system, normally a stated proportion of the rotation age.

Damping Off.   Rotting of seedlings, before or soon after emergence, by soil fungi attacking at ground level.

Deciduous.   Of perennial plants that are normally leafless for some time of the year.

Decay.   Decomposition of wood by fungi and other micro-organisms, resulting in softening, progressive loss of strength and weight, and often changes of texture and color. Also called dote or rot.

Deck.   Pile or stack of logs; if stored they form a cold deck, otherwise a (hot) deck.

Defect.   Any irregularity or imperfection in a tree, log, or wood product that reduces the soundness, durability, strength, or utility.

Deflection. Amount of sag in a cable used in cable logging; the greater the deflection the greater the load the cable can support. See also Skyline.

Degrade. Any process that lowers the value of timber and forest products.

Density. 1) Weight per unit volume, 2) Number of stocking of trees (stand) or animals per unit area at a given time. See also Stocking.

Diameter Breast High (DBH). Point at which diameters of trees are usually measured, 4½ ft. above the average ground level.

Diameter Class. Any of the intervals (usually two-inch) into which a range of diameters of trees or logs may be divided for classification and use.

Diameter Limit. Smallest, and occasionally the largest, size to which trees or logs are to be cut, measured, or used.

Diameter Tape. Tape measure specially graduated so that the diameter may be read directly when the tape is placed around a tree or log.

Dieback. Progressive dying from the end of any part of a plant.

Dioecious. Having male and female flowers on different plants. See also Monoecious.

Dominant. One main crown class of trees with their tops in the uppermost layers of the canopy. See also Codominant, Intermediate and Suppressed.

Donkey. Portable power unit (originally a steam engine), usually mounted on skids, and equipped with winch drums and cables, used in skidding and loading logs.

Durability. Capacity of wood to last in service, with particular reference to decay.

Ecology. Study of plants and animals in relation to their environment.

Elite Tree. One that has been shown by testing to be capable of producing progeny with superior qualities. See also Plus Tree and Tree Seed Orchard.

Environment. All the living organisms and related factors of a site.

Epidemic. Of populations of living things, e.g., pests, that build up, often rapidly, to highly abnormal and generally injurious levels, in contrast to endemic or normal populations.

Evapo-Transpiration. Conversion of water by plants into vapor that is released to the atmosphere. See also Interception and Transpiration.

Even-Aged. Of a forest composed of no, or relatively small, differences in age. See also All-Aged and Uneven-Aged.

Faller. A person who fells trees, also called chopper in California redwood region.

Field (Moisture) Capacity. Water that a soil in place retains, when drainage has become negligible. See also Wilting Point.

Financial Rotation. A rotation age of a forest determined solely by financial considerations. See also Rotation Age.

Firebreak. Any natural or constructed barrier utilized to segregate, stop and control the spread of fire, or to provide a control line from which to work. See also Fire Line and Fuelbreak.

Fire Hazard. Fuel complex, defined by volume, type, condition, arrangement, and location, that determines the degree of both of ease of ignition and of fire suppression difficulty. See also Fire Risk.

Fire Line. Control line from which flammable materials have been removed by cutting, scraping, or digging down to mineral soil. Also called fire trail. See also Cold-Trail and Firebreak.

Fire Retardant. Any substance that by chemical or physical action reduces flammability of forest fuels, usually added to water.

Fire Risk. Chance of a fire starting, as affected by nature and incidence of causative agencies, e.g., travellers, lightning. See also Fire Hazard.

Fire Scar. A fresh or healing injury of the cambium of a woody plant, caused by fire. See also Catface and Goosepin.

Forb. Any herbaceous plant that is neither a grass nor at all like one. See also Herb.

Forest. Plant community predominantly of trees and other woody vegetation, growing more or less close together.

Forestation. Establishment of a forest, naturally or artificially, on an area, whether previously carrying a forest or not. See also Afforestation and Reforestation.

Forest Management. Practical application of economic, scientific, and social principles to the administration and working of a forest.

Forestry. Science, art, and practice of managing and using for human benefit the natural resources that occur on and in association with forest lands.

Forest Type. Category of forest defined by its vegetation, particularly its species composition. See also Type Map.

Form Class (Factor, Quotient). Any of the intervals into which a numerical expression of the taper of a tree or log may be divided for classification or use. See also Taper.

Forty. Land subdivision unit nominally a 40-acre square.

Frass. Waste of insect feeding in wood.

Froe. Long wedge-shaped blade for splitting wood into shingles, shakes, and other split products.

Fuelbreak. Strip from which forest fuels and woody vegetation have been reduced by thinning, pruning, or removal well ahead of time to slow down or stop a wildfire, or to provide a control line from which to work. See also Firebreak.

Fuel Moisture Stick. Special wooden stick of known dry weight that is used to determine changes in moisture content and flammability of forest fuels.

Gall. Pronounced excrescence of greatly modified tissued structure in plants caused by insects or other organisms. See also Canker.

Gill Poke. Originally a horizontal stiff-arm or swinging boom used to poke logs off railroad cars at a log pond; also a tree run over and damaged during skidding usually leaning and thereby being a fire and safety hazard.

Gin Pole. Simple hoisting and loading device, consisting of a block and tackle suspended from near the top of a single pole or mast.

Goosepin. Large hollow at base of tree, particularly in old-growth redwoods, caused by fire and rot, so named because pioneers used such trees and stumps for pens for geese, and other domestic animals.

Grapple. Powered mechanical arms on a tractor, the skidding device, or loading machine to bunch and hold logs during transport or movement.

Growing Stock. All the trees growing in a forest or in a specified part of it, generally expressed in terms of number or volume. See also Normal Growing Stock.

Gun (ning) Stick. A hinged two-legged device inserted into an undercut of a large tree (e.g., old growth redwood) to point direction of fall.

Gy (p) po. Contractor who fells or yards timber on a piece-rate basis.

Habitat. Abode, natural or otherwise, of a plant or animal considered particularly in relation to nutrient supplies and other environmental factors affecting it.

Hardening Off. Preparing seedlings or rooted cutting in a nursery for transplanting or planting out by gradually reducing water, shade, and shelter, and thus making them more resistant to dessication and temperature changes.

Hardwood. See Broadleaved.

Haul-Back (Line). Cable, lighter than associated cables, that travels between the power unit and a block near the logs being transported, to return the main line and chokers for the next load (turn).

Heartwood. Inner layers of wood which have ceased to contain living cells and in which the reserve materials have been removed or converted into more durable substances. See also Sapwood.

Heel-In. To store young plants before transplanting or planting out, by burying the roots in a trench.

Height Class. Any of the intervals (in feet or number of logs) into which tree heights may be divided for classification or use.

Herb. Any seed-producing plant that does not develop persistent woody tissue above the ground, including both forbs and grases. See also Forb.

High-Lead (Cable) Logging. Method of powered cable logging in which the main block is fastened high on a spar tree (or equivalent) to enable the front end of the logs being skidded to be lifted clear of the ground.

Herbicide. Any chemical or other preparation used to control unwanted vegetation. Also called phytocide, silvicide. See also Pesticide.

Hook Tender. Foreman of a skidding or yarding crew.

Humus. More or less decomposed (plant and animal) residues in the soil, duff and litter excluded.

Hypsometer. Any instrument for measuring the heights of standing trees. See also Clinometer.

Increment. Increase during stated period of time in girth, diameter, basal area, area, height, volume, quality, biomass, or value of individual trees or stands.

Increment Borer. Auger-like instrument with hollow bit and an extractor, used mainly to extract a thin radial cylinder of wood from trees having annual growth rings, so as to determine increment and age; but also, in wood preservation, the depth of penetration of the preservative.

Indicator Plant. Any plant that, by its presence, frequency, or vigor, indicates any particular property of the site.

Interception. That part of the precipitation that, in the course of contact with the vegetation, evaporates and so never reaches the ground. See also Evapo- Transpiration and Transpiration.

Intermediate (Crown Class). One main crown class of trees with their tops in the middle canopy. See also Dominant, Codominant, and Suppressed.

Intolerance. Incapacity of a tree to develop and grow in the shade of and in competition with other trees. See also Tolerance.

Jammer. Light-weight, two-drum winch with a wooden spar, generally mounted on a vehicle, which is used for both skidding and loading.

Kerf. Narrow slot cut by a saw in advancing through wood.

Landing. Any place where round timber is assembled for further transport, usually in the woods.

Larva. Early immature form of insect between the egg and adult stage. See also Pupa.

Leave Tree. Tree (usually designated to be) left standing in an area where it would otherwise be felled. Also called residual tree.

Light Burning. Periodic broadcast burning to prevent accumulation of hazardous forest fuels. See also Controlled Burning and Prescribed Burning.

Lignin. Non-carbohydrate, structural constituent of wood and some other plant tissues, which encrusts the cell walls and cements the cells together.

Limb. To sever branches from logs or a felled tree. See also Lop.

Log. Any useable section of the bole, or of the thicker branches, of a felled tree, after limbing and cross-cutting, e.g., a sawlog. Also to harvest timber. See also Peeler (Log) and Sawlog.

Logging. Felling and harvesting of timber, particularly as logs.

Logging Arch. Stout, arched, steel frame mounted on wheels or tracks, for use with a tractor in skidding, one end of the log(s) being slung beneath the arch.

Log Rules. Tables showing the estimated or calculated amount of board feet in logs of given diameter and length. See also Scale.

Long Butt. A section of the lower end of a felled tree, cut off to remove and discard cull material.

Lop. To sever, and sometimes scatter, branches from a felled tree, so that the resulting slash will lie close to the ground. See also Limb.

Magnetic Declination. Angle between true and magnetic north at any point.

Management (or Working) Plan. Written document aiming at continuity of policy and action, and both prescribing and controlling basic operations in a forest over a period of years.

Marking Timber. Act of selecting and designating trees to be cut or left for harvesting, usually done by blaze or paint spray.

Mast. Fruit of oak and other trees, particularly where considered food for wildlife and livestock.

McLeod Tool. Short-handled combination hoe, or cutting tool and rake, with or without removable blades, used in building fire line. See also Barron Tool and Pulaski Tool.

Mensuration. That branch of forestry concerned with the determination of the dimensions, form, increment, and age of trees, individually or collectively, and of their products.

Milacre. An area of one thousandth of an acre (6.6 ft. x 6.6 ft.) commonly used in vegetation and regeneration studies. See also Quadrat.

Molly Hogan. Circle of a twisted strand of wire rope used for temporary linking of eyesplices of cable, especially Straw Line or accessory equipment. Also called molle.

Monoecious. Having male and female flowers on the same plant. See also Dioecious.

Mopping Up. Making a fire safe after it has been controlled, especially concentrating the work near control lines.

Mortality. The loss to a population of trees, other plants, and animals from all lethal causes.

Multiple Use. Management practice to wisely use without impairment, two or more resources associated with forest and related lands.

Normal Growing Stock. Growing stock found in an ideal forest, its attributes including optimum stocking, volume, and yield relative to objects of management. See also Growing Stock.

Overrun. The excess of the amount of a conversion process (e.g., lumber sawing) over the estimated volume or log scale, usually expressed as a percentage. See also Underrun.

Peavey. Stout wooden lever, fitted with a spike at the end, and a hinged hook, used in handling and turning logs. See also Cant Hook.

Peeler (Log). Log considered suitable in size and quality for producing rotary-cut veneer. Also called veneer log.

Pesticide. Any chemical or other preparation used to control populations of injurious organisms, particularly animal. Also insecticide, rodenticide, etc. See also Herbicide.

Phreatophyte. Plant, usually riparian, that uses large amounts of water from underground, or nearby water bodies, and is more or less independent of precipitation.

Pitch (Resin) Pocket. Well-defined, lens-shaped opening between or within annual rings of conifer wood, usually containing pitch, either solid or liquid, and occasionally bark.

Piling. Collective term for piles—long, round timbers that are driven deep into the ground to support structures.

Piling and Burning. Piling logging slash by hand or machine and subsequently burning the individual piles.

Pith. Soft central core of the stem and some roots of trees and other plants.

Plantation. Forest crop or stand raised artificially, usually by planting.

Planting Stock. Seedlings, transplants, cuttings, and occasionally wild plants (wildings) for use in planting.

Plus Tree. Tree judged, but not tested, to be unusually superior in genetic qualities. See also Elite Tree and Tree Seed Orchard.

Point Sampling. Forest sampling by variable sized plots, using prisms or other optical devices. Also called prism sampling.

Pole. 1) Young tree from 4 to 12 inches in diameter breast height, 2) Round timber of stated length ready for use without conversion (except peeling and preservation) for utility lines or construction.

Post. Round, split, or sawn length of timber used for fencing, pillars, and in construction.

Prescribed Burning. Controlled application of fire to wildland fuels, in either their natural or modified state, under such conditions of weather, fuel moisture, soil moisture, etc., as to allow the fire to be confined to a predetermined area and at the same time to produce results to meet planned objectives of management. See also Area Ignition, Controlled Burning, and Light Burning.

Pruning, Artificial. Considered removal, close to or flush with the stem, of side branches, live or dead, and of multiple leaders, from a standing tree for improvement of the tree or its products.

Psychrometer. Instrument consisting of two thermometers, one with a dry bulb and the other with a wet bulb, used to determine relative humidity.

Pulaski Tool. Combination axe and adz-like hoe used in fire line construction. See also Barron Tool and McLeod Tool.

Pulpwood. Cordwood or logs prepared primarily for manufacture into paper, fibreboard, or other wood pulp products.

Pupa. Advanced, but yet immature, generally immobile, insect stage between larva and adult. See also Larva.

Quadrat. Small, clearly demarcated, sample area of known size on which forestry and ecological observations are made. See also Milacre.

Quarter Corner. Land subdivision corner for a quarter of a section (160-acre unit) other than a section corner or the section center.

Range Management. Art and science of planning and directing the utilization of grazing land so as to secure sustained maximum production of livestock and forage, consistent with other uses and conserving natural resources.

Reforestation. Re-establishment of a tree crop on forest land. See also Afforestation and Forestation.

Regeneration. Renewal of a tree crop, whether by natural or artificial means, also the young crop itself.

Regulation. Manipulation of the Growing Stock so that it contains a proper proportion of young, middle-aged, and mature trees in order to obtain continuous production, or sustained yield.

Release. Freeing a tree or group of trees from immediate competition by cutting, or otherwise eliminating, growth that is overtopping or closely surrounding them.

Rigging. Cable, guy lines, blocks, and hooking equipment used for hauling and loading (logs).

Rotation (Age). Planned number of years between the formation or regeneration of a tree crop or stand and its final cutting at a specified stage of maturity. See also Financial Rotation.

Sapwood. Outer layers of wood which, in the growing tree, contain living cells and reserve materials, and generally lighter in color than Heartwood.

Sawlog. Log considered suitable in size and quality for producing sawn timber or lumber. See also Log and Peeler (Log).

Scale. To measure cut timber and fuelwood, usually with a graduated (scale) stick, the contents of cut timber in terms of the log rule or measuring unit. See also Log Rules.

Schoolmarm. Coniferous tree with a forked or double trunk.

Second Growth. Loose term for young trees, left or grown since the first harvest. See also Young Growth.

Section. Standard subdivision of land used in official surveys, intended to be one mile square.

Seed-Tree Cutting. Removal in one cut of the mature timber from an area, save for a small number of seed-bearing trees left singly or in small groups.

Selection Cutting. Periodic removal of crop-sized trees, individually or in small groups, usually from an uneven-aged forest. Also called selective cutting.

Shake. 1) Lengthwise separation of wood, usually between and parallel to annual rings. 2) Thin section split from a Bolt used for roofing.

Shelterwood Cutting. Even-aged silvicultural system in which, in order to provide a source of seed and/or protection for regeneration, the old crop is removed in two or more successive stages.

Silvics. Study of the life history and general characteristics of forest trees and stands. See below.

Silviculture. Science and art of growing and tending forest crops, based on a knowledge of Silvics.

Sinker. Log heavier than water.

Site. Productive capacity of an area to produce forests or other vegetation, related to climatic, biotic, and soil factors. For forest crops, it is expressed by a site index based on height of dominant trees in a stand at a certain age. Site indices are sometimes grouped into site classes.

Skidding. Loose term for hauling logs as developed originally from stump to a landing or roadside. Also called Yarding.

Skyline (Cable) Logging. Loose term for powered cable logging where the log is partly or wholly suspended in the air. See also Deflection.

Slash. Residue of trees left on the ground after logging, fire, or storm.

Snag. Standing dead tree or section thereof.

Softwoods. Pertaining to conifer trees. See also Broadleaved and Hardwoods.

Soil Horizon. Any layer of soil that may be distinguished from adjacent layers because it differs in physical, chemical, or biological characteristics, usually designated as A, B, and C horizons.

Soil Series. Basic unit of soil classification, consisting of soils that are alike in all major profile characteristics save texture of the surface layer, and having similar horizons. See also above.

Spar (-Tree). Tall standing tree, trimmed and topped, and generally braced with guy lines, near whose top cables and other rigging are hung in cable logging or loading. See also Tail Tree.

Spot Fire. Fire set outside of perimeter of main fire by flying sparks or embers.

Springboard. Short board or plank, its end (usually equipped with a metal lip) that is notched into the trunk, on which the faller stands when necessary to work at a level not reachable from the ground. Other boards termed staging are sometimes placed on springboards to build a working platform partly around large trees.

Springwood. More or less open and porous tissue marking the inner part of each annual ring, formed early in the growing season. See also Summerwood.

Spud. Hand tool for barking or peeling round timber.

Stand. 1) Community of trees possessing sufficient uniformity in composition, structure, age, arrangement, or condition to be distinguishable from adjacent forest communities to form a silvicultural or management unit. 2) Amount of timber on an area, generally expressed in volume per area.

Stand Table. Summary table showing Stocking or number of trees by species and diameter class for a given area.

Stem Analysis. Analysis of a complete tree (felled) stem by counting and measuring the annual growth rings on a series of cross sections taken in different heights, in order to determine its past rates of growth.

Stereo(scopic) Pair. Two aerial photographs with sufficient overlap and consequent duplication of detail, to make possible stereoscopic (three dimensional) examination of an object, or an area, common to both.

Stocking. Loose term for an amount of anything on a given area, particularly in relation to what is considered the optimum, used in forest, range, and wildlife management. See also Density (2).

Strap. Short length of cable with an eye spliced at each end for attaching blocks and other rigging to trees, stumps, etc.

Straw Line. Light wire rope used for moving logging cable and accessory equipment into positions.

Stumpage. 1) Standing timber itself or volume thereof. 2) Value of standing timber in terms of amount per unit (e.g., thousand bd. ft.).

Stump Scaling. Measurement of stump diameters to estimate volume of removed trees by using special or adjusted volume tables, frequently in case of timber trespass or cutting of unauthorized trees.

Succession. Gradual supplanting of one community of plants by another as the site changes with time. See also Climax.

Summerwood. Dense, fibrous outer portion of each annual ring, usually without conspicuous pores, formed late in the growing period, not necessarily in the summer. See also Springwood.

Suppressed (Crown Class). One main crown class of trees with their tops in the lower canopy, beneath the Dominant, Codominant, and Intermediate trees, and of poor vigor.

Sustained Yield. Yield that a forest can produce continuously at a given intensity of management, planned to achieve at the earliest practical time a balance between growth and cutting.

Sweep. Gradual bend in a tree, log, pole, or piling, considered as a defect. See also Crook.

Tail Tree. Spar Tree at outer end of a cable logging operation.

Tally Counter (or Whacker). Any device for recording numbers mechanically, e.g., in pacing or timber cruising.

Taper. Decrease in thickness, generally in terms of diameter, of a tree stem or log from the base upward. See also Form Class.

Thinning. Felling made in an immature crop or stand in order primarily to accelerate diameter increment but also, by suitable selection, to improve the average form of trees that remain, classically without permanently breaking the canopy.

Tier. Stack of fuelwood, pulpwood, or other material of a width equal to the length of the pieces, 4 ft. high x 8 ft. long. Also called rick. See also Cord.

Tight-Lining. Procedure in cable logging whereby the cables are tightened so as to 1) lift the load of logs as it is being yarded, such as in a running skyline system, or 2) move cable laterally from one location to an adjacent one after merely changing the location of the tail-block.

Timber. Broad term for standing trees, and certain products thereof.

Timber Stand Improvement (TSI). Loose term for thinning, pruning, and weeding a timber stand to improve the composition, structure, condition, and growth.

Tolerance. Capacity of a tree to develop and grow in the shade of and in competition with other trees. See also Intolerance.

Transpiration. Process by which water vapor passes from foliage of other parts of a living plant to the atmosphere. See also Interception and Evapo-Transpiration.

Transplant. Seedling after it has been lifted and replanted one or more times to another bed in a nursery.

Tree. Woody perennial plant, typically large and with a single well-defined stem carrying a more or less definite crown.

Tree Farm. Area, privately owned, dedicated by the owner to the production of timber crops.

Tree Seed Orchard. Plantation of trees, assumed or proven genetically to be superior, that is intensively protected and managed to improve the genetic quality of seed crops, and to obtain frequent, abundant, and easily harvestable seed. See also Elite Tree and Plus Tree.

Type Map. Map showing the distribution of various types of trees, other vegetation, soil, or site throughout a forest area. See also Forest Type.

Undercut.   Deep notch cut into the base of a tree to govern the direction in which it is to fall and also to prevent butt splitting. See also Back Cut.

Underrun.   Amount by which the conversion of logs into other products (e.g., lumber) is less than the estimated volume or log scale, usually expressed as a percentage. See also Overrun.

Uneven-Aged.   Of a forest, crop, or stand, composed of intermingling trees that differ markedly in age. Also called All-aged. See also Even-aged.

Virgin Forest.   Natural forest virtually uninfluenced by human activity, such as cutting. Also called old-growth forest.

Volume Table.   Table showing, for one or more species, the average volume of trees of given sizes in a specified unit.

Weed Tree.   Any tree, or tree species, of little or no economic value, more particularly when menacing more desirable timber trees. See also Wolf Tree.

Widow-Maker.   Loose limb or piece of tree hanging in the crown of a tree that is dangerous to woods workers.

Wilderness.   Undeveloped, uninhabited area established by a government in order to conserve its primeval character and influence for public enjoyment, under primitive conditions, in perpetuity.

Wildland.   Uncultivated land, other than fallow, neglected or maintained for such purposes as wood or range-forage production, wildlife, recreation, protective watershed cover, wilderness.

Wildlife Management.   Practical application of scientific and technical principles to wildlife populations and habitats so as to maintain them, essentially for recreational or scientific purposes.

Wildling.   Naturally grown, in contrast to a nursery-raised seedling, sometimes used in forest planting.

Wilting Point.   Soil moisture content at which plants will wilt beyond recovery. See also Field (Moisture) Capacity.

Windfall.   Tree or trees thrown or their stems or parts broken off by wind. Also called blowdown in the collective sense.

Witches Broom.   Abnormally bushy, local growth of parts of branch systems on woody plants, characterized by short intervals and excessive branching (brooming), generally caused by disease.

Witness Tree.   One of several trees scribed and officially recorded to mark locations of a Section Corner or Quarter Corner. Also called bearing tree.

Wolf Tree.   Vigorous tree generally of bad growth form with a dominantly wide crown, that occupies more growing space than its value warrants, so harming potentially better neighbors.

Working Circle.   Unit of a large forest organized for a particular object and under one set of management plan prescriptions, and embodying one silvicultural system or a designated combination of systems.

Yarding.   Moving timber from stump to a central point or landing by animal or motive power, usually followed by loading into a transport by trucks or other carriers to a conversion plant. Also called Skidding.

Yield Table.   Table showing, usually for one tree species, the growth pattern of a normal or managed even-aged forest, derived from measurements at regular intervals covering its useful life, and including data on site, diameter, height, stocking, and volume.

Young Growth.   Young trees left or grown since the first or subsequent harvest. See also Second-Growth and Virgin Forest.

Table A-1. Length; unit conversion factors, with appropriate values.

Inches	Links	Feet	Yards	Rods	Chains [1]	Miles [2]	Centi-meters	Meters	Kilo-meters
[3] 1	0.126263 (1/8)	0.083333 [1/12]	0.027778 [1/36]	0.00505 (1/200)	---------	---------	2.540005 (2½)	0.0254 (1/40)	---------
7.92	1	0.66 (2/3)	0.22	0.04 [1/25]	0.01 [1/100]	---------	20.11684 (20)	0.201168 (1/5)	---------
12	1.515152 (1½)	[3] 1	0.333333 [1/3]	0.060606 (1/16)	0.015152 [1/66]	0.000189	30.48006 (30)	0.304801 (3/10)	0.000305
36	4.545455 (4½)	3	[3] 1	0.181818 (1/5)	0.045455 (1/22)	0.000568	91.44018	0.914402 (9/10)	0.000914
0.3937 (2/5)	0.04971 (1/20)	0.032808 (1/30)	0.010936 (1/90)	---------	---------	---------	[4] 1	0.01	---------
39.37 (40)	4.97096 (5)	3.280833	1.09361	0.198838 (1/5)	0.04971 (1/20)	0.000621 (1/1600)	100	1	0.001
							Furlongs		
198	25	16.5	5.5	1	0.25 [1/4]	0.003125 [1/320]	0.025 [1/40]	5.02921 (5)	0.005029 (1/200)
792	100	66	22	4	1	0.0125 [1/80]	0.1	20.1168 (20)	0.020117 (1/50)
	---------	5,280	1,760	320	80	1	8	1,609.347 (1,600)	1.609347 (1 3/5)
	---------	660	220	40	10	0.125 [1/8]	1	201.168	0.201168 (1/5)
	---------	3,280.83	1,093.61	198.838 (200)	49.7096 (50)	0.62137 (5/8)	4.97096 (5)	1,000	1

[1] Surveyor's chain; the engineer's chain=100 links of 1 foot each is not used.
[2] 1 nautical mile (termed "knot" as unit of velocity)=1.1516 statute miles=1.85325 km=1 minute of arc on the earth's surface at the Equator.
[3] British units: 1 yard=0.914399 m; 1 foot=30.47997 cm; 1 inch=2.539998 cm; 1 hand=4 inches=10.16 cm; 1 span=9 inches=22.86 cm; 1 cubit=18 inches=45.72 cm.
[4] 1 millimeter=0.1 cm=0.03937 inch=0.00328 foot.

U.S.D.A. Misc. Publication No. 225

Table A-2. Area or surface; unit conversion factors, with appropriate values.

Square inches	Square links	Square feet	Square yards	Square chains	Acres	Square centi-meters	Square meters	Hectares	Square kilo-meters
1	0.015942 (1/63)	0.006944	---------	---------	---------	6.451626 (6½)	0.000645	---------	---------
62.7264 (63)	1	0.4356 (3/7)	---------	0.0001	0.00001	404.6873	0.040469 (1/25)	---------	---------
144	2.295684	1	0.111111 [1/9]	0.00023	0.000023	929.034	0.092903 (1/11)	---------	---------
1,296	20.6612 (20)	9	1	0.002066 (1/500)	0.000207	8,361.31	0.836131 (4/5)	---------	---------
0.155 (1/7)	---------	0.001076 (1/1000)	---------	---------	---------	[1] 1	0.0001	---------	---------
1,549.997	24.7104	10.76387 (11)	1.19599 (1 1/5)	0.002471 (1/400)	0.000247	10,000	1	0.0001	---------
						Square miles			
	10,000	4,356	484	[2] 1	0.1	0.000156 [1/6400]	404.687	0.040469 (1/25)	0.000405 (1/2500)
		43,560	4,840	10	[3] 1	0.0015625 [1/640]	4,046.87 (4,000)	0.404687 (2/5)	0.004047 (1/250)
		27,878,400	3,097,600	6,400	640	1	2,589,998	258.9998 (260)	2.589998 (2 3/5)
		107,638.7	11,959.9 (12,000)	24.7104 (25)	2.471044 (2½)	0.003861 (1/250)	10,000	1	0.01
		10,763,867	1,195,985	2,471.04	247.104 (250)	0.386101 (2/5)	1,000,000	100	1

[1] 1 mm^2=0.01 cm^2=0.00155 square inch.
[2] 1 square chain=16 square rods.
[3] 1 acre=area 208.710 (210) feet square=3.16 chains square.

U.S.D.A. Mis. Publication No. 225

Table A-3. Volume and capacity; unit conversion factors and values.

United States measure of volume [1]		United States dry measure, quarts	United States apothecaries' and liquid measure [2]				Metric system		
Cubic inches	Cubic feet		Fluid ounces	Pints	Quarts	Gallons	Cubic centimeters [3]	Liters [4]	Cubic meters (steres)
1	0.000579	0.014881	0.554113 (1/2)	0.034632 (1/30)	0.017316 (1/60)	0.004329	16.3872 (16)	0.016387 (1/60)	----
1,728	[5] 1	25.714 (26)	957.5	59.8442 (60)	29.9221 (30)	7.48052 (7 1/2)	28,317	28.316 (28)	0.028317 (1/35)
1.80469 (1 4/5)	----	----	1	0.0625 [1/16]	0.03125 [1/32]	----	29.5737 (30)	0.029573 (1/34)	----
28.875 (30)	----	0.429684 (2/5)	16	1	0.5 [1/2]	0.125 [1/8]	473.179 (475)	0.473167 (1/2)	----
57.75 (58)	0.033420 (1/30)	0.859367 (5/6)	32	2	1	0.25 [1/4]	946.359 (950)	0.946333 (1)	0.000946
231	0.133681 (1/8)	3.43747	128	8	4	[6] 1	3785.43 (4,000)	3.785332 (4)	0.003785 (1/265)
0.061023 (1/16)	----	0.000908	0.033814 (1/30)	0.002113 (1/1000)	0.001057 (1/1000)	----	[7] 1	0.0010 (1/1000)	0.000001
61.0250 (61)	0.035315	0.908102	33.8147 (34)	2.11342 (2)	1.05671 (1)	0.264178 (1/4)	1,000.027 (1,000)	1	0.001 (1/1000)
			Bushels						
67.200625 (67)	0.038889 (1/25)	1	0.03125 [1/32]	----	1.163647 (1 1/6)	0.290912	1,101.23	1.101198	0.001 (1/1000)
2,150.42	1.24446 (1 1/4)	32	[5] 1	----	37.2367 (37)	9.309177 (9)	35,239.28	35.23833 (35)	0.035239 (1/30)
----	35.3145 (35)	908.078 (910)	28.3774	----	1,056.68 (1,000)	264.170 (265)	1,000,000	999.973 (1,000)	[9] 1

[1] 1 cubic yard = 27 cubic feet = 21.696 bushels = 0.764559 m³ (stere).
[2] 1 gill = 7.21875 cubic inches = 4 fluid ounces = 0.25 [1/4] liquid pint = 0.125 [1/8] liquid quart = 0.03125 [1/32] gallon = 0.118292 liter.
[3] 1 cubic millimeter = 0.001 cm³ = 0.000061 cubic inch.
[4] 1 liter = volume pure water at 4° C. and 760 mm pressure weighing 1 kg = 0.028378 bushel = 0.001308 cubic yard.
[5] 1 cubic foot = 0.80356 bushel = 0.037037 cubic yard.
[6] The British imperial gallon = 10 pounds distilled water at 62° F. (and barometer at 30 inches) = 277.418 cubic inches = 1.20094 U. S. gallons = 0.16054 cubic foot = 4.545963 liters.
[7] 1 cubic centimeter = 0.999973 milliliter (ml).
[8] The British imperial bushel = 8 British gallons = 2219.340 cubic inches = 1.032050 United States bushels = 36.37 liters.
[9] 1 m³ = 1.308 cubic yards.

Table A-4. Weight; unit conversion factors and values.

Grains [1]	Avoirdupois weight [3]			Troy and apothecaries' weight			Metric system		
	Drams	Ounces	Pounds	Drams	Ounces	Pounds	Milli-grams	Grams	Kilo-grams
1	0.03657 (1/27)	0.002286 [1/1000]	0.000145	0.016667 [1/60]	0.002083 (1/500)	0.000174	64.7989 (65)	0.064799 (1/15)	----------
27.34375	1	0.0625 [1/16]	0.003906 (1/250)	0.45573 (1/2)	0.056966	0.004747 (1/210)	----------	1.771845	----------
437.5 (440)	16	[3]1	0.0625 [1/16]	7.292	0.9115	0.075955 (1/13)	----------	28.34953 (28)	----------
7,000	256	16	1	116.667	14.5833 (14 1/2)	1.21528 (1 1/5)	----------	453.592 (450)	0.453592 (1/2)
60	2.19428 (2)	0.137143 (1/7)	0.008571	1	0.125 [1/8]	0.010417 (1/96)	----------	3.887935 (4)	----------
480	17.55429	1.09714 (1)	0.06857 (1/15)	8	1	0.083333 [1/12]	----------	31.10348 (31)	----------
5,760	210.651	13.1657 (13)	0.822857 (4/5)	96	12	1	----------	373.2418 (375)	0.373242 (2/5)
0.015432 (1/65)	0.000564	----------	----------	0.000257	----------	----------	[4]1	0.001	----------
15.43236 (15)	0.564383 (1/2 8)	0.035274 (1/28)	0.002205	0.257206	0.032151 (1/30)	0.002679	1,000	1	0.001
	Hundred-weight			Short tons	Long tons		Milliers, tonnes, or metric tons		
	1	----------	100	0.05 [1/20]	0.045 (1/20)	----------	0.045359 (1/20)	----------	45.3592 (45)
	20	----------	2,000	1	0.89286 (9/10)	----------	0.90718 (9/10)	----------	907.1849 (900)
	22.4	----------	2,240	1.12 (1 1/10)	1	----------	1.01605 (1)	----------	1,016.05 (1,000)
	22.05	----------	2,204.62	1.10231 (1 1/10)	0.984206	----------	[5]1	----------	1,000
15,432.4	0.022046	35.27396 (35)	2.204622 (2 3/5)	0.001102	0.000984	2.679228 (2 1/2)	0.001	1,000	1

[1] The grain is common to avoirdupois, troy, and apothecaries' systems.
[2] British units include 1 hundredweight (long, or one-twentieth long ton)=4 quarters=8 stone=112 pounds=50.8 kg; 1 stone=14 pounds=6.35 kg.
[3] 1 ounce (avoirdupois)=0.001 cubic foot of water at 16.7° C., or 62.06° F.
[4] 1 metric carat=200 mg=3.086471 grains.
[5] 1 tonne=10 quintals=100 myriagrams.

U.S.D.A. Misc. Publication 225 (Tables A-3 and 4)

Table A-5. Velocity; unit conversion factors and values.

Feet per minute	Feet per second	Miles per hour	Knots per hour	Meters per minute	Meters per second	Kilometers per hour
1	0.016667 [1/60]	0.011364 (1/100)	0.009868 (1/100)	0.304801 (3/10)	0.00508 (1/200)	0.018288 (1/60)
60	1	0.681818 (2/3)	0.592086 (3/5)	18.2880 (18)	0.304801 (3/10)	1.0973 (1.1)
88	1.46667 (1 1/2)	1	0.868393 (7/8)	26.8225 (27)	0.447041 (3/10)	1.60935 (1 3/5)
101.337 (100)	1.68894 (1 2/3)	1.15155 (1 1/7)	1	30.8875 (31)	0.514791 (1/2)	1.85325 (1 7/8)
3.28083 (3 1/4)	0.054681 (1/20)	0.037282 (1/27)	0.032376 (1/30)	1	0.016667 [1/60]	0.06 (1/17)
196.850 (200)	3.28083 (3 1/4)	2.23693 (2 1/4)	1.94253 (2)	60	1	3.6
54.6806 (55)	0.911343 (1)	0.621370 (5/8)	0.539593 (1/2)	16.6667 (17)	0.27778 (1/4)	1

Table A-6. Power; unit conversion factors and values.

Foot-pounds per minute	Foot-pounds per second	Watts	Kilogram-meters per second	Force de cheval	Horse-power	Kilowatt
1	0.01667 [1/60]	0.0226 (1/45)	0.0023	----------	----------	----------
60	1	1.35582 (1 1/3)	0.138255	0.00184	0.00182	----------
44.2537 (45)	0.73756 (3/4)	[1] 1	0.101972 (1/10)	0.00136	0.00134	0.001
433.9799 (434)	7.23300	9.80665 (10)	1	0.01335	0.01315	0.0098
32,548.5	542.475	735.499	75	[2] 1	0.98632 (1)	0.7355 (3/4)
33,000	550	745.7 (750)	76.04	1.01387 (1)	1	0.7457 (3/4)
44,253.7 (45,000)	737.56	1,000	101.972 (100)	1.3596 (1 1/3)	1.341 (1 1/3)	1

[1] 1 watt=10⁷ ergs per second=1 joule per second.
[2] 1 force de cheval=1 metric horsepower.

Table A-7. Weight or pressure as applied to area;[1] unit conversion factors and approximate values.

Pounds per square foot	Pounds per square inch	Feet of water column or head [2]	Kilograms per square meter	Grams per square centimeter	Millimeters of mercury column [3]	Atmospheres
1	0.006944 [1/144]	0.016018 (1/60)	4.88241 (5)	0.488241 (1/2)	----------	0.000473
144	[4] 1	2.306645	703.067	70.3067 (70)	51.7134	0.068044 (1/15)
62.4283	0.433530	[5] 1	304.801	30.4801	22.4195 (22 1/2)	0.029499 (3/45)
0.204817 (1/5)	0.001422	0.003281	1	0.1	----------	0.0000968 (1/10000)
2.04817 (2)	0.01422 (1/70)	0.03281	10	1	----------	0.000968
2.784578 (2 3/4)	0.019337 (1/50)	0.044604	[6] 13.59545	1.359545 (1 1/3)	[7] 1	0.001316
2,116.28	14.6964 (14 7/10)	33.8993	10,332.54	1,033.254	760	[8] 1

[1] Pressure unit=1 barye=1 dyne per square centimeter=0.0010197 gram per square centimeter=0.010197 kilogram per square meter=(approximately) 0.000001 atmosphere. 1 megadyne=10⁶ dynes per square centimeter=0.98692 atmosphere.
[2] At 4° C., or 39.2° F.
[3] At 0° C., or 32° F. 1 inch of mercury column=70.728 pounds per square foot=1.13295 feet of water=345.325 kilograms per square meter=25.40005 millimeters of mercury=0.033421 atmosphere.
[4] 1 pound per square inch=0.072 ton per square foot.
[5] 1 foot of water=0.882648 inch of mercury=0.304801 meter of water.
[6] The specific gravity of mercury at 0° C.
[7] 1 millimeter of mercury=0.03937 inch of mercury=0.013595 meter of water.
[8] 1 atmosphere=29.9212 inches of mercury=10.332542 meters of water.

U.S.D.A. Misc. Publication No. 225 (all tables above)

Table A-8. Weight as applied to volume; unit conversion factors and approximate values.

Grains per cubic inch	Pounds per cubic yard	Pounds per bushel	Pounds per cubic foot	Pounds per gallon	Kilograms per cubic meter	Grams per cubic centimeter
1	----------	0.307203	0.246857 (¼)	0.0330 (⅟₃₀)	3.95425 (4)	0.003954 (⅟₂₅₀)
	1	----------	0.037037 [⅟₂₇]	----------	0.593273 (⅗)	0.000593
3.25518 (3¼)	----------	1	0.803564 (⅘)	0.107421 (⅟₁₀)	12.8718 (13)	0.012872
4.05093 (4)	27	1.24446 (1¼)	¹1	0.133681 (⅐)	16.0184 (16)	0.016018 (⅟₆₀)
30.3030 (30)	----------	9.3092 (9⅓)	7.48052 (7½)	²1	119.826 (120)	0.119826 (⅛)
	1.68556 (1⅔)	0.077689	0.062428 (⅟₁₆)	0.008345 (⅟₁₂₀)	1	0.001
252.893 (250)	1,685.56 (1,700)	77.6893 (80)	62.4283 (62½)	8.34545 (8)	1,000	³1

[1] 1 pound per cubic foot = 1.60188 kilograms per hectoliter = 0.0135 ton per cubic yard.
[2] 1 pound per gallon = 0.1198 kilogram per liter.
[3] 1 gram per cubic centimeter = 1 tonne (metric ton) per cubic meter = (approximately) 1 kilogram per liter.

Table A-9. Grade percent and equivalent degree of slope.

Grade (Percent)	Slope in degrees ° ′	Grade (Percent)	Slope in degrees ° ′	Grade (Percent)	Slope in degrees ° ′	Grade (Percent)	Slope in degrees ° ′
1	0 34.4	11	6 16.6	21	11 51.6	55	28 48.6
2	1 8.7	12	6 50.6	22	12 24.4	60	30 57.8
3	1 43.1	13	7 24.4	23	12 57.2	65	33 1.4
4	2 17.4	14	7 58.2	24	13 29.7	70	34 59.5
5	2 51.7	15	8 31.8	25	14 2.2	75	36 52.2
6	3 26.0	16	9 5.4	30	16 42.0	80	38 39.6
7	4 0.3	17	9 38.9	35	19 17.4	85	40 21.9
8	4 34.4	18	10 12.2	40	21 48.1	90	41 59.2
9	5 8.6	19	10 45.5	45	24 13.7	95	43 31.9
10	5 42.6	20	11 18.6	50	26 33.9	100	45 0

[1] Equivalents of customary expressions of grade are as follows:
Grades and slopes: 1 foot per chain = 1.515 percent; 1 foot per mile = 0.018939 percent; 1 millimeter per meter = 0.1 percent; 1 foot per thousand = 0.1 percent; 1-percent grade = 633.6 inches per mile = 52.8 feet per mile = 10 millimeters per meter = 10 feet per thousand feet = 1 foot per 1.515 chains = 0.66 feet per chain.

Table A-10. Degree of slope and equivalent grade percent.

Degree of slope ° ′	Grade Percent	Degree of slope ° ′	Grade Percent	Degree of slope ° ′	Grade Percent	Degree of slope ° ′	Grade Percent
0 30	0.873	5	8.749	9 30	16.734	18	32.492
1	1.746	5 30	9.629	10	17.633	19	34.433
1 30	2.619	6	10.510	11	19.438	20	36.397
2	3.492	6 30	11.394	12	21.256	22 30	41.421
2 30	4.366	7	12.278	13	23.087	25	46.631
3	5.241	7 30	13.165	14	24.933	30	57.735
3 30	6.116	8	14.054	15	26.795	35	70.021
4	6.993	8 30	14.945	16	28.675	40	83.910
4 30	7.870	9	15.838	17	30.573	45	100.0

U.S.D.A. Misc. Publication No. 225 (all tables above)

Table A-11.   Areas of circles (basal area).

Diameter Inches	Area Sq.Ft.	Diameter Inches	Area Sq.Ft.	Diameter Inches	Area Sq.Ft.
1	0.005	21	2.405	41	9.168
2	0.022	22	2.640	42	9.621
3	0.049	23	2.885	43	10.085
4	.087	24	3.142	44	10.559
5	.136	25	3.409	45	11.045
6	.196	26	3.687	46	11.541
7	.267	27	3.976	47	12.048
8	.349	28	4.276	48	12.566
9	.442	29	4.587	49	13.095
10	.545	30	4.909	50	13.635
11	.660	31	5.241	51	14.186
12	.785	32	5.585	52	14.748
13	.922	33	5.940	53	15.321
14	1.069	34	6.305	54	15.904
15	1.227	35	6.681	55	16.499
16	1.396	36	7.069	56	17.104
17	1.576	37	7.467	57	17.721
18	1.767	38	7.876	58	18.348
19	1.969	39	8.296	59	18.986
20	2.182	40	8.727	60	19.635

Approximate basal area can be calculated
by multiplying $(DBH)^2$ x .00545

Farm Forester Handbook, U.S.F.S. Region 6, 1969

Table A-12.   Volume, young-growth coast redwood, board feet, Spaulding rule to an 8-inch top.

D.B.H. (inches)	Volume by total height in feet																No. of trees
	40	50	60	70	80	90	100	110	120	130	140	150	160	170	180	190	
11	20	22	25	27	29	32	34	36									9
12	25	31	36	41	46	51	56	61									9
13	31	39	47	55	64	72	80	88	96								8
14	36	48	59	71	82	94	105	117	128								16
15	42	57	72	87	102	117	132	147	162	177							13
16	47	66	85	104	123	142	160	179	198	217							20
17	52	75	98	121	144	167	190	213	236	259	283						16
18	57	85	112	139	167	194	222	249	277	304	331						20
19	62	94	126	159	191	223	255	287	319	351	383						21
20	67	104	141	178	215	252	289	326	363	400	437						22
21		115	157	199	241	283	325	367	409	452	494	536					14
22		125	172	220	268	315	363	410	458	505	553	601					19
23		136	189	242	295	349	402	455	508	562	615	668					14
24		146	206	265	324	383	442	502	561	620	679	739					31
25		157	223	288	354	419	485	550	616	681	746	812	877				21
26			241	313	384	456	528	600	672	744	816	888	960				27
27			259	337	416	495	574	652	731	810	888	967	1046				25
28			277	363	449	535	620	706	792	877	963	1049	1134				36
29			297	390	483	576	669	762	855	948	1040	1133	1226	1319			18
30			316	417	517	618	718	819	920	1020	1121	1221	1322	1422			24

Row														No. of trees
31	445	553	661	770	878	986	1095	1203	1311	1420	1528	1636	1745	17
32	474	590	706	823	939	1056	1172	1288	1405	1521	1637	1754	1870	32
33	503	628	752	877	1002	1127	1251	1376	1501	1626	1750	1875	2000	16
34	533	666	800	933	1066	1200	1333	1466	1600	1733	1866	2000	2133	24
35	564	706	848	991	1133	1275	1417	1559	1702	1844	1986	2128	2270	16
36		747	898	1050	1201	1352	1504	1655	1806	1958	2109	2260	2412	13
37		789	949	1110	1271	1432	1592	1753	1914	2075	2235	2396	2557	8
38		832	1002	1172	1343	1513	1683	1854	2024	2195	2365	2535	2706	14
39		875	1056	1236	1416	1597	1777	1957	2137	2318	2498	2678	2859	1
40		920	1111	1301	1492	1682	1873	2063	2254	2444	2634	2825	3015	4
41			1167	1368	1569	1770	1971	2172	2373	2573	2774	2975	3176	2
42			1224	1436	1648	1859	2071	2283	2494	2706	2917	3129	3341	4
43			1282	1505	1728	1940	2173	2396	2618	2841	3063	3286	3509	3
44			1343	1577	1811	2045	2279	2513	2746	2980	3214	3448	3682	4
45			1405	1650	1895	2141	2386	2631	2877	3122	3367	3613	3858	4
46				1724	1982	2239	2496	2753	3010	3267	3524	3781	4039	4
47				1800	2070	2339	2608	2877	3146	3415	3684	3954	4223	1
48				1878	2159	2441	2722	3004	3285	3567	3848	4129	4411	2
49				1957	2251	2545	2839	3133	3427	3721	4015	4309	4603	1
50				2037	2344	2651	2958	3265	3572	3878	4185	4492	4799	7
No. of trees	2	4	10	39	32	20	69	90	122	94	45	13	13	6	1	560

U.C., Lindquist and Palley, 1959

Table A-13.   Volume, young-growth coast redwood, cubic feet to a 4-inch top.

D.B.H. (inches)	Total height (feet)																		No. of trees
	20	30	40	50	60	70	80	90	100	110	120	130	140	150	160	170	180	190	
4		.3	.7	1.0	1.3														2
5	.4	.9	1.4	1.8	2.3														6
6	.9	1.6	2.2	2.9	3.6	4.2													2
7		2.3	3.1	4.0	4.9	5.7													4
8		3.0	4.1	5.2	6.3	7.4	8.5												9
9		3.9	5.2	6.6	7.9	9.3	11												6
10		4.7	6.4	8.1	9.8	11	13												4
11		5.6	7.6	9.6	12	14	16	18	20	22									9
12		6.6	8.9	11	14	16	18	21	23	25									9
13		7.7	10	13	16	18	21	24	27	29	32	35							8
14		8.7	12	15	18	21	24	28	31	34	37	40							16
15		10	13	17	21	24	28	31	35	38	42	46							13
16		11	15	19	23	27	31	35	39	43	48	52	56						20
17		12	17	22	26	30	35	40	44	49	53	58	62						16
18		14	19	24	29	34	39	44	49	54	59	64	69	74					20
19		15	21	26	32	38	43	49	54	60	66	71	77	82					21
20		16	23	29	35	42	47	54	60	66	72	78	85	91					22
21		18	25	32	38	45	52	59	66	72	79	86	93	100					14
22		19	27	34	42	49	57	64	72	79	87	94	102	109					19
23		21	29	37	45	54	62	70	78	86	94	102	110	119	127	135			14
24		23	32	40	49	58	67	76	84	93	102	111	120	129	138	146			31
25		24	34	43	53	62	72	82	91	101	110	120	130	139	149	158			21
26		26	36	47	57	67	78	88	98	109	119	129	140	150	160	171	181		27
27			39	50	61	72	83	94	106	117	128	139	150	161	172	183	194		25
28			41	53	65	77	89	101	113	125	137	149	161	173	185	197	208		36

																	No. of trees
29	44	57	70	82	95	108	121	134	146	159	172	185	196	210	223		18
30	47	61	74	88	102	115	129	143	156	170	184	197	211	224	238	252	24
31		64	79	94	108	123	137	152	166	181	196	210	225	239	254	268	17
32		68	84	99	115	130	146	161	177	192	208	223	239	254	270	285	32
33		72	89	105	122	138	154	171	188	204	220	237	253	270	286	303	16
34		76	94	111	129	146	164	181	199	216	233	251	268	286	303	321	24
35		81	99	118	136	154	173	191	210	228	247	265	284	302	321	339	16
36		85	104	124	144	163	182	202	222	241	261	280	300	319	339	358	13
37			110	130	151	172	192	213	234	254	275	295	316	336	357	378	8
38			116	137	159	181	202	224	246	267	289	311	332	354	376	398	14
39			121	144	167	190	213	236	258	281	304	327	350	373	395	418	1
40			127	151	175	199	223	247	271	295	319	343	367	391	415	439	4
41			133	158	184	209	234	259	284	310	335	360	385	410	436	461	2
42			139	166	192	219	245	271	298	324	351	377	404	430	456	483	4
43				173	201	229	256	284	312	339	367	394	422	450	478	505	3
44				181	210	239	268	297	326	355	384	412	442	470	499	528	4
45				189	219	249	280	310	340	370	400	431	461	491	522	552	4
46				197	228	260	292	323	355	386	418	450	481	513	544	576	4
47				205	238	271	304	337	370	403	436	468	502	534	568	600	1
48				213	247	282	316	350	385	419	454	488	522	557	591	626	2
49				221	257	293	329	365	400	436	472	508	544	579	615	651	1
50				230	267	305	342	379	416	454	491	528	565	603	640	677	7
No. of trees	5	10	13	19	41	32	20	69	90	122	94	45	13	13	6	1	593

U.C., Lindquist and Palley, 1959

Table A-14. Volume, old-growth coast redwood, board feet, Scribner rule, to a top utilization diameter of 50 percent of D.O.B. at 20 feet.

D.O.B. 20 Ft.	Number of 20-Foot Logs										Top D.I.B.
	1	2	3	4	5	6	7	8	9	10	
16	120										12
18		230	310	470	600						12
20		240	370	570	740						12
22		280	430	710	910						12
24		330	530	880	1,100						12
26			670	1,060	1,300						13
28			810	1,270	1,530						14
30			950	1,470	1,790	2,180					15
32			1,100	1,690	2,030	2,490	2,900				16
34			1,300	1,910	2,300	2,800	3,290	3,790			17
36			1,450	2,150	2,590	3,180	3,680	4,230			18
38			1,750	2,400	2,900	3,500	4,100	4,680			19
40			1,840	2,690	3,220	3,860	4,500	5,200			20
44			2,050	3,240	3,980	4,650	5,500	6,210			22
48			2,500	3,810	4,700	5,580	6,580	7,420			24
52				4,570	5,600	6,470	7,640	8,800			26
56				5,300	6,500	7,960	8,950	10,450			28
60					7,420	9,120	10,330	12,030	13,350		30
64					8,450	10,390	11,730	13,680	15,150		32
68					9,600	11,570	13,770	15,360	17,560		34
72					10,800	12,980	15,450	17,130	19,640		36
76					12,200	14,360	17,100	19,100	21,770	23,720	38
80					13,800	15,870	17,960	21,030	23,990	26,150	40
86					15,900	18,880	21,740	24,230	27,640	30,120	43
92					18,100	20,890	24,790	28,650	31,530	34,370	46
98					20,750	23,660	28,070	31,300	35,670	38,880	49
104					23,250	26,620	31,610	35,240	40,160	43,750	52
110					25,750	29,720	35,240	39,270	44,780	48,830	55

U.S.F.S., Hallin, 1941

Table A-15. Volume, young-growth Douglas-fir, board feet, Scribner rule to an 8-inch top.

D.b.h. (inches)	Board-foot volume when total height of tree in feet is—																			
	50	60	70	80	90	100	110	120	130	140	150	160	170	180	190	200	210	220	230	240
12	32	50	69	87	105	124	140	155	176	196	225									
13	35	61	83	107	130	150	170	190	212	238	270									
14	47	74	101	129	155	175	201	225	252	282	318									
15		88	116	148	180	207	233	262	290	324	364	354								
16		102	136	170	205	235	265	296	330	368	410	410								
17		115	154	193	230	263	296	331	370	412	460	460								
18			172	215	257	294	329	367	410	460	510	522	584							
19			192	239	283	325	363	403	450	508	564	580	640	714						
20			213	259	311	355	397	440	494	558	618	640	710	782						
21				285	338	383	438	480	538	608	676	694	774	854	850					
22				309	367	420	470	520	584	658	732	754	844	930	942					
23					397	451	507	562	630	708	788	820	914	1,010	1,026	1,032				
24					426	489	545	607	676	758	848	882	980	1,090	1,114	1,122				
25					458	524	583	648	724	811	909	950	1,058	1,172	1,204	1,222	1,438	1,670		
26					492	562	626	692	770	866	971	1,013	1,134	1,257	1,296	1,322	1,548	1,801		
27					524	598	666	728	821	920	1,034	1,083	1,210	1,346	1,393	1,438	1,667	1,938		
28						638	708	782	870	975	1,096	1,158	1,287	1,435	1,495	1,548	1,794	2,075		
29						674	750	828	920	1,032	1,162	1,230	1,368	1,535	1,597	1,645	1,921	2,215		
30						712	792	876	972	1,083	1,228	1,309	1,435	1,627	1,699	1,757	2,075	2,354		
31							836	922	1,023	1,148	1,296	1,379	1,536	1,720	1,803	1,874	2,180	2,497		
32							878	970	1,076	1,207	1,360	1,435	1,622	1,813	1,909	1,989	2,308	2,635		3,246
33							922	1,016	1,129	1,267	1,434	1,529	1,711	1,906	2,014	2,104	2,436	2,778	3,019	3,424
34							964	1,060	1,182	1,327	1,512	1,601	1,797	1,999	2,100	2,222	2,569	2,921	3,180	3,598
35								1,112	1,238	1,387	1,565	1,694	1,880	2,092	2,226	2,340	2,702	3,084	3,338	3,780
36								1,158	1,291	1,477	1,628	1,727	1,964	2,180	2,333	2,458	2,833	3,227	3,496	3,956
37								1,203	1,347	1,510	1,692	1,818	2,046	2,278	2,439	2,576	2,963	3,370	3,818	4,132
38								1,256	1,401	1,575	1,753	1,889	2,126	2,372	2,541	2,694	3,096	3,514	3,981	4,315
39											1,811		2,208	2,465	2,651	2,812	3,225	3,800	4,136	4,488
40											1,932		2,286	2,558	2,759	2,931	3,491	3,943	4,299	4,657
41											1,990		2,362	2,651	2,867	3,049	3,619	4,086	4,459	4,844
42											2,045		2,437	2,740	3,008	3,167	3,885	4,229	4,622	5,022
43											2,101		2,513	2,839	3,168	3,280	4,018	4,372	4,781	5,200
44											2,156		2,586	2,932	3,266	3,516	4,149	4,520	4,939	5,373
45											2,207		2,659	3,011	3,365	3,632	4,282	4,663	5,102	5,526
46											2,262		2,732	3,094	3,463	3,747	4,413	4,807	5,258	5,720
47											2,320		2,801	3,174	3,559	3,978	4,546	4,950	5,420	5,890
48											2,373		2,869	3,298	3,762	4,096	4,683	5,097	5,585	6,065
49											2,426		2,946	3,348	3,859	4,219	4,816	5,245	5,744	6,236
50											2,435		3,027	3,516	3,960	4,335	4,949	5,388	5,907	6,409
51											2,540		3,107	3,599	4,059	4,453	5,082	5,536	6,060	6,579
52											2,593		3,189	3,760	4,150	4,565	5,215	5,679	6,225	6,752
53											2,658		3,331	3,853	4,259	4,686	5,348	5,822	6,388	6,925
54													3,434		4,327	4,806	5,481	5,965	6,554	7,093

U.S.F.S., McArdle, 1930

Table A-16.   Volume, young-growth Douglas-fir, cubic feet to a 4-inch top.

D.b.h. (inches)	Cubic-foot volume when total height of tree in feet is—																						
	20	30	40	50	60	70	80	90	100	110	120	130	140	150	160	170	180	190	200	210	220	230	240
6	1.2	1.9	2.7	3.4	4.1	4.8	5.6																
7	2.0	3.0	4.0	5.1	6.0	7.1	8.3																
8	2.7	4.1	5.4	6.8	8.0	9.5	11.1	12.1	13.2	14.6	16.0												
9	3.6	5.3	7.1	8.7	10.4	12.3	14.1	15.4	16.9	18.7	20.4												
10	4.5	6.6	8.7	10.6	12.9	15.1	17.2	18.8	20.7	22.9	24.8	27.3											
11		8.1	10.7	13.0	15.7	18.2	21.2	22.8	25.0	27.9	30.2	33.0											
12		9.7	12.6	15.5	18.6	21.3	24.3	26.6	29.4	32.9	35.7	38.7	42.2	46.0									
13		11.2	14.7	18.0	21.7	24.9	28.5	31.4	34.7	38.3	41.8	45.2	49.3	53.6									
14		12.8	16.8	20.6	24.8	28.6	32.8	36.3	40.0	43.6	48.0	51.8	56.4	61.2	65.8	70.0							
15			19.2	23.5	28.1	32.7	37.8	41.5	45.6	49.4	54.5	58.6	64.1	69.4	74.4	79.7							
16			21.6	26.5	31.5	36.8	41.9	46.7	51.2	55.2	61.0	65.5	71.8	77.7	83.0	85.4	96	102					
17				29.6	35.3	41.0	46.5	51.9	57.2	61.4	67.5	72.7	79.9	86.8	92.5	99.7	107	114					
18				32.8	39.2	45.2	51.2	57.1	63.3	67.7	74	80	88	96	102	110	118	126	136				
19				36.1	43.1	49.7	56.2	62.5	69.2	74.1	81	88	96	105	112	121	130	139	150				
20				39.5	47.0	54.2	61.2	67.9	75.1	80.6	88	96	105	114	123	133	143	153	164	174	187		
21				43.2	50.9	58.8	66.4	73.6	81.0	87.3	96	104	113	123	133	143	155	166	178	189	203		
22				47.0	54.8	63.5	71.6	79.3	86.9	94	103	112	121	133	144	154	167	179	192	205	219	234	
23					59.1	68.3	76.7	85.1	92.5	100	110	119	129	141	153	165	179	192	207	221	236	251	
24					63.5	73.2	81.9	91.0	98.2	107	117	126	137	150	163	177	191	204	222	238	254	269	287
25							87.3	97	105	114	124	134	145	160	174	188	204	220	238	255	272	288	308
26							92.8	103	112	121	131	142	154	170	185	200	218	235	253	273	291	308	329
27								108	119	128	139	150	163	179	195	212	231	250	269	290	311	328	351
28								113	126	136	147	159	172	189	206	224	244	265	286	307	331	349	374
29								120	132	143	154	167	181	199	217	236	258	280	301	325	350	370	398
30								128	139	150	161	175	190	209	228	248	272	296	317	343	370	392	423

31	—	—	—	—	—	—	—	—	—	145	156	169	183	199	219	239	260	286	310	333	360	389	414	446
32	—	—	—	—	—	—	—	—	—	152	163	177	191	208	229	251	273	300	324	350	378	408	436	469
33	—	—	—	—	—	—	—	—	—	—	170	184	199	217	239	263	285	312	338	366	396	427	458	492
34	—	—	—	—	—	—	—	—	—	—	178	191	208	227	250	276	297	325	352	382	414	447	481	516
35	—	—	—	—	—	—	—	—	—	—	—	198	216	236	260	286	309	338	366	398	432	467	503	540
36	—	—	—	—	—	—	—	—	—	—	—	206	224	245	271	296	321	351	381	415	450	488	526	565
37	—	—	—	—	—	—	—	—	—	—	—	213	232	254	281	306	332	364	396	432	468	508	548	589
38	—	—	—	—	—	—	—	—	—	—	—	221	241	263	291	316	344	377	411	449	486	529	570	613
39	—	—	—	—	—	—	—	—	—	—	—	—	—	271	299	325	355	390	425	465	505	550	593	638
40	—	—	—	—	—	—	—	—	—	—	—	—	—	280	307	335	366	403	440	482	524	571	616	663
41	—	—	—	—	—	—	—	—	—	—	—	—	—	—	—	345	378	415	455	498	542	591	638	687
42	—	—	—	—	—	—	—	—	—	—	—	—	—	—	—	356	390	428	470	515	561	611	661	712
43	—	—	—	—	—	—	—	—	—	—	—	—	—	—	—	366	401	441	485	532	580	632	685	739
44	—	—	—	—	—	—	—	—	—	—	—	—	—	—	—	377	413	455	501	550	600	653	709	762
45	—	—	—	—	—	—	—	—	—	—	—	—	—	—	—	387	425	468	515	566	619	673	731	789
46	—	—	—	—	—	—	—	—	—	—	—	—	—	—	—	397	437	481	529	583	638	694	753	816
47	—	—	—	—	—	—	—	—	—	—	—	—	—	—	—	407	448	493	544	600	656	714	775	838
48	—	—	—	—	—	—	—	—	—	—	—	—	—	—	—	417	460	506	559	617	674	735	798	861
49	—	—	—	—	—	—	—	—	—	—	—	—	—	—	—	427	471	519	573	634	694	755	820	885
50	—	—	—	—	—	—	—	—	—	—	—	—	—	—	—	437	483	532	587	652	714	776	843	910
51	—	—	—	—	—	—	—	—	—	—	—	—	—	—	—	447	495	544	602	668	732	796	866	934
52	—	—	—	—	—	—	—	—	—	—	—	—	—	—	—	458	507	557	617	685	751	817	889	959
53	—	—	—	—	—	—	—	—	—	—	—	—	—	—	—	468	518	570	631	703	770	836	911	983
54	—	—	—	—	—	—	—	—	—	—	—	—	—	—	—	478	530	583	646	721	790	855	934	1,008

U.S.F.S., Briegleb, 1953

Table A-17.   Volume, old-growth Douglas-fir, board feet, Scribner rule to an 8-inch top.

D.b.h. (inches)	Volume in tens of board-feet when number of 16-foot logs is—																
	2	3	4	5	6	7	8	9	10	11	12	13	14	15	16	17	18
16	11	19	26	33	40	47	53	59	---	---	---	---	---	---	---	---	---
18	13	22	30	39	48	56	63	71	---	---	---	---	---	---	---	---	---
20	15	25	35	46	56	65	74	83	92	102	---	---	---	---	---	---	---
22	17	29	41	53	65	76	87	99	109	122	---	---	---	---	---	---	---
24	19	33	47	61	74	87	101	115	128	143	---	---	---	---	---	---	---
26	21	37	53	69	84	101	116	132	147	165	---	---	---	---	---	---	---
28	23	41	59	77	96	115	132	150	168	188	---	---	---	---	---	---	---
30	25	46	66	87	108	130	149	170	190	214	235	255	---	---	---	---	---
32	---	51	73	97	120	145	166	190	215	242	265	290	---	---	---	---	---
34	---	56	80	107	134	160	185	214	241	270	300	325	---	---	---	---	---
36	---	62	88	117	148	175	205	238	267	300	335	362	395	---	---	---	---
38	---	67	96	129	163	193	227	262	295	333	365	400	435	470	---	---	---
40	---	72	105	141	178	213	249	290	326	366	400	440	475	515	---	---	---
42	---	---	114	153	193	233	273	318	357	399	440	480	520	560	605	650	690
44	---	---	123	165	210	253	299	344	389	435	480	520	570	615	655	705	750
46	---	---	133	180	228	275	326	375	422	472	520	565	620	665	710	765	815
48	---	---	143	195	247	300	353	405	456	510	560	610	665	715	765	825	875
50	---	---	153	210	267	325	380	435	490	550	600	655	710	770	825	885	945
52	---	---	163	225	288	350	410	470	525	590	645	700	765	830	880	950	1,015
54	---	---	175	240	310	375	440	505	560	630	690	755	820	890	945	1,025	1,095
56	---	---	187	258	333	400	470	540	595	675	740	810	875	950	1,010	1,100	1,175
58	---	---	200	276	356	428	500	575	635	720	790	865	935	1,010	1,085	1,170	1,255
60	---	---	216	297	379	457	530	610	680	765	840	920	995	1,085,	1,160	1,245	1,335

Age																		
62	—	—	—	—	—	402	486	565	645	725	810	895	975	1,065	1,150	1,230	1,320	1,415
64	—	—	—	—	—	428	515	600	685	770	855	950	1,030	1,130	1,220	1,310	1,400	1,500
66	—	—	—	—	—	454	545	635	725	815	910	1,005	1,095	1,195	1,290	1,390	1,480	1,585
68	—	—	—	—	—	480	578	670	770	860	965	1,060	1,160	1,260	1,360	1,470	1,570	1,665
70	—	—	—	—	—	506	612	705	815	910	1,020	1,120	1,225	1,335	1,440	1,545	1,650	1,750
72	—	—	—	—	—	532	646	745	860	960	1,080	1,180	1,290	1,410	1,515	1,625	1,730	1,840
74	—	—	—	—	—	560	680	785	905	1,010	1,140	1,250	1,360	1,485	1,595	1,700	1,815	1,930
76	—	—	—	—	—	583	715	830	950	1,065	1,200	1,320	1,430	1,560	1,675	1,780	1,900	2,015
78	—	—	—	—	—	619	750	875	995	1,120	1,260	1,390	1,500	1,635	1,750	1,860	1,985	2,100
80	—	—	—	—	—	650	785	920	1,050	1,180	1,320	1,450	1,570	1,705	1,825	1,940	2,065	2,175
82	—	—	—	—	—	—	815	965	1,105	1,240	1,380	1,510	1,630	1,775	1,900	2,020	2,145	2,250
84	—	—	—	—	—	—	850	1,010	1,160	1,300	1,440	1,580	1,710	1,850	1,980	2,100	2,225	2,330
86	—	—	—	—	—	—	890	1,055	1,215	1,360	1,500	1,650	1,790	1,925	2,060	2,180	2,300	2,420
88	—	—	—	—	—	—	930	1,100	1,270	1,420	1,570	1,720	1,870	2,000	2,140	2,260	2,380	2,510
90	—	—	—	—	—	—	970	1,150	1,325	1,480	1,640	1,790	1,930	2,075	2,210	2,320	2,460	2,600
92	—	—	—	—	—	—	—	1,200	1,380	1,540	1,710	1,860	1,990	2,145	2,280	2,400	2,550	2,700
94	—	—	—	—	—	—	—	1,250	1,440	1,600	1,780	1,930	2,070	2,215	2,350	2,490	2,640	2,800
96	—	—	—	—	—	—	—	1,300	1,500	1,660	1,850	2,000	2,140	2,285	2,420	2,580	2,740	2,890
98	—	—	—	—	—	—	—	1,355	1,560	1,720	1,920	2,070	2,210	2,355	2,510	2,670	2,830	2,980
100	—	—	—	—	—	—	—	1,410	1,620	1,780	1,980	2,125	2,280	2,430	2,600	2,750	2,920	3,070
102	—	—	—	—	—	—	—	1,470	1,660	1,840	2,040	2,180	2,340	2,500	2,690	2,830	3,010	3,170
104	—	—	—	—	—	—	—	1,500	1,710	1,900	2,100	2,240	2,410	2,590	2,770	2,920	3,100	3,270
106	—	—	—	—	—	—	—	1,570	1,780	1,960	2,160	2,300	2,480	2,680	2,840	3,010	3,190	3,360
108	—	—	—	—	—	—	—	—	1,830	2,020	2,220	2,360	2,560	2,760	2,920	3,100	3,280	3,450
110	—	—	—	—	—	—	—	—	1,900	2,080	2,280	2,420	2,640	2,840	3,000	3,190	3,370	3,540
112	—	—	—	—	—	—	—	—	—	2,130	2,330	2,480	2,710	2,920	3,070	3,280	3,450	3,630
114	—	—	—	—	—	—	—	—	—	2,180	2,390	2,530	2,780	3,000	3,150	3,370	3,540	3,720
116	—	—	—	—	—	—	—	—	—	2,240	2,450	2,590	2,850	3,080	3,220	3,460	3,630	3,810
118	—	—	—	—	—	—	—	—	—	2,300	2,500	2,650	2,930	3,160	3,300	3,550	3,720	3,910
120	—	—	—	—	—	—	—	—	—	2,360	2,560	2,710	3,000	3,240	3,370	3,650	3,820	4,000

U.S.F.S., Meyer, 1932

Table A-18. Volume, Sitka spruce (old and young), board feet, Scribner rule to an 8-inch top.

D.b.h. (inches)	Volume in tens of board-feet when total height of tree in feet is—																		
	40	50	60	70	80	90	100	110	120	130	140	150	160	170	180	190	200	210	220
12	3	4	6	8	10	11	12	13	14										
13	5	7	9	11	13	14	16	17	18										
14	7	9	11	14	16	18	20	22	24	26	27								
15	9	12	14	16	18	21	24	26	28	30	33								
16	11	14	16	19	22	25	28	31	34	36	39	44	48						
17	13	16	19	22	25	28	32	36	40	43	46	50	54						
18	14	18	22	25	28	32	36	41	46	50	53	56	60						
19	15	20	24	28	32	36	40	46	51	55	59	62	66						
20	16	21	26	30	35	40	44	50	57	62	66	70	73						
21	17	22	28	34	39	44	49	56	63	68	74	77	80						
22	18	24	30	36	42	48	54	62	70	76	81	85	89	94	100				
23			32	39	46	52	59	68	76	82	88	92	97	104	110				
24			35	42	50	57	64	74	83	90	96	101	106	113	120	126	132		
25			37	46	55	62	70	80	90	97	104	110	116	124	132	138	145		
26			40	50	59	68	76	86	97	104	112	118	125	135	145	152	158		
27			43	53	63	72	82	93	104	112	120	128	136	146	157	164	172		
28			46	57	68	78	88	100	111	120	129	138	146	158	170	178	186		
29			49	61	73	84	95	106	118	128	138	147	156	168	180	190	200		
30			53	65	77	89	101	114	126	136	147	158	168	180	192	203	214	222	230

31	57	70	82	95	108	120	133	144	156	168	179	192	205	216	228	236	245
32	62	74	87	100	114	127	140	152	165	178	190	205	220	232	243	252	260
33			93	107	121	134	148	161	174	188	202	216	230	244	257	266	276
34			98	113	128	142	156	170	184	198	213	228	244	257	270	280	291
35			103	120	136	150	165	179	193	209	225	240	256	270	284	296	307
36			109	126	143	158	173	188	203	220	237	253	269	284	298	310	322
37			114	132	150	166	182	198	213	231	249	265	281	296	311	324	337
38			120	138	157	174	191	208	224	243	262	278	295	310	325	338	352
39			126	145	164	182	200	217	234	254	274	290	307	323	339	354	368
40			132	152	171	190	210	228	246	266	286	303	320	336	353	369	385
41			138	158	178	198	219	238	257	278	298	316	334	350	367	384	402
42					186	207	228	248	268	290	311	329	347	364	382	401	420
43					194	216	238	259	280	301	322	341	360	379	398	418	438
44					201	224	247	269	291	313	335	355	375	395	415	436	457
45					209	233	257	280	303	324	346	368	390	410	430	452	475
46					217	242	267	290	314	336	359	382	405	426	447	471	495
47					226	252	278	302	326	348	371	396	420	442	465	490	515
48					234	261	288	312	337	360	383	410	436	460	485	511	537
49					242	270	298	324	349	373	397	426	454	480	506	532	559
50					250	279	308	334	360	385	410	440	470	499	528	555	582
51					258	288	318	346	373	399	425	457	489	520	550	578	605
52					267	298	328	357	386	413	440	472	507	538	570	598	627
53					276	308	340	370	400	428	456	491	526	558	590	620	650
54					284	317	350	382	414	443	462	504	545	578	612	643	674
55							362	395	428	458	488	526	565	600	634	666	697
56							372	408	443	474	505	545	585	620	655	688	722
57							384	421	458	490	521	563	605	641	677	712	747
58							396	435	474	506	539	582	624	661	698	734	771
59							407	448	490	523	556	600	645	682	720	758	795
60							419	462	506	540	574	620	665	702	740	780	820

U.S.F.S., Skinner, 1953

Table A-19.   Volume, Sitka spruce (old and young), cubic feet to a 4-inch top.

D.b.h. (inches)	Cubic-foot volume when total height of tree in feet is—												
	20	40	60	80	100	120	140	160	180	200	220	240	260
6	1.3	2.9	4.6										
8		6.0	9.1	13.5									
10		9.9	13.7	18.0	22.2								
12		13.1	19.6	26.6	32.6								
14		17	25	34	42								
16			30	41	50	60							
18			37	50	62	75							
20			44	60	75	90	107	120					
22			51	70	87	107	125	140					
24			59	82	103	124	144	162	179				
26			68	95	119	142	164	185	203	230			
28			78	108	136	159	184	209	235	264			
30			90	121	151	179	207	237	268	296			
32			103	134	168	200	232	267	301	331	366		
34				147	183	220	255	293	331	364	404		
36				160	200	241	280	322	361	401	441		
38				173	219	264	307	352	395	439	481	524	
40				187	241	287	335	381	430	476	523	568	
42				204	258	308	360	409	462	511	565	612	
44					277	329	387	439	495	548	610	661	714
46					294	350	414	468	527	586	650	704	763
48					314	375	443	502	564	631	694	753	820
50					332	399	469	534	599	674	734	799	874
52					370	447	520	600	680	754	823	901	981
54						501	583	676	762	850	931	1,013	1,095
56						520	610	703	791	882	966	1,052	1,133
58						541	632	733	824	919	1,005	1,096	1,177
60						563	664	765	863	961	1,049	1,145	1,231
62						593	698	804	906	1,006	1,099	1,199	1,292
64						630	739	848	956	1,060	1,162	1,262	1,368
66						672	788	904	1,013	1,121	1,234	1,345	1,461
68						721	845	970	1,083	1,197	1,321	1,449	1,569
70							909	1,039	1,166	1,293	1,427	1,570	1,694
72							980	1,114	1,262	1,406	1,554	1,704	1,846
74							1,063	1,209	1,379	1,529	1,700	1,856	2,030
76							1,156	1,331	1,521	1,678	1,867	2,044	2,220
78								1,471	1,671	1,861	2,064	2,260	2,440
80								1,632	1,840	1,959	2,277	2,469	2,670
82								1,827	2,053	2,293	2,519	2,723	2,930
84									2,295	2,535	2,780	3,005	3,230
86									2,571	2,827	3,084	3,324	3,570
88									2,882	3,152	3,432	3,692	3,950

U.S.F.S., Dilworth, 1947

Table A-20. Volume, western hemlock (old and young), board feet, Scribner rule to an 8-inch top.

Species.........................: WESTERN HEMLOCK (Tsuga heterophylla)
Unit of measure.................: Board-foot
Variables.......................: D.b.h. and number of 16-foot logs
Log rule........................: Scribner
Scaling length for logs.........: 16 feet
Stump height....................: 2 feet
Top d.i.b.......................: 8 inches
Trim allowance per log..........: 0.3 feet
Method..........................: Alinement chart
Number of trees.................: 1,526
Location of trees...............: Young and old stands in Oregon and Washington
Accuracy........................: Aggregate deviation 0.25 percent low
Author..........................: W. H. Meyer, Pacific Northwest Forest and Range Expt. Sta.
Source..........................: Table 49 in U. S. Dept. Agr. Tech. Bul. 544
Year............................: 1937

D.b.h. (inches)	Volume in tens of board-feet when number of 16-foot logs is--											
	2	3	4	5	6	7	8	9	10	11	12	13
12	10	16	22	--	--	--	--	--	--	--	--	--
14	12	19	27	34	--	--	--	--	--	--	--	--
16	14	22	32	41	50	--	--	--	--	--	--	--
18	15	26	37	49	60	70	--	--	--	--	--	--
20	17	30	43	57	71	83	96	--	--	--	--	--
22	19	34	50	67	83	97	113	129	--	--	--	--
24	21	39	58	77	96	113	132	150	168	184	--	--
26	24	45	67	88	110	131	152	172	192	212	231	--
28	27	51	76	100	126	150	173	195	219	240	263	--
30	--	57	85	113	142	169	194	219	247	270	298	325
32	--	64	94	126	158	188	216	244	274	302	333	360
34	--	71	104	140	174	207	239	270	303	334	368	400
36	--	77	115	154	190	226	262	297	332	367	400	435
38	--	85	126	168	207	247	286	325	364	400	440	470
40	--	--	138	182	226	269	311	354	396	435	475	515
42	--	--	150	196	246	292	337	384	430	470	510	555
44	--	--	162	212	266	316	365	410	460	505	550	600
46	--	--	173	228	286	339	393	440	490	540	590	640
48	--	--	184	244	306	362	420	470	525	580	630	680
50	--	--	196	260	326	386	445	500	560	615	670	725
52	--	--	--	276	344	408	470	530	590	650	710	765
54	--	--	--	290	362	427	490	555	620	680	745	805
56	--	--	--	303	380	446	510	580	650	710	780	845
58	--	--	--	317	396	465	535	610	675	740	815	885
60	--	--	--	330	412	485	560	635	700	770	850	925

U.S.F.S., Meyer, 1937

Table A-21. Volume, western hemlock (old and young), cubic feet to a 4-inch top.

Cubic-foot volume when total height of tree in feet is—

D.b.h. (in.)	40	50	60	70	80	90	100	110	120	130	140	150	160	170	180	190	200	210	220	230	240	250	260
6—	2.3	3.3	4.4	5.4	6.7	6.9																	
7—	3.3	4.7	6.1	7.5	9.1	10.0																	
8—	4.3	6.1	7.9	9.6	11.5	13.1																	
9—		8.0	10.0	12.3	14.2	16.5																	
10—		10	12	15	17	20																	
11—			15	18	20	24	27	30	33	36	39												
12—			18	22	24	28	32	35	39	42	46	49	52	56°									
13—			21	25	29	33	37	41	45	49	54	57	61	66									
14—			24	29	34	39	43	48	52	57	62	66	71	76									
15—			28	33	39	44	49	55	60	65	71	76	80	87									
16—			32	38	44	50	56	62	68	74	80	86	90	99	105	112	118						
17—			36	42	49	56	63	69	76	83	90	96	102	110	117	124	130						
18—			40	47	54	62	70	77	84	92	100	107	114	122	129	136	143						
19—				52	60	69	77	85	93	102	111	118	126	134	142	149	157						
20—				57	66	76	85	94	103	113	122	129	138	147	155	163	171	179	187				
21—					72	83	93	103	113	123	132	136	150	160	169	177	186	194	203				
22—					79	90	101	112	123	133	143	153	163	173	183	192	201	210	220				
23—						96	109	121	133	144	154	165	175	186	197	207	217	227	237				
24—						103	117	131	143	155	166	177	188	200	212	222	233	244	254				
25—						110	126	140	153	166	178	189	201	214	227	238	250	262	273				
26—						117	136	150	164	177	190	202	215	229	242	254	267	280	292				
27—							145	160	175	189	203	216	230	245	258	271	285	298	311				
28—							155	171	186	201	216	230	245	261	275	289	303	317	331				
29—							165	181	197	213	229	244	260	277	292	307	321	336	351				
30—							175	192	209	226	242	258	275	293	310	325	340	356	372				

	1	2	3	4	5	6	7	8	9	10	11	12	13	14	15	16	17	18	19	20	21	22	23
31——	—	—	—	—	—	—	186	209	221	239	256	273	291	310	327	343	360	377	393	—	—	—	—
32——	—	—	—	—	—	—	197	227	234	252	270	288	308	327	345	362	380	399	414	439	459	—	—
33——	—	—	—	—	—	—	207	232	245	265	284	303	324	344	363	382	401	420	438	463	483	—	—
34——	—	—	—	—	—	—	218	238	257	278	299	319	340	362	382	402	422	442	462	487	507	—	—
35——	—	—	—	—	—	—	—	—	—	292	315	335	359	381	402	421	444	464	486	511	531	—	—
36——	—	—	—	—	—	—	—	—	—	306	331	351	376	401	421	441	466	486	511	536	556	—	—
37——	—	—	—	—	—	—	—	—	—	—	347	370	395	420	442	462	487	510	535	560	582	—	—
38——	—	—	—	—	—	—	—	—	—	—	364	389	414	439	464	484	509	534	559	584	609	—	—
39——	—	—	—	—	—	—	—	—	—	—	380	405	430	458	483	505	530	558	583	608	633	—	—
40——	—	—	—	—	—	—	—	—	—	—	397	422	447	477	502	527	552	582	607	632	657	682	707
41——	—	—	—	—	—	—	—	—	—	—	414	439	466	499	524	549	576	606	632	656	684	711	739
42——	—	—	—	—	—	—	—	—	—	—	431	456	486	521	546	571	601	631	658	681	711	741	771
43——	—	—	—	—	—	—	—	—	—	—	447	475	505	540	567	595	625	655	683	710	740	770	800
44——	—	—	—	—	—	—	—	—	—	—	464	494	524	559	589	619	649	679	709	739	769	799	829
45——	—	—	—	—	—	—	—	—	—	—	480	510	545	580	613	643	673	703	733	763	795	828	858
46——	—	—	—	—	—	—	—	—	—	—	497	527	567	602	637	667	697	727	757	787	822	857	887
47——	—	—	—	—	—	—	—	—	—	—	516	546	591	626	661	691	721	753	786	816	851	884	921
48——	—	—	—	—	—	—	—	—	—	—	535	565	615	650	685	715	745	780	815	845	880	912	955
49——	—	—	—	—	—	—	—	—	—	—	554	584	631	671	706	739	769	806	841	874	911	947	986
50——	—	—	—	—	—	—	—	—	—	—	573	603	648	693	728	763	793	833	868	903	943	983	1,018
51——	—	—	—	—	—	—	—	—	—	—	—	—	671	716	754	786	819	859	896	934	974	1,014	1,049
52——	—	—	—	—	—	—	—	—	—	—	—	—	695	740	780	810	845	885	925	965	1,005	1,045	1,080
53——	—	—	—	—	—	—	—	—	—	—	—	—	716	764	804	836	871	914	954	994	1,034	1,074	1,111
54——	—	—	—	—	—	—	—	—	—	—	—	—	738	788	828	863	898	943	983	1,023	1,063	1,103	1,143
55——	—	—	—	—	—	—	—	—	—	—	—	—	759	809	852	887	924	969	1,009	1,049	1,092	1,132	1,172
56——	—	—	—	—	—	—	—	—	—	—	—	—	781	831	876	911	951	996	1,036	1,076	1,121	1,161	1,201
57——	—	—	—	—	—	—	—	—	—	—	—	—	802	852	899	939	979	1,022	1,062	1,104	1,149	1,189	1,232
58——	—	—	—	—	—	—	—	—	—	—	—	—	823	873	923	968	1,008	1,048	1,088	1,133	1,178	1,218	1,263
59——	—	—	—	—	—	—	—	—	—	—	—	—	842	897	949	992	1,032	1,074	1,114	1,159	1,207	1,249	1,297
60——	—	—	—	—	—	—	—	—	—	—	—	—	861	921	976	1,016	1,056	1,101	1,141	1,186	1,236	1,281	1,331

U.S.F.S., Dilworth, 1947

Table A-22. Volume, old-growth white fir (A. concolor), Site II, board feet, Scribner Decimal C to an 8-inch top.

Diameter breast high	Number of 16-foot logs											Basis
	1	2	3	4	5	6	7	8	9	10	11	
	Volume—board feet, in tens											
Inches												*Trees*
10	4	6	12	15								
12	5	8	13	18								1
14	5	9	15	22								3
16	5	11	18	25	33							5
18	5	12	20	30	39							10
20		13	23	35	46	58						16
22		15	28	42	55	69						23
24		16	31	48	64	80	96	112	128			23
26		18	36	55	75	93	112	130	148			26
28			42	63	85	107	128	150	172			30
30			46	70	94	120	144	169	194			38
32			52	79	106	134	162	189	216			31
34			58	88	118	148	179	209	239	269		28
36					131	165	197	234	266	298		14
38					144	181	218	256	293	330		10
40					158	199	240	281	323	365		14
42					172	218	263	308	353	397		17
44					196	237	286	335	385	433	482	4
46					210	264	310	364	418	470	524	3
48					221	280	338	396	454	512	569	2
50					242	300	366	428	491	554	616	1
52					269	333	394	461	528	595	662	
54					280	349	424	493	566	638	710	1
56					305	373	453	526	603	679	756	
58					317	400	492	561	644	726	808	
60					336	422	517	599	687	775	864	
62					363	452	556	645	738	832	929	
64					382	481	578	678	783	880	989	
66					411	518	622	731	832	945	1050	
68					428	538	645	774	875	990	1110	
70					442	567	691	801	922	1042	1156	
72					473	598	725	849	978	1102	1225	
Total												300

U.S.F.S., Bruce, 1921

Table A-23. Volume, young-growth white fir (A. concolor), board feet, International 1/8″ rule to a five-inch top.

DBH	TOTAL HEIGHT IN FEET — VOLUME IN BOARD FEET														Basis Number of Trees	Average Height Feet
	40	50	60	70	80	90	100	110	120	130	140	150	160	170		
8	17	23	32	42	52										49	52
9	21	30	43	55	67	79									53	58
10	25	39	54	69	86	103	118								57	64
11	29	46	65	85	106	127	147	168							54	69
12	33	53	77	101	127	151	177	203							41	74
13	37	63	90	118	149	180	211	241	272						46	79
14		73	105	140	175	211	247	283	318	354					42	84
15		83	122	162	203	244	285	327	369	410					34	89
16		94	140	185	233	280	325	374	420	468					29	94
17		105	157	208	260	314	366	422	475	531	585				22	99
18		118	174	232	290	350	412	470	533	593	654				15	103
19				257	324	392	458	525	594	660	727				15	107
20				282	355	429	503	576	652	725	800				12	111
21				311	390	472	554	636	720	804	885				8	115
22				340	426	515	607	698	790	882	972				9	119
23				372	469	567	666	764	863	961	1060	1155			9	122
24				404	508	615	722	829	936	1045	1150	1255	1365		9	126
25				439	554	672	790	907	1025	1145	1260	1375	1490		5	129
26				479	604	732	860	990	1120	1250	1375	1505	1630		6	133
27					652	793	935	1075	1215	1360	1500	1640	1780		4	136
28					707	858	1010	1160	1315	1470	1620	1770	1920		2	139
29					768	930	1090	1255	1420	1585	1745	1910	2070		4	143
30					826	1005	1180	1355	1535	1710	1880	2065	2240	2420		146
31							1265	1450	1645	1835	2030	2220	2410	2600	1	148
32							1340	1545	1750	1955	2155	2355	2560	2760	3	151
33							1430	1650	1865	2080	2300	2515	2735	2950	4	154
34							1515	1740	1975	2205	2435	2665	2895	3130		157
35							1600	1840	2085	2330	2579	2810	3055	3290	1	159
36									2205	2460	2710	2970	3225	3480	1	162
37									2320	2590	2865	3140	3410	3680		164
38									2445	2730	3015	3295	3580	3860	1	166
39									2570	2870	3170	3475	3775	4080		168
40									2690	3000	3320	3635	3950	4270		170
Total															536	

U.C., Schumacher, 1926

Table A-24. Volume, young-growth white fir (A. concolor), cubic feet

DBH	TOTAL HEIGHT IN FEET — VOLUME IN CUBIC FEET 25	30	35	40	45	50	60	70	80	90	100	110	120	130	140	150	160	170	Basis Number of Trees	Average Height Feet
4	0.85	1.05	1.24	1.43	1.59															26
5	1.26	1.55	1.85	2.16	2.48	2.77														33
6	1.78	2.16	2.56	3.00	3.46	3.89	3.37													39
7		2.87	3.37	3.94	4.53	5.15	4.80	5.62											54	45
8		3.66	4.38	4.98	5.72	6.51	6.34	7.52											64	51
9			5.35	6.14	6.99	7.94	8.11	9.58	11.2	12.7									53	57
10				7.44	8.44	9.47	9.96	12.0	13.9	15.8	21.9								57	63
11				8.84	9.98	11.2	11.8	14.4	16.8	19.2	25.7	28.4							54	69
12				10.4	11.7	13.1	13.8	16.7	19.9	22.8	30.0	33.4							42	74
13				12.1	13.6	15.1	16.0	19.1	23.0	26.6	34.9	38.8	42.6						45	80
14					15.6	17.4	18.4	21.8	26.1	30.5	39.6	44.3	49.0	53.2					42	85
15					17.7	19.8	21.0	24.8	29.2	34.6	44.6	50.2	55.6	60.6					34	90
16						22.4	23.9	28.1	32.7	38.6	49.5	56.3	62.5	68.4					29	95
17						25.2	26.9	31.6	36.6	42.4	54.5	62.6	69.8	76.7	83.2				22	99
18						28.1	30.2	35.4	40.8	47.0	59.7	68.9	77.6	85.4	92.6				15	103
19							33.7	39.4	45.4	51.8	65.4	75.8	85.6	94.5	103				16	108
20							37.6	43.9	50.4	57.3	71.6	82.4	93.9	104	113				11	112
21							41.6	48.3	55.5	63.2	77.7	88.4	102	114	124				8	115
22							45.5	53.2	60.8	69.0	84.7	95.1	109	123	136	147			9	119
23							50.0	58.3	66.5	75.4	91.8	103	117	133	147	160			12	122
24								63.6	72.8	82.2	99.8	111	125	143	159	174	187		9	126
25								69.3	79.1	89.5	108	120	134	153	171	187	202		6	129
26								75.3	86.0	96.7	116	129	143	162	183	201	218		6	132
27								81.3	92.9	104	125	139	153	172	194	215	233		4	135
28									100	112	135	149	164	183	206	230	251	270	2	138
29									108	121	145	159	176	194	218	245	267	289	4	140
30									116	130	155	171	188	207	231	261	286	308		143
31									124	140	165	182	200	220	243	275	303	328	1	145
32											176	194	213	233	257	290	321	348	2	148
33											187	206	226	247	271	304	339	368	4	150
34											198	218	238	261	285	319	357	389		153
35											210	231	253	276	302	335	376	411	1	155
36													268	291	317	351	394	432	1	157
37													282	308	334	367	411	455		159
38													297	323	352	384	427	475	1	161
39													313	341	369	401	444	496		163
40													329	358	388	421	462	517		165
Total																			608	

U.C., Schumacher, 1926

Table A-25. Volume, old-growth sugar pine, Site II, board feet, Scribner Decimal C rule.

Diameter breast high, inches	Number of 16-foot logs											
	1	2	3	4	5	6	7	8	9	10	11	12
	Volume—board feet, in tens											
12	3	8	13									
14	3	10	15	22								
16	5	11	17	26	33							
18	5	12	20	29	39	48						
20	6	13	23	33	43	55	65					
22	8	15	26	38	52	65	77	88				
24	10	17	30	44	61	75	90	104				
26		18	24	51	70	89	106	122				
28		20	40	59	81	102	122	142	162			
30			46	68	92	116	139	163	187			
32			51	78	105	131	159	186	214			
34				89	118	148	179	211	242			
36				100	134	166	202	237	272	308		
38				111	148	185	225	264	303	342		
40				122	165	205	249	292	336	379	423	
42					182	227	275	323	371	417	466	
44					201	251	304	357	410	464	517	
46					222	278	337	395	454	513	572	
48					244	306	371	435	501	565	629	694
50					269	337	408	478	550	621	693	763
52					294	370	448	525	603	680	758	835
54					323	406	489	574	658	742	827	911
56					354	443	534	627	718	810	902	994
58					382	482	582	682	782	882	982	1082
60						517	622	729	836	942	1048	1156
62						551	657	768	880	993	1107	1235
64						576	690	805	918	1041	1165	1288
66						594	711	832	950	1075	1207	1333
68							732	854	976	1110	1242	1370
70							753	878	1007	1146	1277	1410
72							785	914	1054	1191	1331	1468
74							822	966	1100	1246	1392	1532
76							858	1007	1149	1302	1454	1598
78							898	1053	1202	1362	1522	1671

U.S.F.S., Dunning, 1925

Table A-26. Volume, young-growth sugar pine, board feet, International ¼″ rule to a 4-inch top.

Diameter breast high	Total height of tree—feet											Basis
	30	40	50	60	70	80	90	100	110	120	130	
	Volume—board feet											
Inches												*Trees*
8	5	10	18	29								103
9	6	15	26	40	54							64
10	8	20	34	50	67	83						75
11	10	26	41	61	80	98	118					75
12		32	50	72	93	115	135					54
13		39	58	84	107	131	155	175				39
14		45	68	95	123	150	174	200				35
15			79	108	138	168	195	225				23
16			90	122	156	189	220	253				24
17				136	173	211	247	284				31
18				151	193	234	275	317	355			20
19				166	213	259	305	352	394			13
20				182	235	285	338	388	433	485		5
21					258	317	371	425	475	532		3
22					282	342	407	465	520	583		2
23					306	372	443	505	568	637		2
24					332	405	478	547	618	693		
25						440	518	592	670	753	846	
26						475	560	637	725	814	920	
27						512	600	685	782	877	992	
28						550	642	735	838	942	1063	
29						588	685	786	896	1005	1136	
30						627	729	839	955	1070	1213	
31						668	777	890	1015	1135	1283	
32						709	825	941	1065	1200	1353	
Total	23	107	140	100	77	61	40	18	1	1		568

U.S.F.S., Dunning, 1923

Table A-27. Volume, young-growth sugar pine, cubic feet.

Diameter breast high	Total height of tree—feet												Basis
	10	20	30	40	50	60	70	80	90	100	110	120	
	Total volume—cubic feet												
Inches													*Trees*
4	0.5	0.9	1.6										48
5	1.0	1.6	2.3	3.0									47
6		2.3	3.2	4.0	5.3	6.8							80
7		3.2	4.2	5.3	6.8	8.5							81
8			4.0	5.2	6.7	8.5	10.5	13.0					96
9				6.4	8.2	10.2	12.8	15.6	18.4				64
10				7.8	10.0	12.5	15.3	18.8	21.7				75
11					9.3	11.9	14.8	18.0	21.7	25.6			73
12				14.0	17.3	21.1	25.2	29.5	33.8	38.2			52
13				16.3	20.2	24.5	29.0	33.7	38.6	43.5			39
14				18.6	23.0	28.0	33.0	38.5	44.0	49.5			37
15					26.0	31.7	37.6	43.8	50.0	56.0			23
16					29.3	35.6	42.3	49.0	56.0	62.8			23
17						40.0	47.5	55.0	62.3	70.0			33
18						44.5	52.9	61.0	68.8	77.5	86.3		19
19						49.6	58.4	67.0	75.0	84.8	94.7		13
20						54.8	64.0	73.0	81.3	92.2	103.5	113.3	4
21							69.7	79.0	88.0	99.8	111.7	123.3	3
22							75.3	85.0	94.8	107.2	120.0	133.2	2
23							80.8	90.9	101.4	114.7	128.5	143.0	2
24							86.4	97.0	108.0	122.2	137.0	153.0	
25									114.3	129.8	145.5	162.6	
26									121.0	137.0	154.0	172.0	
27									127.3	144.7	162.7	181.5	
28									133.9	152.0	171.0	190.9	
29									140.2	159.7	179.2	200.0	
30									146.7	167.2	187.7	209.8	
31									153.0	174.8	196.0	219.2	
32									159.8	182.4	204.2	229.0	
Total													814

U.S.F.S., Dunning, 1923

Table A-28. Volume, old-growth ponderosa pine, board feet, Scribner Decimal C rule.

Diameter breast high, inches	Number of 16-foot logs												Diameter inside bark of top inches
	1	2	3	4	5	6	7	8	9	10	11	12	
	Volume—board feet, in tens												
10	4	7											7
12	4	8	15										8
14	5	10	17										8
16	6	12	19	27									8
18	7	14	23	32	41								8
20	9	18	29	38	48	58							9
22	11	24	35	46	58	71	84						9
24	15	30	44	57	71	86	102						9
26	20	39	55	70	87	104	123	143					10
28	26	48	68	86	106	126	146	169					10
30	35	60	83	105	128	150	172	196	230				10
32		72	100	125	152	176	201	230	260				10
34		86	119	148	176	200	230	260	290	330			11
36			110	140	170	200	230	260	290	330	360		11
38				170	200	230	260	290	330	360	400	450	11
40				200	230	260	290	330	370	400	450	500	11
42			240	270	300	330	370	410	450	500	550		11
44				300	330	370	410	450	500	550	600	660	12
46				330	370	420	460	500	560	610	660	710	12
48				360	420	470	510	560	610	660	720	770	12
50					470	520	570	610	670	720	780	830	12
52					520	570	630	670	730	780	840	890	12
54					570	630	690	730	790	850	910	960	12
56						690	750	790	850	920	980	1040	12
58						750	790	860	920	990	1060	1130	12
60						790	860	920	990	1070	1150	1230	13
62							920	980	1060	1150	1240	1340	13
64							980	1060	1130	1230	1340	1450	13
66							1060	1130	1210	1320	1440	1570	13
68								1200	1300	1410	1550	1690	13
70								1280	1390	1500	1660	1820	14
72								1360	1480	1600	1770	1950	
74									1580	1700	1880	2090	
76									1680	1800	1990	2230	

U.S.F.S., Region 5, 1909–1911

Table A-29.   Volume, young-growth ponderosa pine, board feet, Scribner rule to an 8-inch top.

Tree diameter at breast height (inches)	Board foot volume (Scribner log rule) by total tree height in feet									
	60	70	80	90	100	110	120	130	140	150
12	50	60	80	100	110	120	140	150		
14	80	110	130	150	180	200	220	240	260	
16	120	160	180	210	240	270	300	340	360	
18	170	210	240	290	340	370	410	460	500	
20	220	270	320	370	440	480	530	580	640	
22	270	340	410	470	540	600	670	740	810	890
24	330	420	500	580	660	740	830	910	1,000	1,090
26	410	510	600	690	790	900	1,000	1,090	1,190	1,290
28	480	590	700	820	940	1,060	1,170	1,270	1,380	1,480
30	560	690	810	960	1,090	1,220	1,340	1,450	1,570	1,670
32		800	950	1,100	1,240	1,380	1,510	1,630	1,750	1,860
34		910	1,090	1,240	1,400	1,540	1,680	1,810	1,940	2,060
36		1,040	1,230	1,380	1,560	1,710	1,850	1,990	2,130	2,260
38		1,170	1,370	1,520	1,720	1,880	2,030	2,180	2,320	2,470
40		1,300	1,500	1,670	1,880	2,040	2,210	2,370	2,520	2,680
42				1,820	2,030	2,210	2,380	2,560	2,730	2,890
44				1,970	2,180	2,380	2,570	2,750	2,930	3,090
46				2,110	2,340	2,550	2,750	2,940	3,130	3,290
48				2,250	2,490	2,720	2,930	3,130	3,330	3,500
50				2,400	2,640	2,890	3,110	3,320	3,530	3,710

U.S.F.S., Meyer (1938), Josephson, 1941

Table A-30.   Volume, young-growth ponderosa pine, cubic feet.

Diameter at breast height (inches)	Volume* by total height													
	20 feet	30 feet	40 feet	50 feet	60 feet	70 feet	80 feet	90 feet	100 feet	110 feet	120 feet	130 feet	140 feet	150 feet
	Cu. ft.	Cu. ft.	Cu. ft.	Cu. ft.	Cu. ft.	Cu. ft.	Cu. ft.	Cu. ft.	Cu. ft.	Cu. ft.	Cu. ft.	Cu. ft.	Cu. ft.	Cu. ft.
4	0.8	1.2	1.5	1.9	2.2									
6	1.7	2.3	2.9	3.6	4.2	4.8	5.5							
8		3.7	4.9	6.0	7.1	8.3	9.5	11	12					
10		5.8	7.7	9.5	11.5	12.5	15.5	17.5	20	22	24			
12			11	14	17	20	23	26	29	32	35	38		
14			15	19	23	28	32	36	40	44	48	52	56	
16			20	26	31	36	42	47	52	58	63	68	72	76
18			26	33	40	46	53	60	66	74	80	86	92	98
20			32	41	50	58	66	74	83	91	99	107	114	121
22				49	60	70	80	90	100	110	119	129	137	146
24				59	71	83	96	107	119	130	141	151	162	171
26				70	84	98	112	125	139	152	164	177	186	199
28					98	114	130	144	160	175	189	203	216	229
30					112	130	148	165	182	198	214	230	244	259
32					126	146	167	186	204	222	239	257	272	288
34					140	165	186	208	226	246	265	284	300	316
36						182	206	230	250	271	290	311	328	344
38						200	227	252	274	296	315	337	356	374
40						220	248	274	298	321	341	364	384	404
42							269	296	322	346	367	391	412	433
44							290	318	346	371	393	418	440	462
46								340	370	396	419	445	468	492
48								362	394	421	445	472	496	521
50								385	418	446	471	499	524	550

U.S.F.S., Meyer, 1938

Table A-31.　Volume, old-growth incense-cedar, board feet, Scribner Decimal C rule to an 8-inch top.

Diameter breast high, inches	Number of 16-foot logs								
	1	2	3	4	5	6	7	8	9
	Volume—board feet, in tens								
12	3	5	11						
14	4	7	13						
16	5	9	15						
18	7	11	18						
20	8	13	21	30					
22		16	25	34					
24		19	29	39	51				
26		23	34	45	57				
28		27	40	51	65	83			
30		33	46	59	73	92			
32		40	53	67	83	102	121		
34		47	61	76	94	112	131		
36		55	70	87	105	124	143		
38		64	80	98	117	137	157	178	
40		73	92	111	131	152	174	196	
42		85	104	125	146	169	192	217	
44			118	142	163	186	211	238	267
46			134	159	182	205	231	260	293
48			151	178	202	224	251	283	320
50			169	197	221	244	274	308	350
52			188	217	239	265	296	336	384
54				239	255	285	320	365	420
56				262	271	305	345	396	457
58				286	290	325	370	429	497
60				311	320	344	396	461	540

U.S.F.S., Region 5, 1909–1911

Table A-32.　Volume, young-growth, incense-cedar, board feet, International ¼″ rule to a 4-inch top.

Diameter breast high	Total height of tree—feet						Basis
	30	40	50	60	70	80	
	Volume—board feet						
Inches							Trees
8	5	13	21				3
9	5	15	27				5
10	5	18	32	46			3
11		22	38	57			2
12		25	47	66	85		3
13			55	77	97		4
14			61	87	113		4
15			72	99	126	152	1
16			82	113	144	174	
17			91	125	161	197	3
18				141	182	222	
19				155	201	249	2
20				174	226	277	
21					254	310	
22					283	344	
23					317	383	
24					352	425	
Total							30

U.S.F.S., Dunning, 1923

Table A-33. Volume, young-growth incense-cedar, cubic feet.

Diameter breast high	Total height of tree—feet							Basis
	20	30	40	50	60	70	80	
	Total volume—cubic feet							
Inches								Trees
4	0.6	1.5						1
5	1.1	2.0						
6	1.6	2.8	4.1	5.6				
7	2.1	3.6	5.1	7.0				3
8		4.5	6.2	8.5				3
9		5.4	7.6	10.1				5
10		6.5	9.0	12.0	15.3			2
11			10.9	14.1	17.7			3
12			12.9	16.4	20.4	24.5		4
13				19.0	23.5	28.0		4
14				21.8	26.8	31.8	37.0	4
15				24.9	30.3	35.9	41.9	1
16				28.0	34.0	40.6	47.2	
17				31.5	38.5	45.6	53.4	3
18				35.3	43.2	51.2	60.3	
19				39.1	48.2	57.2	68.0	2
20				42.9	53.0	63.0	76.0	
Total								35

U.S.F.S., Dunning, 1923

Table A-34. Volume, old growth lodgepole pine, board feet, Scribner Decimal C rule to an 8-inch top.

Diameter breast high, inches	Number of 16-foot logs					
	1	2	3	4	5	6
	Volume—board feet, in tens					
12	3	6	11	16		
14	5	9	14	19		
16	7	12	17	23	31	
18	11	16	21	28	38	
20	18	20	27	35	45	
22	20	25	33	41	53	64
24	25	30	39	50	62	75
26	30	35	46	59	74	90
28	36	42	54	69	90	105
30	40	49	65	80	100	120
32	54	57	75	94	111	130
34	65	68	88	109	130	143
36		70	103	123	142	155
38		92	118	140	162	180
40			134	158	181	205
42			150	178	202	228
44			169	198	224	252
46			188	222	248	276
48				238	272	302

U.S.F.S.

Table A-35.   Volume, young-growth Sierra redwood, board feet, Scribner rule to a 6-inch top.

DBH (INCH)	MERCH. HEIGHT (FEET)															
	10	20	30	40	50	60	70	80	90	100	110	120	130	140	150	160
12	5	15	30	47	68	92	118	147	178	211	246	284	323	365	408	453
14	6	18	36	57	82	111	142	177	215	255	298	343	391	441	493	548
16	7	22	42	67	97	131	168	209	253	300	351	404	460	519	581	646
18	8	25	49	78	112	151	194	241	292	347	405	467	532	600	672	746
20	9	29	55	89	128	172	221	274	332	395	461	531	605	683	764	849
22	10	32	62	100	143	193	248	308	374	444	518	597	681	768	859	955
24	12	36	69	111	160	215	276	343	416	494	577	665	757	854	956	1062
26	13	40	77	122	176	237	305	379	459	545	636	733	835	943	1055	1172
28	14	43	84	134	193	260	334	415	503	597	697	803	915	1033	1155	1284
30	15	47	91	146	210	282	363	451	547	649	759	874	996	1124	1258	1397
32	16	51	99	158	227	306	393	489	592	703	821	946	1078	1217	1361	1512
34	18	55	106	170	245	329	424	526	638	757	885	1019	1162	1311	1467	1629
36	19	59	114	182	263	353	454	565	684	812	949	1094	1246	1406	1573	1748
38	20	63	122	195	281	378	486	604	731	868	1014	1169	1332	1502	1681	1868
40	22	67	130	208	299	402	517	643	779	925	1080	1245	1418	1600	1791	1989
42	23	71	138	221	317	427	549	682	827	982	1147	1322	1506	1699	1901	2112
44	24	75	146	234	336	452	581	723	876	1040	1214	1399	1594	1799	2013	2236
46	26	80	154	247	355	478	614	763	925	1098	1282	1478	1684	1900	2126	2362
48	27	84	163	260	374	503	647	804	974	1157	1351	1557	1774	2002	2240	2488
50	29	88	171	273	393	529	680	845	1024	1216	1421	1637	1865	2105	2355	2616
52	30	93	179	287	412	555	714	887	1075	1276	1491	1718	1957	2209	2471	2745
54	31	97	188	300	432	581	748	929	1126	1337	1562	1799	2050	2313	2589	2876
56	33	101	196	314	452	608	782	972	1177	1398	1633	1882	2144	2419	2707	3007
58	34	106	205	328	472	635	816	1015	1229	1459	1705	1964	2238	2526	2826	3140
60	36	110	214	342	492	662	851	1058	1281	1522	1777	2048	2333	2633	2946	3273

U.C., Wensel, Jan, Schoenheide, 1970

Table A-36. Volume, young-growth Sierra redwood, cubic feet.

DBH (INCHES)	TOTAL HEIGHT (FEET)													
	40	50	60	70	80	90	100	110	120	130	140	150	160	170
12	7	9	12	15	17	20	23	26	29	33	36	39	43	46
14	9	12	15	19	22	26	30	33	37	42	46	50	54	59
16	11	15	19	23	27	32	36	41	46	51	56	61	67	72
18	13	18	22	27	33	38	44	49	55	61	67	74	80	87
20	16	21	26	32	38	45	51	58	65	72	79	87	94	102
22	18	24	31	37	44	52	59	67	75	83	92	100	109	118
24	21	28	35	43	51	59	68	77	86	95	105	115	125	135
26	23	31	40	48	57	67	77	87	97	108	119	130	141	153
28	26	35	44	54	64	75	86	97	109	121	133	146	159	171
30	29	39	49	60	72	84	96	108	121	135	148	162	176	191
32	32	43	55	67	79	92	106	120	134	149	164	179	195	211
34	35	47	60	73	87	101	116	132	147	163	180	197	214	231
36	39	52	65	80	95	111	127	144	161	178	196	215	234	253
38	42	56	71	87	103	120	138	156	175	194	214	234	254	275
40	45	61	77	94	112	130	149	169	189	210	231	253	275	297
42	49	65	83	101	121	140	161	182	204	226	249	273	296	321
44	53	70	89	109	130	151	173	196	219	243	268	293	319	345
46	56	75	96	117	139	162	185	210	235	261	287	314	341	369
48	60	80	102	125	148	173	198	224	251	278	306	335	364	394
50	64	86	109	133	158	184	211	239	267	296	326	357	388	420
52	68	91	115	141	168	195	224	253	284	315	347	379	412	446
54	72	97	122	149	178	207	237	269	301	334	367	402	437	473
56	76	102	129	158	188	219	251	284	318	353	389	425	462	500
58	81	108	137	167	198	231	265	300	336	373	410	449	488	528
60	85	114	144	176	209	244	279	316	354	393	432	473	514	556

U.C., Wensel, Jan, Schoenheide, 1970

Table A-37. Volume, blue-gum eucalyptus, board feet,
Spaulding rule to a 6-inch top.

DBH	1	2	3	4	Number of 16–foot logs 5	6	7	8	9	10
11	20	48	80	117	160					
12	25	52	86	128	170					
13	32	60	97	140	182					
14	42	75	110	152	199					
15	60	91	125	173	220	300				
16	77	110	145	192	240	328				
17	99	133	170	218	269	357	427	512	665	
18	122	160	193	249	300	392	466	555	710	
19		190	226	282	337	432	510	601	770	
20		222	261	322	375	472	555	650	815	
21			300	362	418	520	605	705	875	
22			351	405	460	580	655	760	938	
23			386	452	510	622	715	821	1005	
24			438	502	560	680	772	885	1072	
25				557	618	741	840	952	1145	1279
26					673	803	910	1028	1225	1350
27					742	875	981	1102	1305	1439
28					815	949	1060	1182	1392	1527
29					887	1023	1142	1271	1482	1620
30					965	1101	1228	1358	1572	1715
31					1047	1190	1313	1450	1670	1812
32					1130	1275	1402	1541	1765	1917
33						1367	1502	1640	1820	2020
34						1460	1596	1745	1973	2129
35						1557	1695	1847	2080	2233
36						1655	1798	1947	2185	2342
37						1760	1900	2050	2295	2455
38						1860	2002	2155	2402	
39						1970	2110	2263	2520	
40								2375		
41								2490		

C.D.F., Barrette, 1974

Table A-38. Volume, blue-gum eucalyptus, cubic feet to a 6-inch top.

DBH	Number of 16-foot logs								
	1	2	3	4	5	6	7	8	9
10	8	12							
11	9	13							
12	10	14							
13	11	16	21	28					
14		18	24	30	37				
15		20	27	34	41	49	56		
16			30	39	47	55	63	72	
17			33	43	52	61	71	80	
18			36	47	58	68	79	88	
19			40	53	64	75	87	97	
20				58	70	82	95	106	
21					76	89	103	116	
22					84	97	112	126	
23					90	105	120	136	152
24					97	114	131	148	165
25					104	122	140	159	178
26					112	131	152	171	191
27					120	141	163	184	204
28						152	174	197	219
29						161	186	210	236
30						171	199	224	249
31						182	212	237	263
32						193	224	251	279
33						204	236	266	294
34						216	249	280	309
35						228	263	295	324
36						240	277	309	339
37						252	290	324	354
38						265	304	338	369
39						278	317	352	382
40							331	366	396
41							344	379	409
42								402	
43								404	

C.D.F., Barrette, 1974

Table A-39. Volume, coast live oak, blue oak, California white oak, interior live oak, tanoak, madrone, for California Central Coast, cubic feet to a 4-inch top.

DBH inches	HEIGHT IN FEET										
	5	10	15	20	25	30	35	40	45	50	55
4	0.3	0.4	0.6	0.7	0.9	1.0					
6	0.6	1.1	1.4	1.8	2.1	2.4	2.7	3.0			
8	1.2	2.0	2.7	3.3	4.0	4.6	5.1	5.7	6.2	6.7	7.2
10		3.2	4.4	5.4	6.4	7.4	8.3	9.2	10.1	10.9	11.8
12		4.8	6.5	8.1	9.6	11.0	12.4	13.7	15.0	16.3	17.5
14		6.7	9.1	11.3	13.4	15.4	17.3	19.2	21.0	22.7	24.5
16			12.1	15.1	17.9	20.6	23.2	25.6	28.0	30.4	32.7
18			15.7	19.5	23.1	26.6	29.9	33.1	36.2	39.3	42.2
20			19.7	24.5	29.1	33.4	37.6	41.6	45.5	49.4	53.1
22				30.2	35.8	41.1	46.3	51.2	56.0	60.7	65.3
24				36.5	43.2	49.7	55.9	61.9	67.7	73.4	78.9
26				43.4	51.4	59.1	66.5	73.6	80.6	87.3	93.9
28				51.0	60.4	69.4	78.1	86.5	94.6	102.5	110.3
30					70.2	80.7	90.7	100.5	109.9	119.1	128.1
32					80.8	92.8	104.4	115.6	126.5	137.1	147.4
34					92.1	105.9	119.1	131.9	144.3	156.4	168.2
36					104.3	119.9	134.9	149.3	163.4	177.1	190.4
38						134.8	151.7	168.0	183.7	199.1	214.2
40						150.7	169.6	187.8	205.4	222.6	239.4
42						167.6	188.5	208.8	228.4	247.5	266.2
44						185.4	208.6	231.0	252.7	273.8	294.5
46						204.2	229.7	254.4	278.3	301.6	324.4
48								279.0	305.3	330.8	355.8
50								304.9	333.6	361.5	388.8
52								332.0	363.3	393.7	423.4
54								360.4	394.3	427.3	459.6

DBH	HEIGHT IN FEET										
inches	60	65	70	75	80	85	90	95	100	105	110
4											
6											
8	7.7	8.2									
10	12.6	13.4	14.1								
12	18.7	19.9	21.0								
14	26.1	27.8	29.4								
16	34.9	37.1	39.3	41.4	43.5	45.6	47.6	49.6	51.6	53.5	55.5
18	45.1	48.0	50.8	53.5	56.2	58.9	61.5	64.1	66.6	69.2	71.7
20	56.7	60.3	63.8	67.3	70.7	74.0	77.3	80.6	83.8	86.9	90.1
22	69.8	74.2	78.5	82.7	86.9	91.0	95.1	99.1	103.0	107.0	110.8
24	84.3	89.6	94.8	100.0	105.0	110.0	114.9	119.7	124.5	129.2	133.9
26	100.3	106.6	112.8	118.9	125.0	130.9	136.7	142.5	148.2	153.8	159.3
28	117.9	125.3	132.6	139.7	146.8	153.7	160.6	167.4	174.0	180.6	187.2
30	136.9	145.5	154.0	162.3	170.5	178.6	186.6	194.4	202.2	209.9	217.4
32	157.5	167.5	177.2	186.8	196.2	205.5	214.7	223.7	232.6	241.5	250.2
34	179.7	191.0	202.2	213.1	223.8	234.4	244.9	255.2	265.4	275.5	285.4
36	203.5	216.3	228.9	241.3	253.4	265.4	277.3	289.0	300.5	311.9	323.2
38	228.9	243.3	257.4	271.3	285.0	298.5	311.8	325.0	337.9	350.8	363.4
40	255.8	272.0	287.8	303.3	318.6	333.7	348.6	363.3	377.8	392.1	406.3
42	284.5	302.4	320.0	337.3	354.3	371.1	387.6	403.9	420.1	436.0	451.7
44	314.7	334.5	354.0	373.1	392.0	410.5	428.8	446.9	464.7	482.4	499.8
46	346.6	368.5	389.9	411.0	431.7	452.2	472.3	492.2	511.9	531.3	550.5
48	380.2	404.2	427.7	450.8	473.6	496.0	518.1	539.9	561.5	582.8	603.8
50	415.5	441.7	467.4	492.6	517.5	542.0	566.2	590.0	613.6	636.8	659.8
52	452.5	481.0	508.9	536.5	563.5	590.2	616.5	642.5	668.1	693.5	718.6
54	491.1	522.1	552.4	582.3	611.7	640.7	669.2	697.4	725.3	752.8	780.0

Cal. Poly State U., S.L.O., Pillsbury and Stephens, 1978

Table A-40. Volume, red alder, board feet, Scribner Dec. C rule to a 10-inch top.

D.B.H. inches	Number of 8-foot logs									
	1	2	3	4	5	6	7	8	9	10
	Volume—board feet, in tens									
10	3									
11	3	6	9							
12	3	6	9	11	14	16				
13		7	10	13	16	18				
14		8	10	14	17	21	25	30		
15		9	11	16	19	23	27	32		
16		10	12	18	22	26	30	36	43	49
17			14	20	25	29	33	40	46	53
18			16	22	27	32	37	44	50	58
19			18	25	30	36	42	48	54	62
20			20	28	33	40	45	52	59	67
21				31	37	44	50	56	64	72
22				35	41	48	55	62	69	77
23					46	54	60	66	74	83
24					51	59	65	72	79	89
25					57	64	70	77	84	94
26						70	76	82	90	100
27						76	82	88	96	106
28						82	88	94	101	111

U.S.F.S., Meyer, 1931

Table A-41. Volume, young-growth madrone, tanoak, and black oak, high site, board feet (8-inch top), cubic ft. (4-inch top).

D.b.h. (inches)	Board Feet Volume, Scribner Dec. C			Cubic Feet Volume		
	Pacific madrone	Tanoak	Calif. black oak	Pacific madrone	Tanoak	Calif. black oak
4	—	—	—	1	—	—
5	—	—	—	2	1	1
6	—	—	—	3	2	3
7	—	—	—	5	4	5
8	—	—	—	7	5	7
9	1	1	1	10	8	9
10	2	2	2	13	10	12
11	3	3	4	16	13	16
12	5	4	5	20	16	20
13	7	5	7	25	19	24
14	9	6	9	30	23	29
15	12	8	12	36	27	34
16	15	10	15	43	32	40
17	18	12	18	50	37	46
18	22	15	21	58	43	52
19	26	18	25	67	49	60
20	30	20	29	76	55	67
21	35	24	33	86	62	76
22	40	27	38	97	69	84
23	45	31	43	109	77	94
24	51	35	48	121	85	104
25	57	40	54	135	94	114
26	64	44	60	149	103	125
27	71	50	66	164	113	137
28	78	55	73	180	123	149
29	86	61	80	196	134	162
30	94	67	88	214	145	176

U.S.F.S., Pacific Southwest Forest and Range Experiment Station, McDonald, 1969

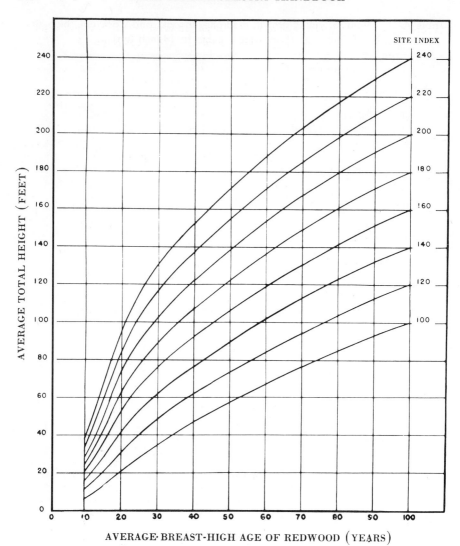

Figure A-1. Site index values of dominant redwood by height and breast-high age classes.

U.C., Lindquist and Palley, 1963

Table A-42. Yield table, young-growth coast redwood stand, all species, per acre, board feet, International $\frac{1}{4}''$ rule, trees larger than 10.5 inches dbh to an 8-inch top.

Age (years)	Site index (feet)							
	100	120	140	160	180	200	220	240
20	. . .	600	2,300	7,000	14,500	23,900	35,000	46,500
30	900	3,100	9,500	19,600	34,500	52,300	71,600	93,200
40	2,800	8,800	20,400	36,900	57,900	82,100	108,700	137,500
50	7,300	16,500	33,700	55,300	82,000	112,700	146,000	181,300
60	14,400	27,400	48,900	74,500	106,100	142,100	180,900	221,900
70	22,800	40,400	65,000	94,500	130,400	170,900	214,400	259,500
80	32,400	53,700	81,500	114,300	153,500	198,200	244,800	293,500
90	44,000	67,400	98,300	133,800	176,400	224,100	273,600	325,700
100	55,760	81,300	114,600	152,300	198,100	248,500	301,700	357,600

U.C., Lindquist and Palley, 1963

Table A-43. Yield table, young-growth coast redwood stand, all species, per acre, cubic feet, trees larger than 4.5 inches dbh to a 4-inch top.

Age (years)	Site index							
	100	120	140	160	180	200	220	240
20	200	450	1,000	2,270	3,990	5,910	7,860	9,940
30	500	1,050	2,500	4,400	7,040	10,000	13,000	16,200
40	1,000	2,300	4,500	7,250	10,550	14,250	18,000	22,000
50	2,100	3,800	6,800	10,100	14,060	18,500	23,000	27,800
60	3,600	5,820	9,220	12,960	17,450	22,480	27,580	33,020
70	5,200	8,000	11,750	15,880	20,820	26,380	32,000	38,000
80	6,900	10,140	14,190	18,640	23,990	29,980	36,060	42,540
90	8,800	12,260	16,580	21,340	27,050	33,450	39,940	46,860
100	10,600	14,280	18,880	23,940	30,010	36,820	43,720	51,080

U.C., Lindquist and Palley, 1963

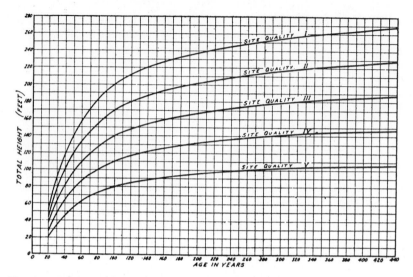

Figure A-2. Site index values of dominant and codominant Douglas-fir trees

U.S.F.S., McArdle, Meyer, Bruce, 1949

Table A-44.   Yield table, Douglas-fir, fully stocked acre, board feet, Scribner rule, trees larger than 12 inches dbh to an 8-inch top.

Age/Site Index	80	90	100	110	120	130	140	150	160	170	180	190	200	210
	Bd. ft.	Bd. ft.	Bd. ft.	Bd. ft.	Bd. ft.	Bd. ft.	Bd. ft.	Bd. ft.	Bd. ft.	Bd. ft.	Bd. ft.	Bd. ft.	Bd. ft.	Bd. ft.
30	0	0	0	0	0	0	300	900	1,500	2,600	4,000	6,000	8,000	10,500
40	0	0	0	200	1,200	2,600	4,500	6,500	9,000	11,900	15,500	19,600	24,100	29,400
50	30	200	1,600	3,300	5,500	8,400	12,400	17,600	22,200	27,400	32,700	38,400	44,100	50,000
60	1,100	2,600	4,800	8,100	12,500	18,000	23,800	29,600	36,200	42,800	49,300	55,900	62,000	68,300
70	2,400	5,300	9,000	14,000	20,600	27,000	35,200	42,500	50,200	57,200	64,600	71,500	78,200	85,000
80	4,400	8,600	13,900	20,100	28,600	37,000	45,700	54,300	62,100	70,200	78,000	85,400	92,500	99,800
90	6,900	12,000	18,600	26,000	35,700	45,200	55,000	64,000	72,000	81,000	89,210	97,100	104,800	112,300
100	9,600	15,400	22,800	31,400	42,000	52,400	62,800	72,400	81,800	90,100	98,900	107,100	115,100	122,900
110	12,200	18,900	26,700	36,300	47,500	58,500	69,400	79,400	89,200	98,300	107,000	115,200	123,700	131,200
120	14,700	21,800	30,400	40,700	52,400	63,900	75,000	85,500	95,300	105,100	114,100	122,300	131,100	139,000
130	17,000	24,600	33,800	44,700	56,700	68,700	80,000	91,000	101,100	111,000	120,000	128,900	137,700	146,100
140	19,200	27,200	36,800	48,300	60,000	72,900	84,500	95,900	106,200	116,000	125,500	134,500	143,500	152,000
150	21,300	29,600	39,700	51,600	64,000	76,600	88,600	100,300	111,000	121,200	130,700	139,500	148,700	157,200
160	23,300	31,900	42,200	54,600	67,100	80,100	92,400	104,400	115,400	125,700	135,400	144,400	153,500	162,000

U.S.F.S., McArdle, Meyer, Bruce, 1949

Table A-45.   Yield Table, Douglas-fir, fully stocked acre, cubic feet, trees larger than 12 inches dbh.

Age/Site Index	80	90	100	110	120	130	140	150	160	170	180	190	200	210
	Cu. ft.	Cu. ft.	Cu. ft.	Cu. ft.	Cu. ft.	Cu. ft.	Cu. ft.	Cu. ft.	Cu. ft.	Cu. ft.	Cu. ft.	Cu. ft.	Cu. ft.	Cu. ft.
20	0	0	0	0	0	0	0	0	0	0	30	80	140	200
30	0	0	0	0	0	70	150	300	490	730	1,020	1,400	1,850	2,450
40	0	0	60	190	430	760	1,190	1,660	2,250	2,960	3,780	4,750	5,650	6,450
50	0	170	470	850	1,430	2,200	3,100	4,120	5,200	6,300	7,380	8,440	9,290	10,000
60	60	680	1,200	1,990	3,030	4,225	5,650	7,000	8,200	9,400	10,400	11,330	12,050	12,770
70	310	1,360	2,190	3,400	4,970	6,550	8,000	9,400	10,650	11,820	12,750	13,650	14,330	14,950
80	720	2,110	3,300	4,800	6,500	8,380	9,940	11,380	12,570	13,720	14,650	15,500	16,230	16,900
90	1,240	2,980	4,370	6,100	8,050	9,800	11,430	12,850	14,100	15,230	16,200	17,050	17,850	18,500
100	1,820	3,690	5,350	7,170	9,130	10,950	12,620	14,000	15,300	16,410	17,440	18,300	19,140	19,820
110	2,410	4,500	6,190	8,050	10,020	11,880	13,530	14,980	16,290	17,430	18,450	19,350	20,200	20,940
120	3,000	5,150	6,800	8,760	10,760	12,620	14,300	15,760	17,100	18,270	19,300	20,220	21,090	21,870
130	3,570	5,720	7,470	9,360	11,360	13,240	14,920	16,410	17,760	18,960	20,000	20,980	21,840	22,660
140	4,120	6,190	7,960	9,860	11,880	13,790	15,450	16,980	18,350	19,580	20,640	21,610	22,520	23,360
150	4,600	6,600	8,390	10,300	12,320	14,250	15,910	17,480	18,870	20,130	21,270	22,250	23,170	24,030
160	5,350	6,950	8,750	10,700	12,750	14,690	16,340	17,950	19,350	20,650	21,820	22,830	23,760	24,660

U.S.F.S., McArdle, Meyer, Bruce, 1949

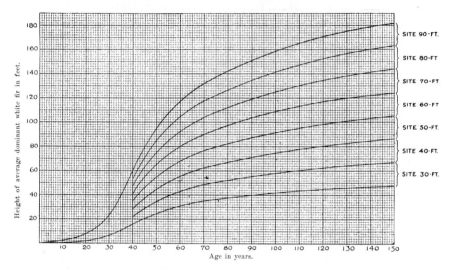

Figure A-3   Site index values of white fir (A. concolor) trees

U.C., Schumacher, 1926

Table A-46   Yield table, normal, white fir (A. concolor), per acre, board feet (in tens), International $\frac{1}{8}'$ rule, trees 8 inches dbh and over to a 5-inch top.

	Site Index at 50 Years					
Age	40	50	60	70	80	90
				board feet in tens		
50	220	970	2060	3190	4320	5240
60	920	2110	3650	5260	6900	8150
70	1570	3050	5000	5960	8930	10440
80	2110	3760	6000	8220	10410	12200
90	2580	4330	6750	9180	11770	13610
100	2900	4840	7400	10070	12740	14780
110	3170	5190	7920	10800	13610	15600
120	3390	5480	8360	11310	14260	16380
130	3600	5780	8810	11810	14850	17100
140	3750	5970	9140	12180	15300	17670
150	3880	6160	9380	12540	15700	18130

U.C. Schumacher, 1926

Table A-47. Yield table, normal, white fir (A. concolor), per acre, cubic feet in tens, trees 4 inches dbh and over.

Age	Site Index at 50 Years						
	30	40	50	60	70	80	90
	cubic feet in tens						
50	215	270	380	530	670	810	900
60	300	380	530	740	940	1140	1260
70	360	450	640	900	1140	1370	1520
80	400	500	710	1000	1270	1520	1690
90	430	550	770	1080	1370	1660	1840
100	460	580	820	1150	1460	1760	1960
110	480	610	860	1200	1540	1850	2050
120	500	635	890	1250	1590	1920	2130
130	515	655	920	1295	1640	1980	2200
140	530	670	940	1330	1680	2030	2260
150	545	690	965	1360	1720	2080	2310

U.C., Schumacher, 1926

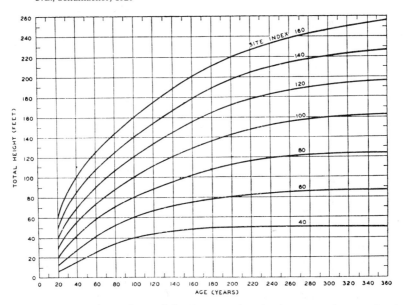

Figure A-4. Site index values of dominant and codominant ponderosa pine trees of average breast high diameter.

U.S.F.S., Meyer, 1938

Table A-48.   Yield table, ponderosa pine, fully stocked acre, board feet, Scribner rule, trees 11.6 inches dbh and over.

Age (years)	Volume per acre, by site index—												
	40	50	60	70	80	90	100	110	120	130	140	150	160
	Bd.ft.	Bd.ft.	Bd.ft.	Bd.ft.	Bd.ft.	Bd.ft.	Bd.ft.	Bd.ft.	Bd.ft.	Bd.ft.	Bd.ft.	Bd.ft.	Bd.ft.
20								100	400	900	1,900	3,800	7,300
30						200	1,000	2,500	5,100	8,400	11,800	16,000	21,400
40				100	600	1,900	4,300	7,500	12,100	17,600	23,100	29,200	36,500
50			100	700	2,300	5,000	9,200	14,000	20,300	27,400	34,600	42,500	51,300
60			600	2,200	5,100	9,100	14,800	21,000	28,400	37,000	45,800	55,300	65,400
70		300	1,800	4,300	8,500	13,800	20,500	27,800	36,400	46,200	56,500	67,300	78,800
80	100	900	3,500	7,000	12,200	18,500	26,000	34,200	43,900	54,800	66,500	78,600	91,300
90	200	2,000	5,500	10,000	16,000	23,000	31,200	40,200	50,800	62,700	75,800	89,200	103,000
100	400	3,800	7,800	13,100	19,700	27,200	36,100	45,800	57,100	70,000	84,400	99,100	113,900
110	800	5,000	10,200	16,200	23,100	31,100	40,600	50,800	62,900	76,700			
120	1,500	7,000	12,500	19,000	26,200	34,700	44,600	55,400	68,200	82,800			
130	2,500	8,900	14,700	21,500	29,000	38,000	48,300	59,600	73,000	88,300			
140	3,800	10,700	16,700	23,700	31,500	40,900	51,700	63,400	77,400	93,200			
150	5,200	12,400	18,500	25,700	33,800	43,600	54,800	66,900	81,400	97,600			
160	6,600	13,900	20,100	27,500	35,900	46,100	57,600	70,100	84,900	101,500			
170	7,900	15,300	21,600	29,200	37,800	48,400	60,100	73,000	88,000	105,000			
180	9,000	16,600	23,100	30,900	39,600	50,500	62,400	75,600	90,900	108,200			
190	10,000	17,800	24,500	32,500	41,300	52,400	64,600	78,000	93,600	111,200			
200	11,000	19,000	25,800	34,000	43,000	54,200	66,700	80,200	96,100	114,100			

U.S.F.S., Meyer, 1938

Table A-49.   Yield table, ponderosa pine, fully stocked acre, cubic feet, trees 11.6 inches dbh and over.

Age (years)	Volume per acre, by site index—												
	40	50	60	70	80	90	100	110	120	130	140	150	160
	Cu.ft.	Cu.ft.	Cu.ft.	Cu.ft.	Cu.ft.	Cu.ft.	Cu.ft.	Cu.ft.	Cu.ft.	Cu.ft.	Cu.ft.	Cu.ft.	Cu.ft.
20								40	120	280	530	1,060	1,880
30						60	200	470	970	1,860	2,750	3,760	4,910
40				30	120	340	820	1,740	2,770	3,990	5,230	6,580	7,950
50			30	150	410	970	2,060	3,230	4,600	6,170	7,670	9,260	10,780
60		30	120	400	990	2,040	3,280	4,710	6,320	8,080	9,830	11,520	13,140
70		90	310	870	1,870	3,090	4,440	6,110	7,910	9,730	11,590	13,380	15,080
80	50	220	710	1,650	2,720	4,110	5,540	7,310	9,210	11,100	13,030	14,880	16,640
90	110	470	1,310	2,400	3,520	5,010	6,520	8,310	10,280	12,230	14,200	16,110	17,940
100	240	870	1,960	3,100	4,270	5,790	7,310	9,130	11,140	13,140	15,160	17,430	19,020
110	460	1,370	2,560	3,710	4,890	6,420	7,950	9,780	11,800	13,900			
120	780	1,820	3,060	4,220	5,410	6,950	8,490	10,330	12,360	14,540			
130	1,140	2,210	3,460	4,640	5,850	7,400	8,950	10,800	12,840	15,070			
140	1,450	2,550	3,810	5,000	6,230	7,780	9,340	11,200	13,250	15,500			
150	1,720	2,840	4,110	5,320	6,560	8,120	9,680	11,550	13,600	15,850			
160	1,950	3,080	4,360	5,600	6,840	8,420	9,990	11,850	13,950	16,200			
170	2,160	3,300	4,590	5,840	7,090	8,680	10,270	12,150	14,250	16,550			
180	2,360	3,510	4,810	6,060	7,320	8,920	10,500	12,400	14,550	16,900			
190	2,550	3,710	5,020	6,270	7,530	9,140	10,750	12,650	14,850	17,250			
200	2,730	3,900	5,220	6,470	7,730	9,340	10,950	12,850	15,100	17,600			

U.S.F.S., Meyer, 1938

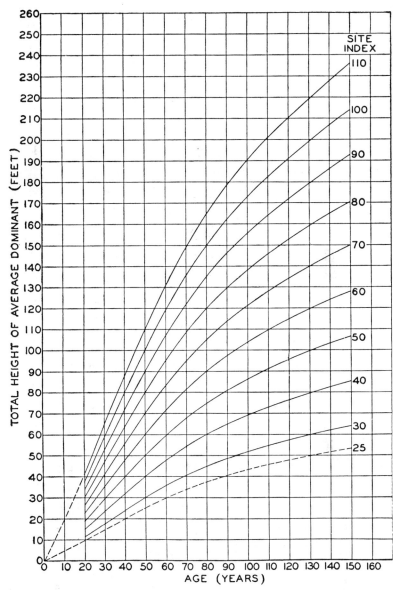

Figure A-5. Site index values of dominant trees in mixed conifer stands in.
California of average basal area.

U.S.F.S., Dunning, 1933

Table A-50.   Yield table, mixed conifer stands, California, per acre, board feet, International ⅛" rule, trees 8 inches dbh and over to a 5-inch top.

Age (years)	Board feet per acre on site index—									
	25	30	40	50	60	70	80	90	100	110
30			85	450	1,100	2,120	3,840	6,030	8,670	11,110
40	700	940	1,740	3,210	5,540	9,100	14,300	20,500	26,800	33,450
50	2,300	2,980	5,050	8,300	13,200	20,340	29,850	40,100	50,500	60,700
60	4,720	6,100	9,970	15,750	23,500	34,300	47,900	61,950	76,750	90,200
70	8,330	10,250	15,950	24,300	35,400	48,950	65,400	83,250	102,100	118,900
80	11,900	14,550	21,950	32,700	45,300	61,650	81,400	102,400	122,800	142,300
90	15,450	18,500	27,950	40,000	54,300	73,000	95,750	118,400	142,200	161,900
100	18,600	22,300	33,100	46,850	63,150	84,250	108,200	133,400	158,200	179,400
110	21,550	25,900	38,100	53,450	70,700	93,850	120,100	146,200	172,200	195,600
120	24,600	29,250	42,400	58,750	78,400	103,400	130,500	158,400	186,200	209,700
130	27,000	31,900	46,350	64,400	85,550	111,400	140,500	170,400	198,000	222,900
140	29,350	34,650	50,250	69,600	92,050	118,600	149,400	180,200	209,700	235,500
150	31,900	37,600	54,400	74,550	98,250	125,800	157,700	189,600	220,400	247,900

U.S.F.S., Dunning, 1933

Table A-51.   Yield table, average mixed conifer stands, California, per acre, cubic feet, trees 8 inches dbh and over.

Age (years)	Volume in cubic feet per acre on site index—									
	25	30	40	50	60	70	80	90	100	110
30	930	1,060	1,420	1,800	2,200	2,650	3,200	3,770	4,380	4,850
40	1,590	1,800	2,410	3,090	3,770	4,550	5,500	6,500	7,450	8,450
50	2,260	2,590	3,480	4,440	5,420	5,560	7,940	9,300	10,700	12,000
60	2,950	3,350	4,510	5,790	7,020	8,550	10,300	12,100	13,900	15,500
70	3,500	4,000	5,350	6,850	8,450	10,200	12,200	14,300	16,500	18,400
80	4,000	4,540	6,100	7,800	9,520	11,500	13,800	16,200	18,600	20,900
90	4,420	5,000	6,750	8,600	10,500	12,700	15,200	17,800	20,700	23,100
100	4,830	5,500	7,400	9,450	11,500	13,900	16,600	19,500	22,600	25,200
110	5,200	5,950	8,000	10,200	12,300	14,900	17,900	21,000	24,250	27,200
120	5,600	6,390	8,550	10,800	13,200	16,000	19,100	22,500	26,000	29,000
130	5,900	6,700	9,050	11,500	14,000	16,900	20,300	24,000	27,500	30,700
140	6,220	7,070	9,550	12,100	14,750	17,750	21,400	25,200	29,000	32,400
150	6,550	7,430	10,000	12,700	15,450	18,550	22,400	26,400	30,400	34,000

U.S.F.S., Dunning, 1938

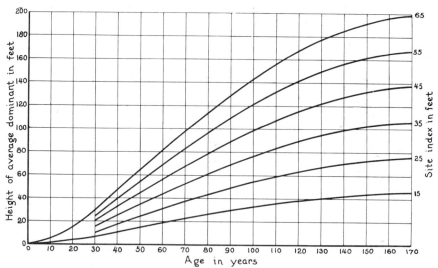

Figure A-6   Site index values of average dominant red fir trees.

U.C., Schumacher, 1928

Table A-52. Yield table, normal, red fir, per acre, board feet in tens, International ⅛' rule, trees 8 inches dbh and over to a 5-inch top.

| Age | Site Index at 50 Years | | | | |
	20	30	40	50	60
			board feet in tens		
50	—	210	605	1200	1920
60	150	695	1440	2380	3370
70	495	1460	2500	3680	5040
80	1030	2360	3710	5200	7110
90	1780	3380	5020	7050	9430
100	2560	4450	6570	9120	11900
110	3460	5770	8400	11250	14500
120	4400	7280	10450	13800	17200
130	5280	8600	12200	15600	19600
140	6040	9660	13600	17300	21600
150	6700	10800	14500	18400	23000

U.C., Schumacher, 1928

Table A-53. Yield table, normal, red fir, per acre, cubic feet in tens, trees 2 inches dbh and over.

| Age | Site Index at 50 Years | | | | |
	20	30	40	50	60
			cubic feet in tens		
50	180	245	320	405	500
60	245	340	435	560	695
70	320	440	570	720	900
80	405	555	720	905	1140
90	495	680	880	1110	1385
100	595	815	1055	1340	1670
110	720	980	1270	1610	2010
120	845	1165	1510	1915	2390
130	965	1320	1715	2170	2720
140	1060	1455	1895	2395	3000
150	1135	1560	2010	2550	3190

U.C., Schumacher, 1928

Table A-54. Revised Scribner Decimal C log rule, logs 8 to 20 feet long, board feet in tens.

DBH inches	8	10	12	Log Length in Feet 14	16	17	18	20
4	1	1	1	1	1	1	1	1
5	1	1	1	1	2	2	2	2
6	1	1	1	2	2	2	2	2
7	1	1	2	2	3	3	3	3
8	1	2	2	2	3	3	3	4
9	2	2	3	3	4	4	4	5
10	3	3	4	4	6	6	6	7
11	3	4	4	5	7	7	8	8
12	4	5	6	7	8	8	9	10
13	5	6	7	8	10	10	11	12
14	6	7	9	10	11	12	13	14
15	7	9	11	12	14	15	16	18
16	8	10	12	14	16	17	18	20
17	9	12	14	16	18	20	21	23
18	11	13	16	19	21	23	24	27
19	12	15	18	21	24	25	27	30
20	14	17	21	24	28	30	31	35
21	15	19	23	27	30	32	34	38
22	17	21	25	29	33	35	38	42
23	19	24	28	33	38	40	42	47
24	20	25	30	35	40	43	45	50
25	23	29	34	40	46	49	52	57
26	25	31	37	44	50	53	56	62
27	27	34	41	48	55	58	62	68
28	29	36	44	51	58	62	65	73
29	30	38	46	53	61	65	68	76
30	33	41	49	57	66	70	74	82
31	36	44	53	62	71	75	80	89
32	37	46	55	64	74	78	83	92
33	39	49	59	69	78	83	88	98
34	40	50	60	70	80	85	90	100
35	44	55	66	77	88	93	98	109
36	46	58	69	81	92	98	104	115
37	51	64	77	90	103	109	116	129
38	53	67	80	93	107	113	120	133
39	56	70	84	98	112	119	126	140
40	60	75	90	105	120	128	135	150
41	64	79	95	111	127	135	143	159
42	67	84	101	117	134	143	151	168
43	70	87	105	122	140	148	157	174
44	74	93	111	130	148	157	167	185
45	76	95	114	133	152	161	171	190
46	79	99	119	139	159	168	178	198
47	83	104	124	145	166	176	186	207
48	86	108	130	151	173	184	194	216
49	90	112	135	157	180	191	202	225
50	94	117	140	164	187	199	211	234

DBH inches	8	10	12	Log Length in Feet 14	16	17	18	20
51	97	122	146	170	195	207	219	243
52	101	127	152	177	202	215	228	253
53	105	132	158	184	210	224	237	263
54	109	137	164	191	218	232	246	273
55	113	142	170	198	227	241	255	283
56	118	147	176	206	235	250	264	294
57	122	152	183	213	244	259	274	304
58	126	158	189	221	252	268	284	315
59	131	163	196	229	261	278	294	327
60	135	169	203	237	270	287	304	338
61	140	175	210	245	280	297	315	350
62	145	181	217	253	289	307	325	361
63	149	187	224	261	299	317	336	373
64	155	193	232	270	309	328	348	386
65	159	199	239	279	319	339	358	398
66	165	206	247	288	329	350	370	411
67	169	212	254	297	339	360	381	424
68	175	219	262	306	350	371	393	437
69	181	226	271	316	361	384	406	451
70	186	232	279	325	372	395	418	465
71	191	239	287	335	383	407	431	479
72	197	247	296	345	395	419	444	493
73	203	254	305	356	406	432	457	508
74	209	262	314	366	418	445	471	523
75	215	269	323	377	430	457	484	538
76	221	277	332	387	443	470	498	553
77	227	284	341	398	455	483	512	569
78	234	293	351	410	468	497	527	585
79	241	301	361	421	481	511	541	601
80	247	309	371	433	494	525	556	618
81	254	317	381	444	508	540	571	635
82	261	326	391	456	521	554	586	652
83	267	334	401	468	535	568	602	668
84	275	343	412	481	549	584	618	687
85	281	351	421	491	561	596	631	702
86	287	359	431	503	575	611	646	718
87	295	368	442	516	589	626	663	737
88	301	377	452	527	603	640	678	753
89	308	385	462	539	616	655	693	770
90	315	393	472	551	629	669	708	787

Prepared by Northwest Log Rule Advisory Group, 1972, recognized by C.D.F., U.S.F.S., State Board of Equalization, and others.

Table A-55. Log volume, cubic feet, Huber formula.

Length (feet)	Contents (cubic feet) according to middle diameter, in inches—																													
	3	4	5	6	7	8	9	10	11	12	13	14	15	16	17	18	19	20	21	22	23	24	25	26	27	28	29	30	31	32
4	0.25	0.25	0.5	1	1	1	2	2	3	3	4	4	5	6	6	7	8	9	10	11	12	13	14	15	16	17	18	20	21	22
5	.25	.5	.5	1	1	2	2	3	3	4	4	5	6	7	8	9	10	11	12	13	14	16	17	18	20	21	23	25	26	28
6	.25	.5	1	1	2	2	3	3	4	4	5	6	7	8	9	11	12	13	14	16	17	19	20	22	24	26	28	29	31	34
7	.25	.5	1	1	2	3	3	4	5	5	6	7	9	10	11	12	14	15	17	18	20	22	24	26	28	30	32	34	37	39
8	.5	.5	1	2	2	3	4	4	5	6	7	9	10	11	13	14	16	17	19	21	23	25	27	29	32	34	37	39	42	45
9	.5	1	1	2	3	3	4	5	6	7	8	10	11	13	14	16	18	19	22	24	26	28	31	33	36	38	41	44	47	50
10	.5	1	1	2	3	4	5	5	7	7	9	11	12	14	16	18	20	22	24	26	29	31	34	37	40	43	46	49	52	56
11	.5	1	2	2	3	4	5	6	7	8	10	12	13	15	17	19	22	24	26	29	32	35	37	41	44	47	50	54	58	61
12	.5	1	2	3	4	5	6	7	8	9	11	13	15	17	19	21	24	26	29	32	35	38	41	44	48	51	55	59	63	67
13	.5	1	2	3	4	5	6	7	9	9	12	14	16	18	20	23	26	28	31	34	38	41	44	48	52	56	60	64	68	73
14	.5	1	2	3	4	6	7	8	9	11	13	15	17	20	22	25	28	31	34	37	40	44	48	52	56	60	64	69	73	78
15	.5	1	2	3	5	6	7	8	10	12	13	16	18	21	24	26	30	33	36	40	43	47	51	55	60	64	69	74	79	84
16	1	1	2	4	5	6	8	9	11	12	14	18	20	23	25	28	32	35	38	43	46	50	55	59	64	68	73	79	84	89
17	1	2	2	4	5	7	8	9	11	13	15	19	21	24	27	30	33	37	41	45	49	53	58	63	68	73	78	83	89	95
18	1	2	3	4	6	7	9	10	12	13	16	20	22	25	28	32	35	39	43	48	52	57	61	66	72	77	83	88	94	101
19	1	2	3	4	6	7	9	10	13	14	17	21	23	27	30	34	37	41	46	51	55	60	65	70	76	81	87	93	100	106
20	1	2	3	5	6	8	10	11	13	15	18	22	25	28	32	35	39	44	48	53	58	63	68	74	80	86	92	98	105	112
21	1	2		5	7	8	11	11	14	16	19	23	26	29	33	37	41	46	50	56	61	66	72	77	83	90	96	103	110	117
22	1	2		5	7	8	11	12	15	16	20	25	27	31	35	39	43	48	53	58	64	69	75	81	87	94	101	108	115	123
23	1	2		5	7	9	12	13	16	18	21	26	28	32	36	41	45	50	55	61	66	72	78	85	91	98	105	113	121	128
24	1	2		6	7	9	13	13	16	19	22	27	29	34	38	42	47	52	57	63	69	75	82	88	95	103	110	118	126	134
25	1	2		6	8	10	13	14	17	20	23	28	31	35	39	44	49	55	60	66	72	79	85	92	99	107	115	123	131	140
26				6	8	10	14	15	18	20	24	29	32	38	41	46	51	57	63	69	75	82	89	96	103	111	119	128	136	145
27				6	8	11	14	15	19	21	25	30	33	39	43	48	53	59	65	71	78	85	92	100	107	115	124	133	142	151
28				7	9	12	15	16	20	22	26	31	34	40	44	49	55	61	67	74	81	88	95	103	111	120	128	137	147	156
29				7	9	12	15	17	20	24	27	32	36	42	46	51	57	63	70	77	84	91	99	107	115	124	133	142	152	162
30				7	9	13	16	17	21	24	28	33	37	43	47	53	59	65	72	79	87	94	102	111	119	128	138	147	157	168
31				7	10	13	16	18	22	26	29	35	38	45	49	55	61	68	74	82	89	97	106	114	123	133	142	152	162	173
32				8	10	13	17	19	22	27	30	36	40	46	50	57	63	70	77	84	92	101	109	118	127	137	147	157	168	179
33				8	10	14	17	20	24	28	31	37	42	47	52	58	65	72	79	87	95	104	112	122	131	141	151	162	173	184
34					11	14	18	20	24	29	32	38	43	49	54	60	67	74	82	90	98	107	116	125	135	145	156	167	178	190
35								21	26	30	33	40	44	50	55	62	69	76	84	92	101	110	119	129	139	150	161	172	183	195
36								21	26	31	34	41	45	52	57	64	71	79	87	95	104	113	123	133	143	154	165	177	189	201
37								22		31	35	43	47	53	58	65	73	81	89	98	107	116	126	136	147	158	170	182	194	207
38											37		48	54	60	67	75	83	91	100	110	119	130	140	151	162	174	187	199	212
39													49	56	61	69	77	85	94	103	113	123	133	144	155	167	179	191	204	218
40															63	71	79	87	96	106	115	126	136	147	159	171	183	196	210	223

Contents (cubic feet) according to middle diameter, in inches—

Length (feet)	33	34	35	36	37	38	39	40	41	42	43	44	45	46	47	48	49	50	51	52	53	54	55	56	57	58	59	60
4	24	25	27	28	30	32	33	35	37	38	40	42	44	46	48	50	52	55	57	59	61	64	66	68	71	73	76	79
5	30	32	33	35	37	39	41	44	46	48	50	53	55	58	60	63	65	68	71	74	77	80	82	86	89	92	95	98
6	36	38	40	42	45	47	50	52	55	58	61	64	66	69	72	75	79	82	85	88	92	95	99	103	106	110	114	118
7	42	44	47	49	52	55	58	61	64	67	71	74	77	81	84	88	92	95	99	103	107	111	115	120	124	128	133	137
8	48	50	53	57	60	63	66	70	73	77	81	84	88	92	96	101	105	109	113	118	123	127	132	137	142	147	152	157
9	53	57	60	64	67	71	75	79	83	87	91	95	99	104	108	113	118	123	128	133	138	143	148	154	159	165	171	177
10	59	63	67	71	75	79	83	87	92	96	101	106	110	115	120	126	131	136	142	147	153	159	165	171	177	183	190	196
11	65	69	73	78	82	87	91	96	101	106	111	116	121	127	133	138	144	150	156	162	169	175	181	188	195	202	209	216
12	71	76	80	85	90	95	100	105	110	115	121	127	133	138	145	151	157	164	170	177	184	191	198	205	213	220	228	236
13	77	82	87	92	97	102	108	113	119	125	131	137	144	150	157	163	170	177	184	192	199	207	214	222	230	239	247	255
14	83	88	94	99	105	110	116	122	128	135	141	148	155	162	169	176	183	191	199	206	214	223	231	239	248	257	266	275
15	89	95	100	106	112	118	124	131	138	144	151	158	166	173	181	188	196	205	213	221	230	239	247	257	266	275	285	295
16	95	101	107	113	119	126	133	140	147	154	161	169	177	185	193	201	210	218	227	236	245	254	264	274	284	294	304	314
17	101	107	114	120	127	134	141	148	156	164	171	180	188	196	205	214	223	232	241	251	260	270	280	291	301	312	323	334
18	107	113	120	127	134	142	149	157	165	173	182	190	199	208	217	226	236	245	255	265	276	286	297	308	319	330	342	353
19	113	120	127	134	141	150	158	166	174	183	192	201	210	219	229	239	249	259	270	280	291	302	313	325	337	349	361	373
20	119	126	134	141	149	158	166	175	183	192	202	211	221	231	241	251	262	273	284	295	306	318	330	342	354	367	380	393
21	125	132	140	148	157	165	174	183	193	202	212	222	232	242	253	264	275	286	298	310	322	334	346	359	372	385	399	412
22	131	138	147	156	164	173	183	192	202	212	222	232	243	254	265	276	288	300	312	324	337	350	363	376	390	404	418	432
23	137	146	154	163	172	181	191	201	211	221	232	243	254	265	277	289	301	314	326	339	352	366	379	393	408	422	437	453
24	143	151	160	170	179	189	199	209	220	231	242	253	265	277	289	302	314	327	340	354	368	382	396	411	425	440	456	471
25	148	158	167	177	187	197	207	218	229	241	252	264	276	289	301	314	327	341	355	369	383	398	412	428	443	459	475	491
26	154	164	174	184	194	205	216	227	238	250	262	275	287	300	313	327	340	355	369	383	398	414	429	445	461	477	494	511
27	160	170	180	191	202	213	224	236	248	260	272	285	298	312	325	340	354	369	383	398	414	429	445	462	478	495	513	530
28	166	177	187	198	209	221	232	244	257	269	282	296	309	323	337	352	367	382	397	413	429	444	462	479	496	514	532	550
29	172	183	194	205	217	228	241	253	266	279	292	306	320	335	349	364	380	395	411	428	444	461	478	496	514	532	551	569
30	178	189	200	212	224	236	249	262	275	289	303	317	331	346	361	377	393	409	426	442	460	477	495	513	532	550	570	589
31	184	195	207	219	231	244	257	271	284	298	313	327	342	358	373	390	406	423	440	457	475	493	511	530	549	569	589	609
32	190	202	214	226	239	252	265	279	293	308	323	338	353	369	386	402	419	436	454	472	490	509	528	547	567	587	608	628
33	196	208	220	233	246	260	274	288	303	317	333	348	364	381	398	415	432	450	468	487	506	525	544	564	585	605	627	648
34	202	214	227	240	254	268	282	297	312	327	343	359	376	392	410	427	445	464	482	501	521	541	561	582	603	624	646	668
35	208	221	234	247	261	276	290	305	321	337	353	370	387	404	422	440	458	477	497	516	536	557	577	599	620	642	665	687
36	214	227	241	254	269	284	299	314	330	346	363	380	398	415	434	451	471	491	511	531	552	573	594	616	638	661	683	707
37	220	233	247	262	276	291	307	323	339	356	373	391	409	427	446	465	485	505	525	546	567	588	610	633	656	679	702	726
38	226	240	254	269	284	299	315	332	348	366	383	401	419	439	458	478	498	518	539	560	582	604	627	650	673	697	721	746
39	232	246	261	276	291	307	324	340	358	375	393	411	431	450	470	490	511	532	553	575	598	620	643	667	691	716	740	766
40	238	252	267	283	299	315	332	349	367	385	403	422	442	462	482	503	524	545	567	590	613	636	660	684	709	734	759	785

U.S.F.S., National Forest Scaling Handbook, 1974

Table A-56. Comparison of log rules.

Top diameter inside bark	International ¼-inch kerf	Scribner decimal C		Spaulding		Humboldt		Doyle	
	Board foot values for 16-foot logs by log rules and in percentage of International log rule, ¼-inch kerf								
	Bd. ft.	Bd. ft.	Percent	Bd. ft.	Percent	Bd. ft.	Percent	Bd. ft.	Percent
4	5	(10)	200						
5	10	(10)	100					1	10
6	20	20	100					4	20
7	30	30	100					9	30
8	40	30	75					16	40
9	50	40	80					25	50
10	65	60	92	50	77			36	55
11	80	70	88	63	79			49	61
12	95	80	84	77	81			64	67
13	115	100	87	94	82			81	70
14	135	110	81	114	84	80	59	100	74
15	160	140	88	137	86	97	61	121	76
16	180	160	89	161	89	113	63	144	80
17	205	180	88	188	92	132	64	169	82
18	230	210	91	216	94	151	66	196	85
19	260	240	92	245	94	172	66	225	87
20	290	280	97	276	95	193	67	256	88
21	320	300	94	308	96	216	67	289	90
22	355	330	93	341	96	239	67	324	91
23	390	380	97	376	96	264	68	361	93
24	425	400	94	412	97	288	68	400	94
25	460	460	100	449	98	315	68	441	96
26	500	500	100	488	98	342	68	484	97
27	540	550	102	528	96	371	69	529	98
28	585	580	99	569	97	399	68	576	98
29	630	610	97	612	97	430	68	625	99
30	675	660	98	656	97	460	68	676	100
31	720	710	99	701	97	492	68	729	101
32	770	740	96	748	97	523	68	784	102
33	820	780	95	796	97	558	68	841	103
34	876	800	91	845	96	592	68	900	103
35	925	880	95	897	97	629	68	961	104
36	980	920	94	950	97	665	68	1,024	105
37	1,040	1,030	99	1,006	97	705	68	1,089	105
38	1,095	1,070	98	1,064	97	745	68	1,156	106
39	1,155	1,120	97	1,124	97	788	68	1,225	106
40	1,220	1,200	98	1,185	97	830	68	1,296	106

List of Tables *

I-1.   The more common native trees of California.

I-2.   Some properties of selected woods.

II-1.   Height of average dominant and codominant ponderosa pine at 100 years.

II-2.   Height (in feet) of average dominant and codominant Douglas-fir at 100 years.

II-3.   Average total heights of dominant coast redwood by breast-high age and site index.

II-4.   Timber site classification systems in California.

II-5.   Interest rates being grown by trees.

II-6.   Percentage of allowable stand cut for various rates of growth and cutting cycles.

II-7.   Number of clean seed per pound and average germination capacity after stratification for selected California conifers.

II-8.   Number of trees per acre for various square and rectangular spacings.

V-1.   Map scale equivalents.

V-2.   Vertical aerial photograph scale equivalents.

V-3.   Conversion of slope distance to horizontal distance for a 100-ft. tape.

V-4.   Size of selected circular and square plots.

V-5.   Number of one-fifth acre plots (evenly spaced) for three classes of accuracy.

V-6.   Tree volume distribution by log position.

V-7.   Prism diopters and basal area factor equivalents.

V-8.   Plot radius factor for selected Basal Area Factors.

VI-1.   Standard division of long logs for scaling with 20-foot maximum scaling length.

VII-1.   Road standards by class of road.

VII-2.   Tangent distances T and external distances E for curves of radius 10 feet.

VII-3.   Volume of cuts and fills per 100 feet of road length and side slopes of 1½ to 1.

VII-4.   Cut slope ratios (horizontal distance to vertical distance) for various conditions.

VII-5.   Culvert openings required for various drainage areas.

VIII-1.   Other forest insects of economic importance in California.

VIII-2.   Principal timber decays of California conifers.

VIII-3.   Additional diseases affecting California forests.

IX-1.   Common forage plants of California forest-ranges with comparative grazing values.

IX-2.   Some indicator plants of range conditions.

IX-3.   Water and salt requirements for range livestock.

---

* The roman numeral refers to chapter number, A to appendix, and arabic number to table sequence number in each.

IX-4. Common noxious or poisonous plants of California forest-ranges.

A-1. Length; unit conversion factors with appropriate values.

A-2. Area or surface-unit conversion factors, with appropriate values.

A-3. Volume or capacity, unit conversion factors and values.

A-4. Weight; unit conversion factors and values.

A-5. Velocity; unit conversion factors and values.

A-6. Power; unit conversion factors and values.

A-7. Weight or pressure as applied to area; unit conversion factors and approximate values.

A-8. Weight as applied to volume; unit conversion factors and appropriate values.

A-9. Grade percent and equivalent degree of slope.

A-10. Degree of slope and equivalent grade percent.

A-11. Area of circles (basal area).

A-12. Volume, young-growth coast redwood, board feet, Spaulding rule to an 8-inch top.

A-13. Volume, young-growth coast redwood, cubic feet to a 4-inch top.

A-14. Volume, old-growth coast redwood, board feet, Scribner rule, to a top utilization diameter of 50 percent of D.O.B. at 20 feet.

A-15. Volume, young-growth Douglas-fir, board feet, Scribner rule to an 8-inch top.

A-16. Volume, young-growth Douglas-fir, cubic feet to a 4-inch top.

A-17. Volume, old-growth Douglas-fir, board feet, Scribner rule to an 8-inch top.

A-18. Volume; Sitka spruce (old and young), board feet, Scribner rule to an 8-inch top.

A-19. Volume,, Sitka spruce (old and young), cubic feet to a 4-inch top.

A-20. Volume, western hemlock (old and young), board feet, Scribner rule to an 8-inch top.

A-21. Volume, western hemlock (old and young), cubic feet to a 4-inch top.

A-22. Volume, old-growth white fir (A. concolor), board feet, Scribner Decimal C to an 8-inch top.

A-23. Volume, young-growth white fir (A. concolor), board feet, International ⅛ " rule to a 5-inch top.

A-24. Volume, young-growth white fir (A. concolor), cubic feet.

A-25. Volume, old-growth sugar pine, site II, Scribner Decimal C rule.

A-26. Volume, young-growth sugar pine, board feet, International ¼ " rule to a 4-inch top.

A-27. Volume, young-growth sugar pine, cubic feet.

A-28. Volume, old-growth ponderosa pine, board feet, Scribner Decimal C rule.

A-29. Volume, young-growth ponderosa pine, board feet, Scribner rule to an 8-inch top.

A-30. Volume, young-growth ponderosa pine, cubic feet.

A-31. Volume, old-growth incense-cedar, board feet, Scribner Decimal C rule to an 8-inch top.

A-32. Volume, young-growth incense-cedar, board feet, International ¼ " rule to a 4-inch top.

A-33. Volume, young-growth incense-cedar, cubic feet.

A-34. Volume, old-growth, lodgepole pine, board feet, Scribner Decimal C rule to an 8-inch top.

A-35. Volume, young-growth Sierra redwood, board feet, Scribner rule to a 6-inch top.

A-36. Volume, young-growth Sierra redwood, cubic feet.

A-37. Volume, blue-gum eucalyptus, board feet, Spaulding rule to a 6-inch top.

A-38. Volume, blue-gum eucalyptus, cubic feet to a 6-inch top.

A-39. Volume, coast live oak, blue oak, California white oak, interior live oak, tanoak, madrone, for California Central Coast, cubic feet to a 4-inch top.

A-40. Volume, red alder, board feet, Scribner Decimal C rule to a 10-inch top.

A-41. Volume, young-growth madrone, tanoak, and black oak, high site, board feet (8-inch top), cubic feet (4-inch top).

A-42. Yield table, young-growth coast redwood stand, all species, per acre, board feet, International ¼" rule, trees larger than 10.5 inches dbh to an 8-inch top.

A-43. Yield table, young-growth coast redwood stand, all species, per acre, cubic feet, trees larger than 4.5 inches dbh to a 4-inch top.

A-44. Yield table, Douglas-fir, fully stocked acre, board feet, Scribner rule, trees larger than 12 inches dbh to an 8-inch top.

A-45. Yield table, Douglas-fir, fully stocked acre, cubic feet, trees larger than 12-inches dbh.

A-46. Yield table, normal, white fir (A. concolor), per acre, board feet (in tens), International ⅛" rule, trees 8 inches dbh and over to a 5-inch top.

A-47. Yield table, normal, white fir (A. concolor), per acre, cubic feet in tens, trees 4 inches dbh and over.

A-48. Yield table, ponderosa pine, fully stocked acre, board feet, Scribner rule, trees 11.6 inches dbh and over.

A-49. Yield table, ponderosa pine, fully stocked acre, cubic feet, trees 11.6 inches dbh and over.

A-50. Yield table, mixed conifer stand, California, per acre, board feet, International ⅛" rule, trees 8 inches dbh and over to a 5-inch top.

A-51. Yield table, average mixed conifer stand, California, per acre, cubic feet, trees 8 inches dbh and over.

A-52. Yield table, normal, red fir, per acre, board feet in tens, International ⅛" rule, trees 8 inches dbh and over to a 5-inch top.

A-53. Yield table, normal, red fir, per acre, cubic feet in tens, trees 2 inches dbh and over.

A-54. Revised Scribner Decimal C log rule for logs 8 to 20 feet long, board feet in tens.

A-55. Log volume, cubic feet, Huber formula.

A-56. Comparison of log rules.

Some Practical References *

All Forestry Subjects
Forestry Handbook, Society of American Foresters, 1955, Washington, D. C. 20014

Tree Identification
Knowing Your Trees, C. H. Collingwood et al, 1974, American Forestry Association, Washington, D. C. 20036

Important Trees of the U. S., Agricultural Handbook No. 519, Elbert L. Little, 1978, U. S. Forest Service, San Francisco, 94111

Reforestation
Planting California Forest Land, Leaflet 2925, Robert J. Laacke et al, 1976, University of California Cooperative Extension, Berkeley 94720

Reforestation Practices for Conifers in California, Gilbert H. Schubert and Ronald S. Adams, 1971, California Department of Forestry, Sacramento 95814

Managing and Marketing California Forest-Grown Christmas Trees, Arthur L. Scarlett and Charles L. Wagener, 1973, University of California Cooperative Extension, Berkeley 94720

Timber Harvesting
Logging Practices, Steve Conway, 1977, Forest Industries, San Francisco 94105

Forest Measurements
Log Scaling and Timber Cruising, J. R. Dilworth, 1977, Oregon State University Book Store, Corvallis 97331

National Forest Scaling Handbook, FSH 2443.71, 1974, U. S. Forest Service, San Francisco 94111

Forest Products Utilization
Wood Handbook, Agricultural Handbook No. 72, 1974, U.S.D.A., U. S. Forest Service, Forest Products Laboratory, Madison, Wisc. 53705

Range Management
Range Management Principles and Practice, A. W. Sampson, 1952, Wily and Sons, New York City

Watershed Management
An Outline of Forest Hydrology, John D. Hewlett and Wade L. Nutter, 1969, University of Georgia, Athens 30601

Forest and Water: Effects of Forest Management on Floods, Sedimentation, and Water Supply, USDA Forest Service General Technical Report PSW-18, Henry W. Anderson et al, 1976, Pacific Southwest Forest and Range Experiment Station, Berkeley, CA 94701

Recreation
Forest Recreation for a Profit, Agricultural Information Bulletin No. 265, 1962, U. S. Department of Agriculture, Forest Service, San Francisco 94111

Fisheries and Wildlife Management
Wildlife Leaflets, University of California Cooperative Extension Service, 1976, Davis 95616

Coordination Guidelines for Fish and Wildlife Habitats, No's. 1–7, 9, and 10, 1973–1978, U. S. Forest Service, San Francisco, 94111

---

* There are many more references and publications of value on specific topics. See your local CDF forest adviser, USFS and BLM offices, and forestry schools for a more complete coverage and places to obtain.

Photoelectronic composition by
CALIFORNIA OFFICE OF STATE PRINTING

78029—356 7-78 15M LDA

NOTES